Microwave Remote Sensing

Active and Passive

Volume I

Microwave Remote Sensing
Fundamentals and Radiometry

REMOTE SENSING

A Series of Advanced Level Textbooks and Reference Works

Consulting Editor: DAVID S. SIMONETT
University of California, Santa Barbara

Other Numbers in Preparation

MICROWAVE REMOTE SENSING
ACTIVE AND PASSIVE

Volume I

Microwave Remote Sensing Fundamentals and Radiometry

Fawwaz T. Ulaby
Richard K. Moore
Adrian K. Fung

Remote Sensing Laboratory
University of Kansas
Lawrence, Kansas

1981

▲
▼▼

Addison-Wesley Publishing Company
Advanced Book Program/World Science Division
Reading, Massachusetts

London ● Amsterdam ● Don Mills, Ontario ● Sydney ● Tokyo

MICROWAVE REMOTE SENSING: Active and Passive (in three volumes)
Volume I: MICROWAVE REMOTE SENSING FUNDAMENTALS
AND RADIOMETRY

Library of Congress Cataloging in Publication Data

Ulaby, Fawwaz T. (Fawwaz Tayssir), 1943-
  Microwave remote sensing.

  (Remote sensing ; no. 2-)
  Contents: v. 1. Microwave remote sensing fundamentals
and radiometry.
  Includes bibliographies and index.
  1. Remote sensing--Equipment and supplies. 2. Micro-
wave devices. I. Moore, Richard K. II. Fung, Adrian K.
III. Title. IV. Series.
G70.6.U4   621.36'78   81-17643
ISBN 0-201-10759-7 (v. 1)   AACR2

Manufactured in the United States of America

ABCDEFGHIJ-HA-8987654321

To our Families,
whose support and encouragement made this work possible

Contents

Editor's Foreword

This volume is one of a series on remote sensing subjects which will be issued in the Addison-Wesley Advanced Book Program. The series is designed to cover remote sensing subjects with the breadth and depth required for use by students in graduate level courses and at the same time to serve as general reference texts for remote sensing engineering and applications scientists. The areas to be covered include theory and techniques, modeling, instruments, and applications.

The first volume, by Dr. Philip N. Slater of the Committee on Remote Sensing and Optical Sciences Center at the University of Arizona, dealt with remote sensing optics and optical systems, an area in which Dr. Slater has published extensively and has established international recognition.

The present volume will be one of three on active and passive microwave remote sensing, by Professors Fawwaz T. Ulaby, Richard K. Moore, and Adrian K. Fung of the University of Kansas. These authors have made important contributions to microwave theory, instrumentation, and practical applications from the earliest days of remote sensing in the United States, as these three volumes amply demonstrate.

It is an especial pleasure to acknowledge that each of these authors has been a patient mentor to me, and that I have learned much from them. A large number of the radar remote sensing engineers and applications scientists in the United States and throughout the world have been trained by them. A list of their engineering Ph.D. students now reads like an international Who's Who—from Korea to Thailand, Canada to Chile, Western Europe to Australia, as well as the United States. The scientists who have visited their Remote Sensing Laboratory over the last two decades have quite literally come from all over the world, and the range of their questions and interests has served to stimulate the already catholic research concerns of the group at Kansas. The extent of their teaching interests and experience, and their international experience, is reflected in this volume in the clear exposition of these experienced teachers and scientists. I commend the volumes in this series to you, and look forward to using them with my own students.

David S. Simonett

Preface

Over the past two decades, *microwave remote sensing* has evolved into an important tool for monitoring the atmospheres and surfaces of planetary objects, with special emphasis on observations of the planet earth. The term "microwave remote sensing" encompasses the physics of radiowave propagation in and interaction with material media, including surface and volume scattering and emission; the techniques used for designing microwave sensors and processing the data they acquire; and the translation of the measured data into information about the temporal or spatial variation of atmospheric or surface and medium parameters or properties. Sensors usually are divided into two groups according to their modes of operation: *active* sensors are those that provide their own source of illumination and therefore contain a transmitter and a receiver, while *passive* sensors are simply receivers that measure the radiation emanating from the scene under observation. Active microwave sensors include *radar imagers*, *scatterometers*, and *altimeters*, and passive microwave sensors are often referred to as *microwave radiometers*.

Aside from their traditional meteorological and military applications, radars have been used extensively for mapping geological structures and features, particularly in those parts of the world where cloud cover presents a serious problem to optical sensors. Other application areas, some demonstrated and others still in the research phase, include vegetation mapping, discrimination of sea-ice types, measuring ocean wind speed and direction, mapping soil moisture content and snow water content, and land-use evaluations. Microwave radiometers have been used from satellite platforms to retrieve the atmospheric temperature and water vapor density over the oceans, to estimate the liquid-water content of clouds and to discriminate between different types of sea ice as an aid to navigation in arctic waters. Other potential applications which are still in the research phase include the monitoring of the spatial distribution of soil moisture content and snow water content, which are important factors in agriculture, hydrology, and meteorology.

The three components of microwave remote sensing—sensor-scene interaction, sensor design and measurement techniques, and the application of microwave remote sensing in geoscience—are the subject of this book. It should be emphasized, however, that the book is written from the standpoint of the physicist or engineer working in microwave remote sensing, rather than from the standpoint of the ultimate user, such as the geologist or hydrologist. We have attempted to establish the link, based on current knowledge, between the microwave sensor response and scene parameters such as soil moisture content, through intermediary parameters like the physical temperature and dielectric properties of the scene. The next step, which usually involves the incorporation of remotely sensed data into appropriate models, or the use of the data in conjunction with other sources of information, is outside the scope of this book. For example, we shall discuss how radar is used to map linear geological features, but the methodology involving the use of such information by the geologist, as one of several inputs, for delineating mineral and petroleum exploration sites, will not be covered.

The material covered in this book is divided into three volumes. Volume I, *Microwave Remote Sensing Fundamentals and Radiometry*, starts out with an introductory chapter on the history and applications of active and passive microwave remote sensing, followed by introductory treatments of electromagnetic wave propagation (Chapter 2), antennas (Chapter 3), and microwave interaction with atmospheric constituents (Chapter 5). These three chapters are intended to provide a review of those fundamental aspects of remote sensing that are common to all types of microwave sensors. The major topic of Volume I is microwave radiometry, which is treated in Chapters 4 and 6 and the latter part of Chapter 5. Chapter 4 begins by introducing radiometric concepts and quantities of interest, and then proceeds to treat the radiometric measurement problem for atmospheric and terrestrial sources of natural radiation. Emission by atmospheric gases, clouds, and rain is covered in Chapter 5 using the radiative-transfer formulations developed earlier in Chapter 4. Chapter 6 discusses the operation and performance characteristics of radiometer receivers, with special emphasis given to measurement precision, calibration techniques, and imaging considerations.

Volume II, *Radar Remote Sensing and Surface Scattering and Emission Theory*, consists of Chapters 7–12. The fundamental principles of radar backscattering measurements are covered in Chapter 7, which include measurement statistics, angle, Doppler and pulse discrimination techniques, and associated ambiguity functions. Chapters 8 and 9 describe the operation of real-aperture and synthetic-aperture sidelooking airborne radar systems, respectively, and Chapter 10 focuses on internal and external calibration techniques employed in scattering measurements.

Approaches used for modeling microwave interaction with material media are covered in Chapters 11–13. The primary purpose of Chapter 11 is to help the reader develop a "feel" for the physical mechanisms responsible for the scattering and emission behavior of homogeneous and inhomogeneous media. This is done through discussions of specific factors governing the scattering and emission (such as surface roughness, dielectric properties, penetration depth and dielectric inhomogeneity): and through the presentation of simple semi-empirical models. Theoretical models involving a higher degree of mathematical sophistication are developed in Chapters 12 and 13, with Chapter 12 being limited to treatments of extended surfaces (as for the ocean and bare soil), while Chapter 13 (of Volume III) considers scattering and emission models for the more general case of a layer of volume scatterers (as in a vegetation canopy) over a rough surface.

As suggested by its title, *Volume Scattering and Emission Theory, Advanced Systems, and Applications*, Volume III contains a chapter devoted to volume scattering and emission (Chapter 13), two chapters on the system configurations and applications of scatterometers (Chapter 14) and altimeters (Chapter 15), a chapter on synthetic-aperture-radar (SAR) processing techniques (Chapter 16), and five chapters on active and passive microwave remote-sensing applications. In addition, Volume III includes a special appendix containing a summary of the dielectric properties of several types of material media, including fresh and saline water, pure and sea ice, snow, soils, and vegetation.

The three-volume combination is intended as a graduate-level, three-semester course sequence in microwave remote sensing, although the organization of the book is such that, through the appropriate selection of relevant chapters, the book may be narrowed in scope to cover one-semester courses in specific subjects, such as active microwave systems, microwave radiometry, scattering and emission theories, or microwave remote-sensing applications. Additionally, this book is intended to serve remote-sensing engineers and scientists as a reference guide to those aspects of the remote-sensing process that pertain to the microwave part of the electromagnetic spectrum.

The authors wish to acknowledge the help and support of the many people who have contributed to the development of this book. Thanks are due to the agencies that have supported our research activities, especially the National Aeronautics and Space Administration, the National Science Foundation, and the Department of Defense. We wish to give special thanks to our students, who have suffered through several semesters of having a text in note form and who have provided many suggestions for improving and clarifying the presentation. We are also grateful to Vera Sehon and her colleagues of the Graphic Arts Service at the University of Kansas Center for Research, Inc., for the artwork and photographic processing associated with this book—with special recognition going to Ricky Nigus, who was the primary graphic artist on this project.

Above all, we wish to thank our secretaries, Lee Blackledge, Julie Banhart, and Debra Shoger, for typing this manuscript, for polishing its prose and syntax, and for their patience throughout this task.

FAWWAZ T. ULABY
RICHARD K. MOORE
ADRIAN K. FUNG

CONTENTS OF VOLUME II

CONTENTS OF VOLUME III

Chapter 1

Introduction

1-1 WHY MICROWAVES FOR REMOTE SENSING?

The use of microwaves for remote sensing is fairly new, having been in application only since the early 1960s, whereas aerial photography has been used for over one hundred years and color photography for over forty years. Furthermore, the success of aerial photography, and more recently of Landsat optical images from space, is well known. Why, then, use microwaves?

This question has several answers. Perhaps the most important reasons for using microwaves are their capability to penetrate clouds—and to some extent rain—and their independence of the sun as a source of illumination. Figure 1.1 illustrates the effect of cloud on radio transmission between space and ground. Ice clouds that are dense enough to completely obscure the ground, thus precluding aerial photography, have almost no effect at any microwavelength. Water clouds have a significant effect only when the wavelength gets below 2 cm, and the effect is really strong only for wavelengths below 1 cm. Rain has a greater effect than clouds, but as shown in Fig. 1.2, this effect is negligible below about 4 cm and becomes important only for wavelengths of the order of about 2 cm when the rain is extremely intense. Even at wavelengths of 1 cm, the percentage of the earth covered with rain sufficiently intense to cause a major degradation in the performance of radar is very small indeed.

In the case of the microwave radiometer the effect is more important, and one must consider that the regions shown in Fig. 1.1 and 1.2, for which the transmission is less than about 80 percent, are effectively blocked for radiometric use. Nevertheless, the radiometer at a wavelength of 3 or 4 cm is blocked only a small fraction of the time. In fact, even at the shorter wavelengths of 1.55 and 0.81 cm, which are the respective wavelengths for the electrically scanning microwave radiometer (ESMR) on Nimbus 5 and 6, the effect of clouds is so small that maps of areas such as Greenland and Antarctica (Gloersen et al., 1974) have been produced with almost no cloud effect, whereas mapping such areas in the visible spectrum is much more difficult.

Another reason for the use of microwaves is that they are able to penetrate more deeply into vegetation than optical waves can. A pictorial illustration of

Fawwaz T. Ulaby, Richard K. Moore, and Adrian K. Fung,
Microwave Remote Sensing: *Active and Passive*,
Vol. I: *Microwave Remote Sensing Fundamentals and Radiometry*   ISBN 0-201-10759-7

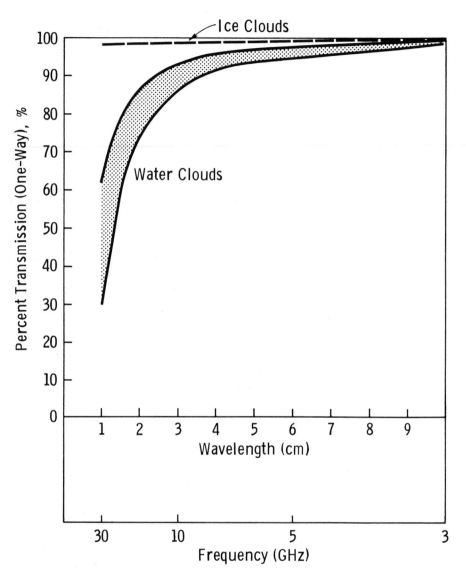

Fig. 1.1 Effect of cloud on radio transmission from space to ground.

the relation between penetration depth and wavelength is shown in Fig. 1.3. The extent of penetration into vegetation depends upon the moisture content and density of the vegetation as well as upon the wavelength of the microwaves. The longer wavelength penetrates much better than the shorter wavelength. Thus, the shorter wavelengths yield information about the upper layers of the vegetation, and the longer wavelengths yield information about the lower layers and the ground beneath. Moreover, microwaves are able to penetrate significantly into the ground itself. Figure 1.4 illustrates the depth at

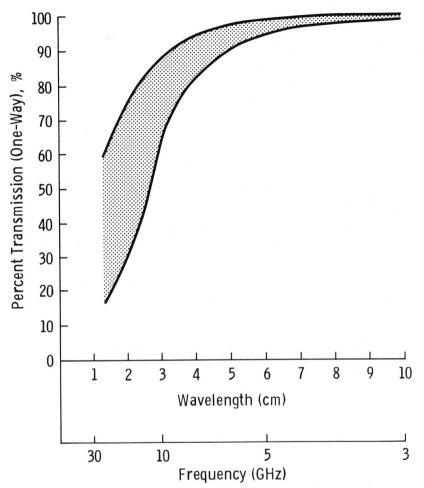

Fig. 1.2 Effect of rain on radio transmission from space to ground.

which the microwave signal decreases by 63 percent for three different frequencies and three different types of soil. Clearly, for dry soil the penetration depth at the lower microwave frequencies is rather substantial, and for wet soil the higher microwave frequencies penetrate only a centimeter or so. Nevertheless, this penetration is larger than that obtainable with visible and infrared radiation.

A third reason for the use of microwaves is simply that the information available from microwaves is different from that available in the visible and infrared regions, so that when conditions are suitable for all three regions, the sensors operating in these regions complement each other. For example, the color observed in the visible and near-infrared region is determined primarily by molecular resonances in the surface layer of the vegetation or soil, whereas

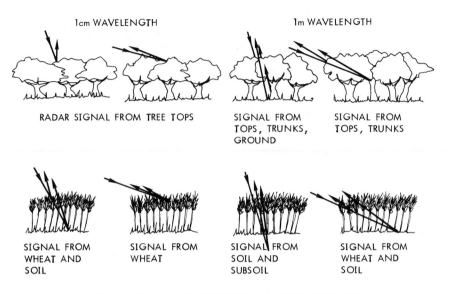

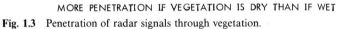

MORE PENETRATION IF VEGETATION IS DRY THAN IF WET

Fig. 1.3 Penetration of radar signals through vegetation.

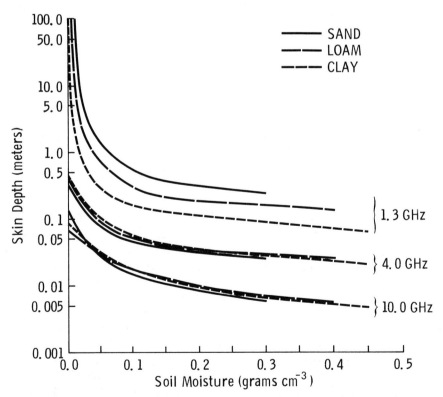

Fig. 1.4 Skin depth as a function of soil volumetric water content, frequency, and soil type (from Cihlar and Ulaby, 1974).

the "color" in the microwave region is a result of geometric and bulk-dielectric properties of the surface or volume studied. Thus, the combined use of microwaves and of visible and infrared radiation allows a study of the geometric, bulk-dielectric, and molecular-resonance properties of a surface, and either one alone is less effective than the combination of the two in delineating all the properties one may wish to sense remotely.

1-2 HISTORY OF MICROWAVE SENSING

1-2.1 Radars

The very first radio experiment was conducted at a frequency that approached the microwave range. Heinrich Hertz, in 1886, experimentally tested Maxwell's electromagnetic theory with resonators at a frequency of about 200 MHz, which is close to the microwave spectrum. In his early tests, Hertz demonstrated that reflections could be received from various metallic and nonmetallic objects. The first demonstration of radar as a detector of ships was in 1903 by Hülsmeyer, who obtained a patent for his idea in 1904 (Hülsmeyer, 1904). Marconi (1922) also predicted the use of radio for detection, but did not develop it.

A. H. Taylor and others at the U. S. Naval Research Laboratory were pioneers in the development of radar as a tool for detecting ships and aircraft; the first experiment was conducted with a continuous-wave system in 1922 (Skolnik, 1980). The first pulse radar, however, was used in a series of interesting experiments conducted by Taylor, Breit, and Tuve in 1925 (Breit and Tuve, 1926) to measure the height of the ionosphere. They transmitted pulses from a radio station (not microwave) and, from a location a few miles distant, observed the pulses that were reflected from the ionosphere. This technique was developed further during the late 1920s, but development of pulse radars for detecting objects closer to the earth did not begin until the early 1930s (Taylor et al., 1934).

Although continuous-wave radars were tried at various times in the early 1930s, the experiment at the U. S. Naval Research Laboratory in the spring of 1934 may have been the first to use a pulse radar designed specifically to detect objects (Guerlac, n.d.). This first NRL pulse radar operated at a frequency of 60 MHz, which is not in the microwave band, but is very close to the frequency of the first synthetic-aperture imaging radar developed some 20 years later.

The first *successful* NRL pulse radar was operated in 1936, about the same time as pulse radars were developed in Great Britain under Sir Robert Watson-Watt (1957). By the time of World War II, all the major participants had pulse-radar systems developed for the purpose of locating aircraft and/or ships, although nothing comparable to today's microwave remote-sensing radars was then in use. The wavelengths were measured in meters or decimeters, not centimeters, and most of the equipment was involved in looking up at aircraft or out at ships. Early in World War II, however, airborne radars were deployed. The first of these also operated at long wavelengths (Rowe, 1948)

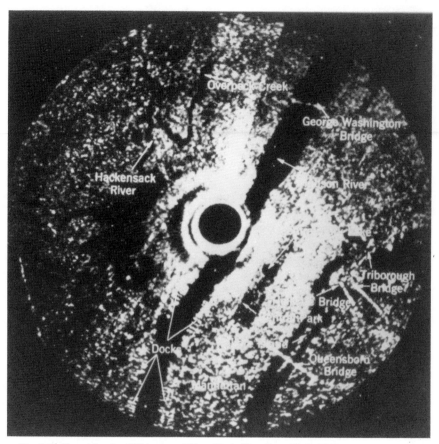

Fig. 1.5   Example of a PPI image of New York City (from Hall, 1947).

and were used for detecting other aircraft and ships-at-sea, but the very extensive effort at the MIT Radiation Laboratory (MIT Rad. Lab., 1948–52) in the United States and comparable laboratories in other countries resulted in airborne radars at microwave frequencies that were capable of producing images of the ground. The development of these microwave systems was based on the perfection of the magnetron as a high-peak-power transmitter in the microwave region and on the klystron as a low-power source for receiver local oscillators. By 1946, radars producing images of the ground were extensively in use in the 3-, 10-, and 24-GHz bands, although the last were not used very much because of the adverse effects of water vapor at that frequency. Figure 1.5 shows a radar picture produced by a World War II microwave system carried in an aircraft.

Before discussing the imaging radars that are the heart of remote sensing, one must consider the radar altimeter. The first airborne radars to be used extensively, just prior to World War II, were frequency-modulated altimeters that were developed commercially for aircraft (Matsuo, 1938). These altimeters operated at about 400 MHz, and even today some radar altimeters are similar with the exception that they use a much higher frequency.

The first imaging radars, developed during World War II, used the *B-scan*, which produced an image in a rectangular format, with distance away from the aircraft (range) as one coordinate, and angle relative to the direction of aircraft orientation as the other coordinate. Such a display had very great distortions because of the nonlinear relations between angle and distance to the side of the aircraft. This distortion was corrected by the development of the *plan-position indicator* (PPI), wherein the antenna beam was rotated through 360° about the aircraft and a picture of the ground was thus produced. Although some distortion remained, the PPI display was quite similar to an accurate ground map. The discussion of distortion in such systems is reserved for later chapters. The PPI still is in use today, although normal systems with this display no longer scan the antenna through 360°; rather, they provide an image of a segment of approximately 120° about the line of flight.

The early imaging radars all displayed the image on a cathode-ray tube with a long-persistence phosphor. The image was bright at the direction corresponding to the instantaneous antenna location, and gradually became dimmer as the antenna moved to different directions. The phosphor on the cathode-ray tube was almost binary in its characteristics except for the decay of intensity, so that the images were essentially maps showing land areas and targets such as ships, as distinguished from water and shadows. There was little gray-scale differentiation. Use of scan converters today makes PPI displays with gray scale possible.

In the 1950s, a new type of radar, the *side-looking airborne radar* (SLAR), was developed. With the SLAR, finer resolution could be achieved because the antenna could be quite long, since it was fixed parallel to the fuselage of the aircraft. Scanning had been achieved with the B and PPI displays by rotation of an antenna, which necessarily limited its size. With the SLAR, scanning was achieved by a fixed beam pointed to the side, with the aircraft's motion moving the beam across the land, hence producing a scan. Since this scan was continuous, and since the use of SLAR was primarily by ground interpreters rather than by the pilot or bombardier of an aircraft, recording on film was necessary. The film was set up initially as a long strip. With the film recording as the primary means of display, the necessity for the long-persistence phosphor was no longer present, so that cathode-ray tubes with phosphors of short persistence were used. The blurring inherent in the long-persistence phosphor was no longer present, and numerous levels of gray could be recorded on the film.

Many different SLAR systems were developed during the 1950s, some of them operating at 10 GHz (3-cm wavelength) and some at higher frequencies such as 16 GHz (1.9-cm wavelength) and 35 GHz (8.6-mm wavelength). With these high frequencies and with antennas that, in some cases, were as long as 15 m, very fine-resolution images could be produced, extending to quite long ranges. By 1960, many of these images had been produced, but were unavailable on an unclassified basis; in 1964, however, the excellent images produced by the 8.6-mm AN/APQ-97 system were declassified. In 1965 and early 1966, about 500,000 km^2 of images were flown with this system over the United States for remote-sensing purposes. These images are still being analyzed today, and much of the development of radar as a tool for earth observation was based upon analysis of this very extensive image set. (An example is shown in Figure 1.19).

In 1952, Wiley developed a radar he called a "Doppler beam-sharpening" system. This first system was at 75 MHz, where some kind of beam sharpening is required if a reasonable resolution in angle is to be achieved with an antenna small enough to be carried on an aircraft (Cutrona, 1970). The early system was not a side-looking radar; rather it was a radar that looked to the side of the aircraft with a beam pointed about 45° ahead (now called *squint mode*). The image, however, was produced in the same manner as for the SLAR. This was the first of what we now know as *synthetic-aperture* radars.

An independent development of a Doppler processing radar was started in 1954 at the Control Systems Laboratory of the University of Illinois (Sherwin et al., 1962). Almost from the beginning, this concept was called synthetic aperture. The research at the University of Illinois was transferred to the University of Michigan about 1956 because it was off the main research path for the Illinois group (Cutrona et al., 1961). During the late 1950s and early 1960s, classified development of synthetic-aperture radar systems took place at the University of Michigan and at numerous companies. The first unclassified papers describing this new type of imaging radar appeared in 1961 (Cutrona et al., 1961, 1962).

The synthetic-aperture radar permitted the production of an image whose pixel dimension in the along-track direction (it was used as a side-looking radar) was independent of distance from the radar and could be much smaller than was possible for a SLAR with a feasibly short antenna, except at very short ranges. This represented a major step forward in improved resolution for airborne radars and made feasible the concept of a spaceborne imaging radar with fine resolution.

At the same time, similar developments were proceeding in other countries, including the USSR (Reutov and Mikhaylov, 1970), France, and the United Kingdom. However, papers in the open literature reporting these developments did not appear as early as the 1961 papers in the U.S.

The first applications of the SLAR were to geological studies (Fischer, 1964), but it was recognized from the beginning that many other land-use, water-resource, and vegetation studies were possible with imaging radars. The first major radar mapping project was conducted by the U. S. Army and the Government of Panama in Oriente Province, Panama, in 1967 (Viksne et al., 1969). Oriente Province is almost perpetually cloud-covered and almost completely devoid of roads; it is mountainous and covered with jungle. Thus, adequate mapping of the area by other means had been impossible prior to the radar project. The radar system used was the real-aperture Westinghouse AN/APQ-97, and numerous analyses were made, not only of the geology of the province (MacDonald, 1969), but also of the potential for agricultural development in some areas where such development previously had been thought impossible.

In 1969 this system became commercially available, and it was used extensively for mapping in various parts of the world, primarily with geology in mind. Soon thereafter, the synthetic-aperture GEMS (Goodyear Electronic Mapping System) was made available commercially, based upon a military radar, the AN/APQ-102, that had been in use for some time. Also widely used for commercial mapping are the real-aperture Motorola AN/APS-94 and its derivatives. Since their initial commercial development, these radars have been used to map many parts of the World that are usually cloudy, including several entire countries in Asia, Latin America, and Africa (Martin-Kaye, 1972), the largest of which is Brazil (van Roessel et al., 1974).

Research synthetic-aperture systems at 1.25 and about 9 GHz were flown by the Environmental Research Institute of Michigan (ERIM) (Rawson and Smith, 1974) and the Jet Propulsion Laboratory (Schaber et al., 1980) during the 1970s. Both of these systems are multiply polarized, and the production of multiple-polarization, multiple-frequency images with them has contributed significantly to the knowledge of the capabilities of imaging radar in remote sensing.

Proposals for spaceborne earth-observation radars (using synthetic aperture) were made in the early 1960s, but the first such radar to fly in space was on the oceanographic satellite Seasat that was launched in June 1978 (Jordan, 1980). This system produced many millions of square kilometers of imagery, both of ocean and of land. At the time of writing, analysis is really just beginning.

Production of an image from the signal received by a synthetic-aperture radar is a complex task. Most of the early processing of synthetic-aperture radar images, with the exception of Wiley's Doppler beam-sharpening system, was done by an optical system similar to that used for producing holograms (Harger, 1970); and, indeed, much of the processing of SAR is still done in this fashion. Efforts to develop electronic processing schemes began early, but successful electronic processing on any major scale had to await the development of modern large-scale integrated circuits (Kirk, 1975). Various electronic processors are now in use, and great improvements are expected in the near future.

The radar *scatterometer* is a device used for measuring the scattering coefficient quantitatively. Any amplitude-calibrated radar can be a scatterometer. The term itself was coined in 1965 by R. K. Moore (1966), but scatterometers were used without any particular name long before that. Scattering-coefficient measurements were made during World· War II by various agencies including the MIT Radiation Laboratory in the U.S. (Kerr and Goldstein, 1951) and several British groups (e.g., Davies and MacFarlane,

1946). Most of these measurements were made by calibrating a standard radar developed for other purposes, but some used special equipment. The technique of calibrating a standard radar has been used ever since, and is still in use, but most satisfactory measurements of scattering coefficient are made with radars designed as scatterometers.

One of the most extensive sets of scattering-coefficient measurements was produced by the Naval Research Laboratory, using a special system. During the 1950s, this four-frequency system (0.428, 1.2, 3.0, and 8.8 GHz) was flown extensively, mostly over the sea but also over land (F. C. MacDonald, 1956). The system was modified in the early 1960s to allow it to be used on a different aircraft, and at that time the 3.0-GHz unit was replaced with a 4.4-GHz unit. This system was used for several years, into the early 1970s in fact, and also made extensive measurements over sea and land (Guinard and Daley, 1970). The purpose of these measurements, which had no direct application other than that of research, was to ascertain the scattering characteristics of the surface. The NRL system was made up of four pulse radars with narrow beams that could be pointed to different elevation angles so that curves could be produced delineating scattering coefficient versus angle of incidence. In 1965, the system was modified so that it also could produce synthetic-aperture images.

In 1964, a fan-beam Doppler system was developed at NASA Johnson Space Center. Initially, the system was designed to make measurements that would predict the behavior of the Apollo-landing radar. Thus, it used components from the 13.3-GHz Apollo-landing Doppler-navigation system. Using a fan beam pointed along the flight track allowed measurements to be taken simultaneously over angles of incidence from 60° down to 5° behind the aircraft and again from 5° to 60° ahead of it. This system and a 0.4-GHz system that was implemented somewhat later were used as research tools to determine the scattering properties of land surfaces and sea conditions of interest (e.g., Rouse, 1969).

One of the objects of taking scattering coefficient measurements was to establish whether or not the radar scattering coefficient was proportional in some way to the wind speed over the ocean. Interpretation of observations with the NASA and NRL scatterometers led to the conclusion that the scattering coefficient is, indeed, proportional to some power of the wind speed (Claasen et al., 1972); consequently, a scatterometer, the S-193, was built for use on Skylab to allow a fuller check of this capability. The Skylab system flew in 1973 and 1974, and verified that wind measurements might be made from space over the world's oceans (Moore and Young, 1977). The result led to the development of an instrument that may have been the first scatterometer designed for purposes other than research. This instrument was a Doppler scatterometer with four orthogonal fan beams (see Fig. 1.6). It was first flown on the Seasat oceanographic satellite launched in 1978 (Grantham et al., 1977). Measurements with this scatterometer were designed specifically to test its

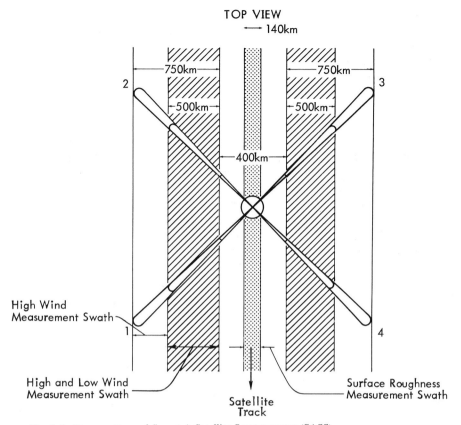

Fig. 1.6   Beam pattern of Seasat-A Satellite Scatterometer (SASS).

ability to determine both wind speed and direction by measuring radar backscatter at orthogonal directions.

One of the most extensive series of specialized scatterometer measurements was made during the 1950s and 1960s at Ohio State University, using a truck-mounted, continuous-wave system. Very careful observations were made at three frequencies covering the range from 9 to 35 GHz. Since the antennas were at a height of only about 6 meters, the illuminated area was quite small; nevertheless, this set of measurements has served as a standard reference of the scattering coefficient for many years (Cosgriff et al., 1960).

Until recently, the most extensive series of scattering-coefficient measurements made near vertical incidence was that performed by the Sandia Corporation in the early 1950s (Edison et al., 1960). These measurements were conducted at 0.4 and 3.8 GHz, and were made with pulse scatterometers with a beam directed straight down. The beam was wide enough to allow measurements to be made to about 25°, with the use of a short pulse allowing discrimination in angle.

In order to look almost horizontally at sea and land, numerous experimenters have used either specialized or standard calibrated radars as scatterometers. However, these measurements are of little importance for the remote sensing of the earth, which normally is carried out from an aircraft or spacecraft, because the angles of incidence they provide are much farther from grazing than one can achieve with a near-horizontal-beam ground-based system.

Starting in 1967 at the University of Kansas, the idea of a radar spectrometer that could cover wide continuous-frequency bands was developed. Previous experimenters, in particular those at NRL and Ohio State University, had used independent systems at spot frequencies, but the frequency response of the terrain was always in question because of differences in the systems and calibrations used in the different bands. The spectrometer concept involves the use of a single system that has the capacity to sweep at least an octave in frequency. The initial University of Kansas spectrometer was a truck-mounted system sweeping the octave from 4 to 8 GHz with a very short-pulse radar (Waite, 1970). In 1971 and 1972, this was modified to a continuous-wave frequency-modulated system (Ulaby et al., 1972). The Kansas truck-mounted system was then extended in frequency coverage so that continuous coverage was available in two subsystems from 1 to 18 GHz and another system provided spot coverage at 35 GHz (Ulaby et al., 1979a). Similar systems now have been built in various other institutions in the U.S. and Europe, and a helicopter version of the system also has been built (Patel, 1979). These systems are designed strictly for the purpose of learning the characteristics of radar backscatter and applying it to remote-sensing system design and performance evaluation. They are not capable of being used operationally because of their very short range.

Many of the measurements made prior to 1975 throughout the world have been summarized by M. W. Long (1975).

1-2.2 Radiometers

All matter radiates electromagnetic energy. The radiation is a consequence of the interaction between the atoms and molecules in the material. A material also may absorb and/or reflect energy incident upon it. When in thermodynamic equilibrium with its environment, a material absorbs and radiates energy at the same rate. A *blackbody* is defined as an ideal material that absorbs all of the incident radiation, reflecting none. Since energy absorbed by a material would increase its temperature if no energy were emitted, a perfect absorber also is a perfect emitter. The blackbody radiation spectrum is given by Planck's radiation law (Chapter 4), which was formulated by Max Planck in 1901 on the basis of the quantum theory of matter. This spectrum is used as a reference against which the radiation spectra of real bodies at the same physical temperature are compared. The spectral, polarization, and angular variations of the radiation emitted, absorbed, and scattered by a medium are governed by the geometrical configuration of the surface and interior of the medium, and by the spatial distributions of its dielectric and temperature.

Radiometry is the measurement of electromagnetic radiation. A microwave radiometer is a highly sensitive receiver capable of measuring low levels of microwave radiation. When a scene, such as terrain, is observed by a microwave radiometer (through its antenna beam), the radiation received by the antenna is partly due to self-emission by the scene and partly due to reflected radiation originating from the surroundings, such as the atmosphere. Through proper choice of the radiometer parameters (wavelength, polarization, and viewing angle), it is sometimes possible to establish useful relations between the magnitude of the energy received by the radiometer and specific terrestrial or atmospheric parameters of interest. For example, observations of bare soil surfaces have shown that the radiometric response in the 20–30-cm wavelength range is influenced strongly by the soil moisture content (Schmugge, 1978). Such a dependence can be used over large areas to remotely map soil moisture content, an important physical parameter in many hydrological, agricultural, and meteorological applications. In some cases, multiwavelength observations can be processed to estimate more than one physical variable or to predict the profile of a particular variable. A notable example of this approach is the Nimbus satellite-atmospheric-sounding program, which employs multiwavelength radiometric observations to generate global maps of atmospheric temperature profiles and of total water vapor and liquid water over the ocean.

Historically, microwave radiometric techniques were first developed in the 1930s and 1940s to measure electromagnetic energy of extraterrestrial origin. Terrestrial microwave radiometric remote sensing had its beginnings in the late 1950s, following about two decades of radioastronomical and atmospheric observations made with antennas pointing in directions away from the surface of the earth. Using a 4.3-mm-wavelength radiometer, which had been developed to measure the solar temperature and atmospheric attenuation, Straiton's group at the University of Texas made radiometric observations of several terrestrial materials, such as water, wood, grass, and asphalt (Straiton et al., 1958). These observations represent the first deliberate effort in which the radiometer antenna was pointed "downward" rather than "upward."

Over the past 20 years, the science of microwave radiometry has established itself as an integral part of the general field of environmental remote sensing. In the process, it also has acquired a new name, *passive microwave remote sensing*, in contrast to radar, which has come to be known as *active microwave remote sensing*. Numerous investigations have been conducted to evaluate the use of passive microwave sensors for meteorological, hydrological, oceanographic, and military applications. Experience with microwave radiometric data acquisition from spacecraft altitude dates back to December 14, 1962, when the sensors aboard the Mariner 2 spacecraft provided man with the first close observation of the planet Venus (Barrett and Lilley, 1963). Among the sensors flown aboard Mariner 2 was a two-channel microwave radiometer

TABLE 1.1

History of Microwave Radiometry on Spacecraft[a]

Year of Launch	Spacecraft/instrument acronym	Frequencies (GHz)	Antenna type	Swath-width of scan (km)	Smallest-resolution element (km)	Principal parameters measured or inferred
1962	Mariner 2 (Venus flyby)	15.8, 22.2	Mechanically scanned parabola	Planetary	1300*	Limb darkening of planetary emission
1968	Cosmos 243	3.5, 8.8 22.2, 37	Nadir-viewing horns		13	Atmosphere: Water-vapor content, liquid-water content
1970	Cosmos 384					Surface: Sea temperature, sea-ice concentration
1972	Nimbus 5 ESMR	19.3	Electrically scanned array	3000	25	Atmosphere: Rain rate Surface: Sea-ice concentration, ice classification, snow cover
	NEMS	22.2, 31.4 53.6, 54.9 58.8	Five lens-loaded horns, nadir-viewing		200	Atmosphere: Temperature profile, water-vapor content, liquid-water content Surface: Ice classification, snow cover.
1973	Skylab S193	13.9	Mechanically scanned parabola	180	16	Surface: Soil moisture, ocean winds Atmosphere: Rain rate
	S194	1.4	Nadir-viewing phased array		115	Surface: Soil moisture
1974	Meteor	37	Dual polarization 35° from nadir			Atmosphere: Liquid-water content
1975	Nimbus 6 ESMR	37	Dual polarization electrically scanned array	1300	20×43	Same as Nimbus 5 ESMR

Date	Instrument	Frequencies	Scan type		Resolution	Applications
	SCAMS	22.2, 31.6, 52.8, 53.8, 55.4	Three rotating hyperbolic mirrors	2700	150	Same as Nimbus 5 NEMS
1978	DMSP SSM/T	50.5, 53.2, 54.3, 54.9, 58.4, 58.8, 59.4	Single rotating mirror	1600	175	Atmosphere: Temperature profile
1978	TIROS N/MSU (2 satellites)	50.3, 53.7, 55.0, 57.9	Dual rotating mirrors	2300	110	Atmosphere: Temperature profile
1978	Nimbus 7 SMMR	6.6, 10.7, 18, 21, 37	Single oscillating-offset parabolic reflector	800	18×27[b]	Atmosphere: Water-vapor content, liquid water content, rain rate
	Seasat 1 SMMR			600	14×21[b]	Surface: Sea state (wind speed), sea temperature, sea-ice concentration, ice classification, snow cover, soil moisture
1982 (planned)	DMSP SSM/I	19.4, 22.3, 37.0, 85.5	Continuously rotating offset parabolic reflector	1300	16×14	Precipitation rate over ocean/land, ocean wind speed, ice type/concentrations, soil moisture
1986 (planned)	TIROS-0 AMSU	18.5, 22.2, 31.6, 50.3–57.9 (7 ch), 90, 150, 183.3 (3 ch)	Continuously scanned mirrors	2000	15	Atmospheric temperature and water vapor profiles

[a] Courtesy of L. King, NASA/GSFC.
[b] Resolution at highest frequency only.

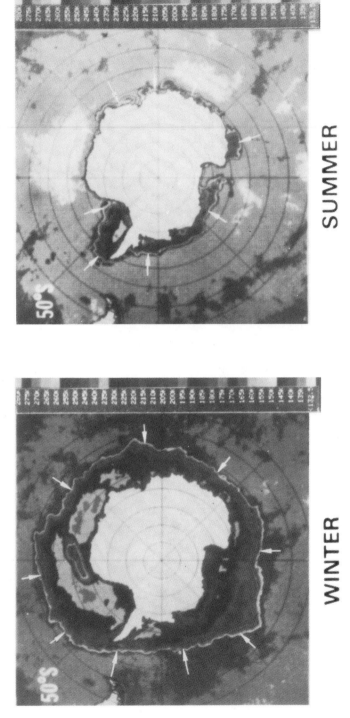

Fig. 1.7 Passive microwave images of the Antarctic region, produced by the Nimbus-5 electrically scanning microwave radiometer (ESMR). The images show maximum and minimum seasonal extent of sea ice (the 150-K brightness temperature contour, indicated by white arrows, defines the sea-ice boundary at 15 percent ice cover). Courtesy of NASA/GSFC.

operating at wavelengths of 1.35 and 1.9 cm. Passive observations of the planet Earth were initiated in 1968 by the Russian satellite Cosmos 243, which was equipped with four microwave radiometers (Basharinov et al., 1971). Since 1968, microwave radiometers have been carried aboard several spacecraft (Table 1.1) including Cosmos 384; Nimbus 5, 6, and 7; Skylab; TIROS; and Seasat. Of particular note among these spaceborne radiometers are the electrically scanning microwave radiometer (ESMR) systems flown aboard Nimbus 5 (1.55-cm wavelength) and Nimbus 6 (0.81-cm wavelength); they have provided synoptic images of microwave emission of the entire globe, with the exception of small areas around the north and south poles. Examples are shown in Fig. 1.7, which contains two mosaics prepared from Nimbus 5 EMSR data. The data are used in conjunction with radiometric emission models to delineate the approximate boundary of sea ice in the Antarctic region, and similar images are used for the Arctic. The different gray levels correspond to different ranges of the *brightness temperature* T_B (the term used to represent the intensity of radiation emitted by the scene under observation). With approximately 15 percent of the surface ice-covered, $T_B \cong 150$ K; lower values usually are characteristic of open water, and higher values correspond to a higher percentage of the surface covered by sea ice.

The linear spatial resolution of ESMR images is of the order of 25 to 50 km; this is typical of all spaceborne radiometers flown to date (Table 1.1). This limitation is a consequence of the fact that the spatial resolution is governed by the antenna beamwidth and platform attitude, and since the beamwidth is approximately equal to the reciprocal of the number of wavelengths across the antenna, very narrow beamwidths require very large antenna sizes. Currently, studies are being conducted to evaluate the feasibility of placing antennas in space in the 1990s with dimensions as large as 1000 wavelengths, in which case spatial resolutions of the order of 10^{-3} of the spacecraft altitude might become attainable. Until this happens, however, the use of spaceborne passive microwave sensors will be limited to applications whose spatial resolution requirements are of the order of tens of kilometers.

1-3 THE ELECTROMAGNETIC SPECTRUM

Figure 1.8 shows the useful part of the electromagnetic spectrum. Obviously, it covers many decades in frequency (or wavelength). The lowest frequencies (longest wavelengths) constitute the radio spectrum. Parts of the radio spectrum are used for radar and passive detection, as is discussed in greater detail in future sections. Above the radio-frequency spectrum lies the infrared spectrum, followed by the visible range, which is quite narrow. Multispectral scanners are operated in the visible and infrared regions of the spectrum, and are used extensively as remote-sensing tools for a wide variety of applications. Above the visible spectrum lies the ultraviolet spectrum and, overlapping it, the X-ray spectrum. Finally, at the highest frequencies are the gamma rays, which

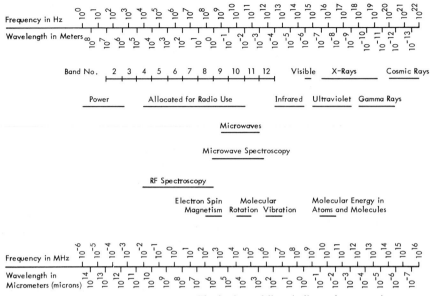

Fig. 1.8 The electromagnetic spectrum. The horizontal lines indicate the approximate spectral ranges of various physical phenomena and practical applications.

are sometimes used in remote sensing; for example, in the determination of the presence of moisture due to the absorption of gamma rays by moisture.

1-3.1 The Radio Spectrum

Figure 1.9(a) illustrates the radio spectrum. The portion shown extends from 1 kHz to 1000 GHz, a range of nine decades. Actually, the radio spectrum usually is considered to end at about 300 GHz, and the lower boundary is somewhat fuzzy. Frequencies down to 0.1 Hz are used in magnetotelluric sensing of the structure of the earth, and frequencies in the range between 0.1 Hz and 1 kHz sometimes are used both for communication with submarines (at least this is a proposed use) and for certain kinds of sensing of the ionosphere and the earth's crust. These frequencies certainly are far from the microwave range, and consequently are not the subject of this book. Letter designations are shown for decade regions of the spectrum above the frequency chart. These designations have been adopted internationally by the International Telecommunication Union (ITU). The very-low-frequency (VLF) region from 3 to 30 kHz is used both for submarine communication and for the Omega navigation system. The Omega system might be considered to be a form of radar—but for use in position location, not for remote sensing. The low-frequency (LF) region, from 30 to 300 kHz, is used for some forms of communication, and for the Loran C position-location system. At the high end of this range are some radio beacons and weather broadcast stations used in air

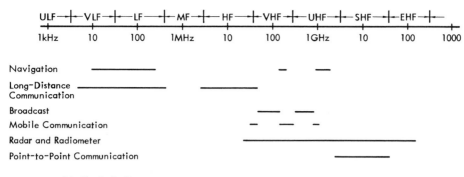

ULF	VLF	LF	MF	HF	VHF	UHF	SHF	EHF	
1kHz	10	100	1MHz	10	100	1GHz	10	100	1000

Navigation

Long-Distance
Communication

Broadcast

Mobile Communication

Radar and Radiometer

Point-to-Point Communication

(a) The Radio Spectrum

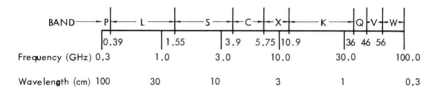

BAND — P — L — S — C — X — K — Q V W

	0.39	1.55	3.9	5.75 10.9	36 46 56	
Frequency (GHz) 0.3	1.0	3.0	10.0	30.0	100.0	

Wavelength (cm) 100   30   10   3   1   0.3

(b) The Microwave Spectrum

Fig. 1.9 (a) Band designation of the radio spectrum and (b) letter designation of the microwave portion.

navigation, although in most areas of the world these are being phased out. The medium-frequency (MF) region from 300 to 3000 kHz contains the standard broadcast band from 500 to 1500 kHz, with some marine communications remaining below the band and various communication services above it. The original Loran A system also was just above the broadcast band at about 1.8 MHz. This, too, is a form of radar system, but it is being phased out.

The high-frequency (HF) region from 3 to 30 MHz is used primarily for long-distance communication and short-wave broadcasting over long distances, because this is the region most affected by reflections from the ionosphere and least affected by absorption in the ionosphere. Because of the use of ionosphere reflection in this region, some radar systems are operated in the HF region. A recent development (since 1970) is an ionospherically reflected long-distance radar for measuring properties of ocean waves from a shore station (Long and Trizna, 1973); a similar system uses a ground wave (Barrick and Snider, 1977).

The very-high-frequency (VHF) region from 30 to 300 MHz is used primarily for television and FM broadcasting over line-of-sight distances and also for communication with aircraft and other vehicles. However, some radars intended for remote sensing have been built in this frequency range, although none is used operationally. Some of the early radio-astronomy work also was done in this range, but radiometers for observing the earth have not ordinarily operated at such long wavelengths because of the difficulty of getting narrow antenna beams with reasonable-size antennas.

The ultra-high-frequency (UHF) region from 300 to 3000 MHz is extensively populated with radars, although part of it is used for television broadcasting and for mobile communications with aircraft and surface vehicles. The radars in this region of the spectrum are normally used for aircraft detection and tracking, but the lower-frequency imaging radars such as that on Seasat and the JPL and ERIM experimental SARs also are found in this frequency range. Microwave radiometers are often found at 1.665 GHz, where nitric oxide (NO) has a resonance. Extensive radio-astronomy research is done using these resonances, and the availability of a channel clear of transmitter radiation is essential. The passive microwave radiometers thus can take advantage of this radio-astronomy frequency allocation.

The super-high-frequency (SHF) range from 3 to 30 GHz is used for most of the remote-sensing radar systems, but has many other applications as well. The remote-sensing radars are concentrated in the region between 9 and 10 GHz and around 14 to 16 GHz. Satellite communications use bands near 4 and 6 GHz and between 11 and 13 GHz as well as some higher frequencies. Point-to-point radio communications and various kinds of ground-based radar and ship radar are scattered throughout the range, as are aircraft navigation systems. Because of a water-vapor absorption near 22 GHz (see Fig. 1.10), that part of the SHF region near 22 GHz is used almost exclusively for radiometric

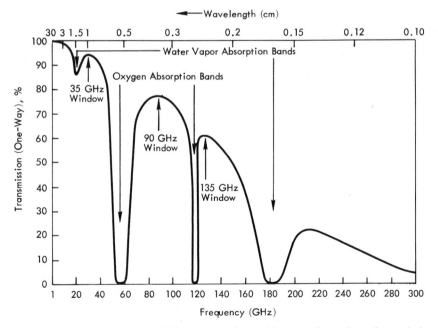

Fig. 1.10 Percentage transmission through the earth's atmosphere, along the vertical direction, under clear sky conditions.

TABLE 1.2
Passive Sensor Frequency Allocations (GHz)

0.404–0.406a	10.60–10.68p	36–37p	150–151p
1.370–1.400s	10.68–10.70a	50.2–50.4p	164–168a
1.400–1.427a	15.20–15.35s	51.4–54.25a	174.5–176.5p
1.6605–1.6684p	15.35–15.40a	54.25–58.2p	182–185a
2.640–2.600s	18.6–18.8s	58.2–59.0a	200–202p
2.690–2.700a	21.2–21.4p	64–65a	217–231a
4.2–4.4s	22.21–22.5s	86–92a	235–238p
4.80–4.99s	23.6–24.0a	100–102p	250–252a
6.425–7.250s	31.3–31.5a	105–116a	
10.60–10.68p	31.5–31.8p	116–126p	

a Protected for radio astronomy—no transmitters allowed.
p Shared. Primary use is for services having transmitters.
s Shared. Secondary use is for services having transmitters.

observations of the atmosphere. Additionally, remote-sensing radiometers operate at several points within the SHF range, primarily within the radio-astronomy allocations centered at 4.995, 10.69, 15.375, and 19.35 GHz (Table 1.2).

Most of the extremely-high-frequency (EHF) range from 30 to 300 GHz is used less extensively, although the atmospheric-window region between 30 and 40 GHz (Fig. 1.10) is rather widely used and applications in the neighborhood of 90 to 100 GHz are increasing. Because of the strong oxygen absorption in the neighborhood of 60 GHz (Figure 1.10), frequencies in the 40–70-GHz region are not used by active systems. However, multifrequency radiometers operating in the 50–60-GHz range are used for retrieving the atmospheric temperature profiles from radiometric observations. Radars are operated for remote sensing in the 32–36-GHz region, and some military imaging radars are around 95 GHz. Radio-astronomy bands exist at 31.4, 37, and 89 GHz, and these are, of course, used by microwave radiometers for remote sensing as well.

1-3.2 The Microwave Spectrum

The microwave spectrum itself is illustrated in Figure 1.9(b). No firm definition exists for the microwave region, but a reasonable convention is that it extends throughout the internationally designated UHF, SHF, and EHF bands from 0.3 to 300 GHz (1 m to 1 mm in wavelength). Numerous schemes of letter designation for bands in the microwave region exist. A set of these schemes is indicated in Figure 1.9(b) and in Table 1.3. The various bands have official subdesignations not identified here. Common usage, however, describes the lower part of K-band as K_u, and the frequency range normally considered for this is from 10.9 to about 22 GHz, whereas frequencies above 22 GHz in the K-band are normally designated K_a. More precise definitions for these subscripts are included in detailed listings, but the designations indicated here are used commonly in spite of the more precise definitions.

TABLE 1.3
Band Designations (GHz)

P	0.225–0.390	K	10.90–36.0
L	0.390–1.550	Q	36.0–46.0
S	1.550–4.20	V	46.0–56.0
C	4.20–5.75	W	56.0–100
X	5.75–10.90		

Radars may be found in all of the bands, with the possible exception of the Q- and V-bands, with most remote sensing radars at X-band or higher frequencies. Frequency allocations are made on an international basis at periodic but infrequent World Administrative Radio Conferences, which classify radars as "radiolocation stations." Several of the radiolocation allocations of the 1979 WARC list radar for earth observation as a secondary service to other radars, and some permit such use as a primary service. Table 1.4 lists these allocations along with some selected non-remote-sensing allocations. Sharing between radar remote-sensing systems and other radars is usually not permitted. Thus, the designer of a remote-sensing radar system cannot simply choose an optimum frequency and use it.

The measurement precision of a microwave radiometer is proportional to $(B\tau)^{-1/2}$, where B is the receiver bandwidth and τ is the integration time. Hence, for precision radiometry it is desirable to use as wide a bandwidth as possible, because for a radiometer on a moving platform the upper (useful) limit on τ usually is constrained by the platform parameters (height and speed) as well as antenna beamwidth and scanning configurations. Thus, in addition to the locations of bands available for microwave radiometry, the bandwidths of these protected bands are important also.

Passive microwave systems share frequency allocations with radio astronomy, and these frequencies are protected against transmission of any kind. Since some of the radio-astronomy bands are too narrow for airborne and spaceborne passive sensors, additional frequencies have been allocated for them on a shared basis, but users of such systems must be aware of the

TABLE 1.4
Radar Frequency Allocations for Remote Sensing (GHz)
(All are shared with other services)

1.215–1.300, 3.1–3.3, 5.25–5.35, 8.55–8.65
9.50–9.80, 13.4–14.0, 17.2–17.3, 24.05–24.25
35.5–35.6, 78.0–79.0

Examples of Other Allocations

Radar altimeter	4.2–4.4
Doppler navigator	8.8, 13.25–13.40
Meteorological radar	5.6–5.65, 9.3–9.5
Coastal radar	5.35–5.65, 9.0–9.2, 10.0–10.55
Ship radar	5.46–5.47, 9.3–9.5, 14–14.3,
	24.25–25.25, 31.8–33.4

likelihood that some points on the globe will be inaccessible for their sensing because of interference from ground transmitters. Allocations for these purposes are shown in Table 1.2.

1-4 APPLICATIONS OF RADAR

1-4.1 Uses of Radar in General

Radar systems may be used on the ground, on ships, on aircraft, and on spacecraft. The applications are different for radars located in different places, but all take advantage of the capability of radar to penetrate clouds, rain, and darkness.

Table 1.5 shows some applications for ground-based radars. One of the most important and widespread is in locating and tracking aircraft. For this purpose it is necessary to determine both the azimuth and elevation of the aircraft and from these to compute the location of the aircraft in three dimensions. Such systems are used in air-traffic control and also in many military functions. Ground-based systems are used to locate an aircraft by triggering a beacon on it that transmits a code unique to that aircraft. The ground station serves as part of the distance-measuring-equipment (DME) system in which the aircraft triggers the ground station, which then retransmits information allowing the determination of the distance of the aircraft from the station.

The ground-controlled approach system was widely used toward the end of World War II and for some time thereafter. In this system, radar operators on the ground at airports were able to "talk down" aircraft pilots by using radar to measure very precisely the position of the aircraft relative to the runway and by giving the pilots directions to make changes in glide slope and direction of flight.

TABLE 1.5
Applications of Ground-Based Radar

Aircraft location
  Azimuth
  Elevation
  Beacons
  DME
Aircraft tracking
Ground-controlled approach
Harbor and river surveillance
Hyperbolic navigation
Speed indicator (e.g., police radar)
Traffic signal actuator
Weather monitor
Astronomy
Ionosphere sounding

Harbors, rivers, and airport surfaces all can be monitored by radars for traffic-control purposes. Hyperbolic navigation systems, including the Omega and Loran systems mentioned earlier, and many different microwave systems for short-range purposes, use a comparison (at the aircraft or ship) between signal characteristics received from two different transmitters at known locations. The time difference, determined in the vehicle, allows the establishment of a hyperbola as a line of position on a map. When two pairs of stations are used, the location of the vehicle is at the intersection of the two hyperbolas.

Simple Doppler radars are used as speed indicators, one of the most widely known being the police radar used for monitoring traffic speeds. Proposals have been made to use similar radars on automobiles to aid in collision prevention and also on aircraft for the same purpose.

The traffic signal actuator is not so well known. It operates on the same principle as a proximity fuse in the microwave band. When a car enters an area beneath the suspended sensor, a signal is communicated to the signal controller telling it that a car is waiting and that the light should be changed. These traffic signal actuators have been in use for over twenty years; their primary use is in experimenting with control systems, because they are much more portable than installations mounted beneath the street.

Weather radars are well-known and are used at meteorological stations throughout the world for monitoring the progress of storms and clouds. Radar astronomy has been used to study the moon and all of the nearer planets, as well as the sun. The synthetic-aperture capability of radar astronomy has allowed the production of radar maps of Mercury, Venus, and Mars.

Ionosphere sounding, the earliest type of pulse radar (Breit and Tuve, 1926), is still carried on extensively throughout the world; frequency-modulated ionosphere sounders are also in use.

Almost since its invention, radar has been used aboard ships. Radars are used extensively in searching the surface for other ships, nearby land masses, buoys, and other beacons. Even vessels in rivers and harbors use radar for navigation purposes.

Table 1.6 outlines some of the applications of aircraft-mounted radars. All airliners today carry radars to assist them in finding their way through intense weather patterns and to aid in navigation over the ground. Many different radar-based collision avoidance systems have been proposed, but world-wide agreement has not yet been reached on a particular system. The DME and beacon application is the same as that discussed in the section on ground-based

TABLE 1.6
Applications of Aircraft Radar

Weather observation and navigation
Collision avoidance
Distance measuring equipment and beacons
Doppler navigation
Altitude measurements
Mapping

TABLE 1.7
Applications of Radar on Spacecraft

Rendezvous
Landing System
Altimeter
Scatterometer for winds at sea
Mapping

radars: the beacon is located in the aircraft, as is the equipment for triggering the ground-based DME system. Doppler navigation radars were developed in the 1950s. These radars permit the determination of the velocity (speed and direction) of an aircraft over the ground, and they greatly assist in aircraft navigation where ground navigation aids such as beacons and DME are not available. The first airborne application of radar was to measure altitude, and radar altimeters are still very widely used.

Radar mapping will be discussed in the next section in much more detail, since it is the primary remote-sensing application.

Radars are also widely used, and will be used even more in the future, on spacecraft. Table 1.7 lists some of these spacecraft applications. The linkup of manned spacecraft, such as the Skylab and Salyut systems, would have been impossible without the rendezvous radars that allowed the spacecraft to find each other and to navigate into docking position. Radar landing systems, including altimeters, are essential for spacecraft landings on planetary bodies without atmospheres, such as the earth's moon, or with thin atmospheres, such as Mars.

The scatterometer on Seasat demonstrated that radar can be used to determine wind speeds over the ocean. The imaging or mapping radar on Seasat also demonstrated for the first time that a synthetic-aperture spacecraft radar can be used for many different earth-observation purposes.

Most of the development of radar has been for military purposes. Some of the specialized military applications of radar are listed in Table 1.8. The earliest applications of radar were for the detection and tracking of aircraft, and this remains a most important military application today. In addition, ships were tracked early in the history of radar, and this is a significant military function as well. The tracking and detection of land vehicles, men, and artillery shells was a later development because of the complications involved in locating these relatively small targets in the presence of radar echoes from the surrounding terrain (ground clutter). However, these applications have been developed widely in the past two decades. Also of military interest today is the tracking of missiles and spacecraft.

Radar fire control for weapons systems started early in World War II, when radars were used to control the firing of antiaircraft guns. Also during this period, fire-control systems for the guns mounted on fighter aircraft were developed so that other aircraft could be intercepted at night. "Bombing radars" were developed during World War II as well, both for special sea-warfare applications and for use over land, and much of the bombing during

TABLE 1.8
Special Military Applications of Radar

Tracking and detecting
  Aircraft
  Missiles
  Spacecraft
  Ships
  Land vehicles
  Men
  Artillery and mortar shells
Fire Control
  Surface-to-air
  Air-to-air
  Air-to-surface
  Surface-to-surface
Missile guidance
Weapon fuses
Reconnaissance

the last years of World War II was done with imaging radars used for fire control. Similarly, ships made extensive use of radars to control the accuracy of their gunfire against other ships. All of these applications have been developed much further since World War II and remain important.

Of course, many of the fire-control systems today control missile systems rather than conventional guns. Some missile guidance systems are completely self-contained when they are placed aboard the missile, and others (called semiactive seekers) use a radar—on the ground or in an aircraft—that illuminates the target and the missile. In the latter system, the missile carries only a receiver. The receiver processes signals received from both the ground radar and the target to compute the intercept path to the target.

The proximity fuse was developed for use in artillery shells during World War II. These fuses permitted the detonation of shells in the immediate vicinity of an aircraft in flight, thus damaging it without the necessity of a direct hit by a shell. It also permitted the bursting of shells well above the ground, thereby dispersing their destructive effect so that, again, a direct hit was not required. The earliest nuclear weapons used radar altimeters as fuses, and many of today's weapon systems—from small artillery shells to intercontinental missiles—use some kind of radar fusing.

Military radar reconnaissance systems were the first high-quality imaging radars. The same general principles apply to mapping radars in civilian use as apply to military systems, although the requirements for military reconnaissance are often more stringent, and in many cases military systems have greater capabilities than can be justified for civilian systems.

1-4.2 Uses of Remote-Sensing Radars

Table 1.9 summarizes some of the applications of airborne and spaceborne imaging radars in remote sensing. The primary application of nonimaging

TABLE 1.9
Some Applications of Airborne/Spaceborne Imaging Radar
in Remote Sensing

Geology:
    Structure
    Lithology
Hydrology:
    Soil moisture
    Watershed mapping
    Flood mapping
    Mapping area of surface water (ponds, lakes, rivers)
    Snow mapping
Agriculture:
    Crop mapping
    Agricultural-practice monitoring
    Identifying field boundaries
    Monitoring growth and harvest progress
    Identifying stress areas
    Rangeland monitoring
    Water problems– same as hydrology
Forests:
    Monitoring cutting practices
    Mapping fire damage
    Identifying stress areas
    Timber volume estimates (a dream so far)
Cartography:
    Topographic mapping in remote cloudy areas
    Land-use mapping
    Monitoring land-use changes, urban developments, etc.
Polar regions:
    Monitoring and mapping sea ice
    Mapping continental ice sheets
    Monitoring iceberg formation and movement
    Monitoring glacial changes
Oceans:
    Monitoring wave patterns
    Monitoring oil spills
    Monitoring ship traffic and fishing fleets

radars to remote sensing is in oceanography, where spaceborne radar altimeters and scatterometers are used. The altimeter has been used to measure the detailed characteristics of the geoid, to establish characteristics of tides and even of current flows by very precise measurement of the deflection of the ocean associated with the currents (Leitao et al., 1978), and to determine the height of waves directly beneath the spacecraft (Gower, 1979). The radar altimeter on Seasat had a precision of 10 cm, which allowed many of these measurements to be made (Townsend, 1980). The radar scatterometer on Seasat permitted determination of the wind speed and direction, although the direction estimates are ambiguous in the sense that one estimate is obtained in each of the four quadrants and other means must be used to determine which one is correct.

Radar application to geology has been more extensive than to any other field. Its primary purpose is in identifying geologic structures with the goal of mineral exploration and general geologic mapping; of lesser importance is the direct determination of lithologies. This is effective in desert regions where the rocks are exposed, but less so in heavily vegetated regions where the radar signal comes largely from the vegetation, since differences in the underlying rock cannot be detected except by surrogates in the vegetation signature.

Although radar has not yet been used operationally for soil moisture determination, an extensive research program has been conducted that demonstrates that radar is a good tool for measuring soil moisture (Ulaby et al., 1978, 1979b). One of the earliest hydrologic applications of radar was to determine the characteristics of watersheds in order to aid in the determination of runoff coefficients (McCoy, 1969). Radar has also been used at various times for mapping floods, a task made easy by the strong contrast between a body of water and a land surface.

The total area of surface water in ponds, lakes, and rivers is not well known, even in the United States. Demonstration experiments have shown that this area can be established reasonably accurately with imaging radar, but no operational use has occurred yet.

Mapping the extent, water content, and state of snow cover is most important in determining future runoff, whether to forecast floods or to forecast the amount of water that will be available for irrigation or hydroelectric power generation. Experimentation with radar to obtain this kind of information shows considerable promise (Stiles and Ulaby, 1980), but much research still is needed before a final system design and a final list of system capabilities can be made available.

Extensive study has been made of the potential application of radar to agriculture. The ability of multitemporal radar observations to distinguish among different crops has been demonstrated but not used operationally (Bush and Ulaby, 1978; Ulaby, 1980). The identification of plant stress with radar has been indicated (Ulaby and Bush, 1976) but not proved definitely. The physics of radar backscatter indicates that the radar return from plants is governed strongly by the moisture content of the plant (Attema and Ulaby, 1978), and since most stress conditions result in a change in the plant's moisture content, it should be possible to identify stress areas; however, extensive proof is lacking. The monitoring of rangeland characteristics is another area with some promise, but little proof exists at present that radar can perform this function.

In forestry, one of the properties that managers wish to determine is the type of cutting practice employed (selective versus slash-and-burn) and the extent of harvest in given areas. Little has been done to demonstrate radar's capability in this area, although a cursory examination of radar images of forest areas indicates that the slash-and-burn practice should be quite easy to identify and quantify. The same is true for the mapping of damage due to fire.

The problems of identifying stress in forests are similar to those for crops, although forest stress has not been studied. Perhaps the most desirable forestry information would be an estimate of timber volume. Unfortunately, this turns out to be much harder for radar to accomplish; in particular, it seems impossible to estimate timber volume in multispecific stands, of trees. For monospecific stands, a recent study conducted in France (Shahin, 1980) using radar imagery has shown good discrimination ability between forests of different ages.

Cartographic application of radar has been studied to some extent and has been used in some developing areas (Hockeborn, 1971). Topographic maps have been produced in many remote, cloudy areas, and numerous studies of radar's ability to map land use have been conducted (Henderson, 1975). Some land-use mapping has been done operationally in developing countries. The monitoring of changes in land use, urban development, etc., appears to be feasible, but radar systems have not been used extensively enough to demonstrate this potential capability.

Radar has particular application in the polar regions because of the long period of darkness and the extensive presence of ice fogs, both of which militate against the use of sensors at visible wavelengths. Radar's ability to map the characteristics of sea ice has been well demonstrated (Page and Ramseier, 1975), although optimum parameters and quantitative definition of the capability for distinguishing ice types in all seasons have yet to be determined. Operational systems are in use for monitoring the extent of sea ice in the Arctic north of the USSR (Shilin and Komarov, 1974) and Canada. Lake ice is quite different from sea ice, but radar's usefulness in monitoring its properties was demonstrated on the Great Lakes during the mid 1970s (Gedney et al., 1975). Following this demonstration, an operational ice-monitoring system was established for the lakes, with great economic benefit. This system, in North America for fresh-water ice and in the Soviet Union with a sea-ice monitoring system located north of Siberia, may represent the first civilian operational uses of radar images to monitor time-varying phenomena.

Radar would appear to have potential for mapping continental ice sheets, but little has been done on this problem in Greenland and nothing in Antarctica. Some efforts have been made to observe icebergs with radar, and the use of a radar system appears to be very promising for this purpose; in fact, it now is used to a limited extent on an operational basis. The major problem with iceberg monitoring is distinguishing between icebergs and ships. With large icebergs and large ships, this is relatively easy because of the differences in their shapes. With smaller ones the distinction is difficult. Radar has been also proposed for monitoring changes in rapidly moving glaciers. This could be accomplished by repeating radar coverage at intervals of a few months to show changes in the position of the edge of the glacier. This has not been applied on an experimental basis or even studied carefully.

The Seasat SAR demonstrated that certain characteristics of wave patterns can be monitored on a global scale. The patterns in the Seasat imagery are indeed impressive (Beal, 1980). However, attainment of the goal of obtaining adequate wave spectra is questionable. Some ocean-wave spectra for the longer waves have been determined both with aircraft and with the Seasat radars, but other shorter-wavelength parts of the spectrum may not be measurable. Radars are being used to monitor oil spills in several countries (Kraus et al., 1977; Moncrief, 1980) because the oil damps the capillary waves on the surface of the ocean and the radar signal from the ocean is largely determined by the capillary waves; thus, the presence of a large dark spot in the middle of an ocean image is an indication that the capillary waves have been damped, and this often is due to the presence of oil. The ability of radar to monitor ship traffic, both from the shore and from other ships, is well known.

At the time of writing, remote-sensing radar is just past its infancy; consequently, many of its applications still fall into two categories: "proved but not used" and "yet to be proved." The applications of radar to geology, ice mapping, oil-spill mapping, and the observation of land use and vegetation in developing areas all have been used operationally, however.

1-5 APPLICATIONS OF MICROWAVE RADIOMETRY

Microwave radiometry is used for (1) astronomical studies, (2) military applications and (3) environmental monitoring. Although both radar and radiometers are employed in radio astronomy, earth-based radars are limited to observations of the sun and nearby targets such as the earth's moon and the inner planets. Radiometers, on the other hand, have been used to measure the radio emission from numerous objects in our galaxy, as well as from objects in other galaxies.

The military use of radiometers is primarily for detecting or locating metal objects. As was mentioned earlier, the term used for characterizing the emission by the scene observed by the radiometer (through its antenna beam) is the brightness temperature T_B, which may vary from zero kelvins (for a non-emitting medium) to a maximum value equal to the physical temperature T_0 of the scene (for a perfect emitter known as a *blackbody*). Equivalently, the emissivity e ($= T_B/T_0$) varies between zero and unity. Theoretically, a perfectly conducting material, such as a metal object, has zero emissivity, thereby making it easy to differentiate from the earth's background (the emissivity for land surfaces is rarely <0.3 and is often >0.7). Although metal objects do not self-emit, their radiometric temperatures are not identically zero because they reflect downward-emitted sky radiation. The radiometric contrast between a *field of view* (FOV) with and without a metal target contained in it is a function of the beam-fill factor (ratio of the cross-sectional area of the metal target to the area of the antenna *footprint* on the ground). The size of the footprint (i.e., the spatial resolution) is governed by the distance between the radiometer and the ground and by the antenna beamwidths, the latter being in turn determined by the size of the antenna and the microwave frequency. Because of its inherently limited spatial resolution even at high microwave frequencies, a missile-borne microwave radiometer used for locating military targets can detect successfully the presence of the target only if the target is within a few hundred meters. A study conducted by Deitz and Constantine (1979), for example, shows that a 35-GHz radiometer, at an altitude of up to 100 m above the ground, can detect a tank against the signal fluctuation due to ground background. This altitude range may be increased by a factor of 3 to 4 by operating at higher microwave frequencies, such as the atmospheric-window frequencies located at 94 and 140 GHz, because, for a given antenna size, the FOV varies as the square of the height-to-frequency ratio, $(h/f)^2$. Operationally, microwave radiometers are used in conjunction with other superior-spatial-resolution sensors such as radars and infrared scanners, which serve as the prime sensors for detecting the presence of military targets. Microwave radiometers are used as the prime sensors in the final stage as a missile approaches a target area, since no warning signal is emitted by a radiometer. Because the microwave radiometer is a wideband incoherent receiver, its output fluctuates less as the antenna beam scans over a relatively homogeneous terrain than does the output from a "coherent" radar system. This smaller fluctuation translates into a lower probability of false alarm for the radiometer if the target's brightness temperature T_B is different from that of the background.

Aside from their use in radio astronomy and for military applications, microwave radiometers have found extensive use in several geoscientific fields including meteorology, oceanography, and hydrology (Table 1.10). In 1978, a team of scientists prepared a panel report outlining the potential and demonstrated applications of satellite-borne passive microwave systems (Staelin and Rosenkranz, 1978). The report recommends the "development of an imaging multi-frequency observatory system covering the region ~ 1.4–185 GHz with ~ 5.25 km resolution on most channels, full earth coverage in ~ 6–12 hours, and a ~ 3–4 meter mechanically scanned antenna." Justification for the proposed passive microwave observatory is based on a combination of "proved" and "potential" capabilities. Because of the coarse spatial resolution of microwave radiometers that have been flown on satellites to date (see Table 1.1), evaluation of the utility of passive microwave sensors operating at satellite altitudes has been limited to applications that are compatible with resolution of the order of 15 km or larger. This means that, with the exception of a few land applications, most of these applications are those involving observations of oceanographic parameters or atmospheric parameters over the ocean. These parameters include sea surface temperature and wind speed (Wilheit, 1979), sea-ice type and concentration (Zwally and Gloersen, 1977), atmospheric water-vapor content, liquid-water content, and temperature profiles (Staelin et al., 1973; Wilheit, 1979) and rainfall rates (Wilheit et al., 1977).

Over land, observations made by the 8.1-mm-wavelength Nimbus 6 microwave radiometer have shown that monitoring snow accumulation and depletion may be feasible (Rango et al., 1979). Another land application that may be served by microwave radiometry is soil-moisture determination. Extensive research has been conducted using ground-based and airborne microwave

TABLE 1.10
Some Applications of Airborne/Spaceborne Microwave
Radiometers in Remote Sensing[a]

Hydrology:
  Soil moisture distribution for
    river-stage and flood forecasts
  Watershed surface drainage
    characteristics
  Flood mapping
  Identification of water surfaces
  Snowcover extent, snow water
    equivalent, and snow wetness

Agriculture:
  Soil moisture distribution for crop-
    yield estimation and for irrigation
    scheduling
  Delineation of freeze-thaw
    boundaries

Polar Regions:
  Monitoring and mapping sea-ice type
  Mapping continental ice sheets

Oceans:
  Monitoring surface wind speeds
  Monitoring surface temperature
  Monitoring surface salinity
  Monitoring surface oil spills

Severe Storms:
  Monitoring tropical cyclones
    (rain maps, temperature and
    humidity profiles, sea temperature
    and wind)
  Severe local storms (temperature
    and humidity profiles, soil
    moisture and rain [as feasible])

Meteorology and climatology (primarily over oceans):
  Temperature profile
  Integrated water vapor
  Water-vapor profile
  Liquid water (rain)
  Ocean temperature and surface
    wind speed

Stratosphere, mesosphere, and lower thermosphere:
  Atmospheric temperature profile
  Magnetic-field profile
  Abundance of atmospheric gases

[a] Portions of this table were extracted from Staelin and
Rosenkranz (1978).

radiometers to determine the radiometric sensitivity to soil moisture content, soil surface roughness, soil type, and (to a lesser extent) vegetation cover. Results obtained to date indicate that a radiometer operating in the neighborhood of 1.4 GHz or lower frequency would be needed to suppress the effects of surface roughness and of modest vegetation cover (Schmugge, 1978). At 1.4 GHz, the linear spatial ground resolution for a nadir-looking radiometer at altitude h (km) with antenna diameter d (m) is approximately $0.2h/d$ (km). Most hydrologic and agricultural models use soil moisture as an input parameter for estimating watershed runoff and crop yield, respectively. A spatial resolution of the order of 0.1 to 3 km is needed for the model input, depending on the specific application, the terrain topography, and other factors. Even for a 3-km resolution, an antenna with a 40-m diameter would be needed from a 600-km satellite altitude. Hence, until the construction of large antenna structures in space becomes a reality, soil moisture estimates provided by satellite-borne passive microwave sensors will be limited to low-spatial-frequency information. Considering that no technique is now available, remote or otherwise, that can provide useful information on the temporal and spatial variability of soil moisture over large areas, even a resolution of the order of 10 to 20 km will probably prove useful. Since radar also has been shown to be capable of measuring soil moisture content, a combination of a fine-resolution radar and a coarser-resolution radiometer may have more immediate potential for mapping soil moisture than the harder-to-build fine-resolution radiometer.

1-6 BASIC OPERATION OF RADAR

The term "radar" stands for radio detection and ranging. This term was coined at a time when the detection of ships and aircraft and the determination of their range was the primary purpose of radar. Today some radio devices measure only amplitude; others measure only speed. In many cases the presence of a target, such as the ground, is known; thus, "detection" is unnecessary. The term "radar," however, is applied to any radio device in which a transmitter illuminates a reflecting or scattering surface or object and a receiver measures some property of the signal returned to the radar from the object or surface.

1-6.1 General Discussion of Radar Operation

Figure 1.11 illustrates the basic components of a radar system. The transmitter is used to produce a signal which is coupled into space through a transmitting antenna. The signal goes out to the "target," from which it is reflected or scattered back to a receiving antenna that couples the scattered wave into the receiver circuits. The receiver amplifies and in other ways processes the scattered signal and then passes it to an indicator of some kind, which also may process the signal in various ways to extract different characteristics of

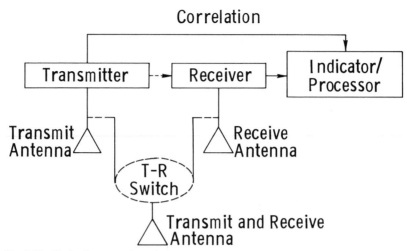

Fig. 1.11 Basic elements of a radar system.

interest. In all but the very simplest amplitude-measuring radars, some kind of correlation between the transmitter and the indicator or processor is required so that the characteristics of the transmitted and received signals may be compared.

In many radars a single antenna is used for transmission and reception. In this case, some kind of a transmit-receive switch (TR switch) is used to switch the antenna alternately between transmitter and receiver, although occasionally with very-low-power radars, isolation may be achieved by the use of a microwave circulator.

Pulse Radar

The most common type of radar transmits short pulses of energy. A block diagram of a typical pulse radar is shown in Fig. 1.12. Timing of the operation of the radar originates in many cases in a synchronizer. Trigger pulses are sent from the synchronizer to the modulator, which generates high-power pulses of suitable shape and duration; these are used to modulate a radio-frequency oscillator or amplifier in the pulsed transmitter. The signal goes through a unit called an anti-TR (ATR), whose purpose is to provide additional isolation (over that provided by the TR switch) between the receiver and the transmitter during the reception period. During the transmission the ATR simply acts as a closed switch, allowing the pulse to pass to the TR switch, which acts as a double-throw switch closed in the direction that sends the signal on to the antenna. The pulsed carrier is radiated by the antenna toward the target. The echo then returns, and by this time the ATR and TR switches are in the other position, so the signal may pass from the antenna to the receiver. A low-noise preamplifier is often used in sensitive radars ahead of the mixer of the superheterodyne receiver, but many radars do not have a preamplifier. The

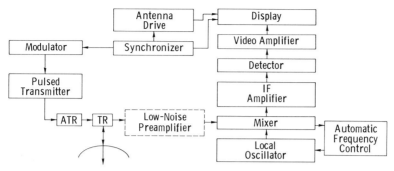

Fig. 1.12   Typical pulse radar.

receiver mixer takes the echoed carrier pulse, mixes it with the output of a local oscillator, and produces an intermediate frequency (IF), which is amplified in an IF amplifier to a suitable level for detection. The detected signal then is further amplified in a video amplifier to a level required to drive a cathode-ray-tube display. The display also receives a trigger pulse from the synchronizer so that the display sweep may start at a suitable time. If a pulsed oscillator is used, as shown in the diagram of Fig. 1.12, the local oscillator in the receiver takes a sample of the transmitted signal and passes it through some form of discriminator, and the discriminator is used as an automatic frequency control to adjust the local-oscillator frequency so that the transmitted carrier frequency is centered in the bandwidth of the IF amplifier. The typical pulse radar has some kind of moving antenna; and the antenna drive is, in part at least, controlled by the synchronizer, the position of the antenna being monitored and provided to the display so that the display may be synchronized with the antenna position. The entire radar, of course, operates with a variety of power supplies that have output voltages and current capabilities suitable for han-dling the different units in the radar.

Figure 1.13 shows the waveforms and timing for a typical pulse radar looking at the ground. The operation is initiated by the periodic transmitter trigger that comes from the synchronizer, as shown on the first line. The second line shows that this causes the modulator to produce a rectangular pulse. Because of the finite bandwidth of the transmitter circuitry, the rectan-gular pulse is converted into a more rounded pulse by the time it is trans-mitted. If only a point target were present, the received pulse would be a replica of the transmitted pulse. The received pulse shown in the figure, however, is the type that would be observed from a ground target, where it is extended because of the different time delays involved in the pulse return from target sections at different distances from the radar. The first part of the received pulse comes from the nearest part of the target that is illuminated by the antenna, and the last part of the received pulse comes either from the farthest part illuminated by the antenna or from a distance such that the signal is no longer strong enough to be detected. The sweep in the cathode-ray-tube

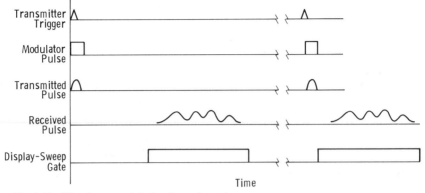

Fig. 1.13 Waveforms and timing for pulse radar.

display need not start at the time the transmitter pulse is radiated. It is turned on at the beginning of the sweep-display gate, just before the first expected return signal, and is left on for a time suitable for display purposes. In Fig. 1.13, this period of time is long enough so that the entire received pulse can be seen. The next trigger occurs after sufficient time delay to assure that the received signal from the first pulse has terminated, so that the received signals from the first and second pulse will not overlap.

Since the transmitted and received signals from two successive pulses are isolated in time, we can consider the received signal for a single pulse without concerning ourselves about the fact that it is a repetitive wave form. Let the transmitter pulse power be described by the amplitude and shape function $P_t(t)$. The received signal for a point target is simply a delayed replica of the transmitted signal, as indicated by

$$P_r(t) = AP_t(t-T) = AP_t\left(t - \frac{2R}{c}\right). \tag{1.1}$$

Here A is an amplitude factor that takes into account the change in signal power level associated with propagation through the atmosphere to the target, scattering from the target, and traveling back to the receiver. Typically A is a very small number. The time delay, T, is related to the velocity of propagation of the wave, c, by the relationship $T = 2R/c$, where R is the distance from radar to target, called the *range*. The factor 2 appears because the signal must travel the distance R twice, once in going from radar to target and once in returning from target to radar.

For an area target such as that producing the signal shown in Fig. 1.13, the return-signal strength is a superposition of the echoes from portions of the target at different ranges. Let the return strength from a segment of range ΔR be $B(R)\Delta R$. This substitutes for A in (1.1) and is based on the presumption that the power returned from an area of range length ΔR is proportional to its length. The superposition of returns from successive lengths may be shown mathematically as the convolution integral, where the limits on the integral are related to the pulse duration:

$$P_r(t) = \int P_t\left(t - \frac{2R}{c}\right) B(R)\, dR \qquad (1.2)$$

The echo strength shown in Fig. 1.13 is the result of such a convolution with an assumed value for $B(R)$.

Doppler Radar

Although a ranging radar must be modulated so that the time delay between transmitted and received signals may be determined, a radar that measures only speed need not have any modulation. The comparison in the speed-measuring radar is between the frequency of the transmitted and received signals, and the actual time delay is unimportant. Figure 1.14 illustrates a simple speed measuring Doppler radar.

The source of the unmodulated carrier is a CW oscillator at frequency f_c. The major portion of its output goes through the microwave circulator to the antenna where it is radiated to the target. The echo signal from the target returns to the antenna through the circulator to the mixer. Because the target is moving, it is at a different frequency, $f_c + f_D$. In the mixer, a sample of the oscillator signal is combined with the received signal producing sum- and difference-frequency outputs:

$$\text{mixer output frequencies} = |f_c + f_D \pm f_c| = 2f_c + f_D,\, f_D. \qquad (1.3)$$

Figure 1.15 illustrates this spectrum. The sum-frequency output is close to the second harmonic of the carrier frequency and is discarded. The difference-frequency output is typically at audio and is amplified to determine the Doppler frequency and hence the speed. This frequency is measured with some

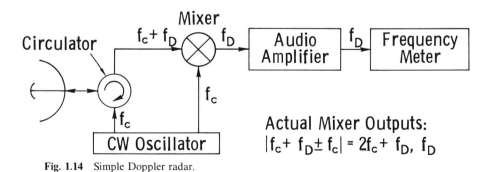

Fig. 1.14 Simple Doppler radar.

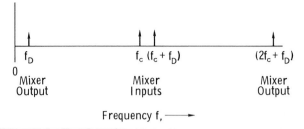

Fig. 1.15 Spectrum for Doppler radar.

sort of frequency meter for a single target, or a spectrum analyzer for a complex of targets moving at different speeds; and the results are presented to the user in a form suitable for his application. For instance, the police speed-monitoring radar displays the output on a meter or on a digital display calibrated in units of speed.

The Doppler frequency is directly proportional to the speed and is given by

$$f_D = -\frac{2u_R}{\lambda}, \tag{1.4}$$

where u_R is the speed in the **R**-direction and λ is the wavelength.

The Doppler radar is very easy to build because it has so few components. Complete, simple Doppler radars have been built on single substrates and are available commercially. These have limited range; systems requiring greater range, of course, are more complicated and use more power. A longer-range Doppler radar also may use a low-noise preamplifier ahead of the mixer.

FM Radar

The third common type of radar is another form of ranging radar, the frequency-modulated (FM) radar. The first airborne radar, an altimeter, was frequency-modulated, and most radar altimeters even today use this type of modulation. FM, however, also can be useful for many other purposes, particularly in view of the availability today of inexpensive filtering components.

Figure 1.16 illustrates the operation of a typical FM radar. In Fig. 1.16(a) the instantaneous frequencies involved in the transmitted waveform and the received waveform for a point target are illustrated. The transmitted waveform is swept linearly in frequency across a band B during a time $T_R/2$ and swept linearly back to the original frequency during the second half of the period T_R. It sweeps between a frequency f_1 and a frequency f_2 so that the bandwidth B is $f_2 - f_1$. The echo from the target is a replica of the transmitted signal, just as it is for the pulse radar, and it is also delayed by a time $T = 2R/c$. The frequency associated with this delay is illustrated in Fig. 1.16(a). During the upward

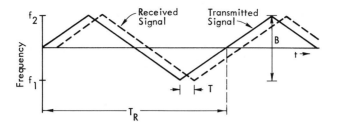

(a) Instantaneous Frequencies for Point Target with Delay T.

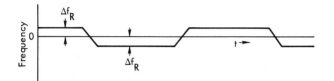

(b) Instantaneous Frequency of Output.

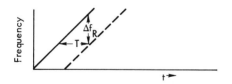

(c) Expanded View of Part of Sweep.

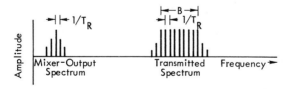

(d) Spectrum of Received and Transmitted Signal.

Fig. 1.16   Operation of FM radar.

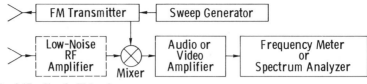

Fig. 1.17 Simple FM radar.

sweep of the transmitted frequency, the received frequency—since it is the frequency which was transmitted earlier—is lower than the transmitted frequency at any given instant. During the downsweep the received frequency is higher at any instant than the transmitted frequency.

Figure 1.17 illustrates the major components of the simple FM radar. A sweep generator is used to produce the triangle waveform that modulates the transmitter carrier frequency. The transmitter output is coupled to a transmitting antenna; the signal goes out to the target and returns to a receiving antenna (most FM radars use separate receiving and transmitting antennas). The received signal may or may not be amplified in a low-noise preamplifier, but at any rate it is conducted to a mixer where it meets a sample of the current transmitter frequency. As with the Doppler radar, the output of the mixer is at the sum and difference of the received and transmitted signal frequencies. The sum frequency is at approximately the second harmonic of the transmitter frequency and is discarded; the difference frequency is used in the FM radar. In some cases only the magnitude of this frequency is important; in other cases its sign is also important, as illustrated in Fig. 1.16(b). If the sign is important, and we adopt the convention that a positive difference frequency corresponds to the transmitted frequency being higher than the received frequency, the output frequency is above zero during the upsweep and below zero during the downsweep. Because of the linearity of the modulation, a smooth linear transition occurs between the up- and downsweep frequencies. Typically, the sweep rate is low enough so that the fraction of the total time occupied by this transition region is very small indeed. Returning to Fig. 1.17, this output frequency, which may be at audio or video, is amplified and supplied to a frequency meter if a point target is to be observed, as for example, in the case of the radar altimeter (frequency meter calibrated in distance); or it may go to a spectrum analyzer where the display illustrates returns from many distances as the outputs at many frequencies.

Returning to Fig. 1.16, we can derive the relationship between the output frequency and the distance. Figure 1.16(c) is an expanded version of a portion of Fig. 1.16(a). Here we observe the relationship between the time delay T and the output frequency Δf_R. Clearly, from the geometry of the diagram, the output frequency is simply the slope of the transmitted frequency shift multiplied by the time delay:

$$\Delta f_R = \frac{df}{dt} T. \tag{1.5}$$

But with the linear sweep, the slope may be described by

$$\frac{df}{dt} = \frac{B}{T_R/2} = \frac{2B}{T_R}. \tag{1.6}$$

Substituting (1.6) into (1.5), we find the output frequency in terms of the time delay as

$$\Delta f_R = \frac{2BT}{T_R}; \tag{1.7}$$

but we know already that

$$T = \frac{2R}{c}. \tag{1.8}$$

Consequently, the output frequency may be expressed in terms of the range by

$$\Delta f_R = \frac{4BR}{cT_R}. \tag{1.9}$$

If an extended target is viewed, as was illustrated for the pulse radar, the output consists of a band of frequencies obtained from a superposition integral in the frequency domain comparable to (1.2).

Because the FM waveform is periodic, the actual output spectrum is a line spectrum with components at harmonics of the fundamental frequency $1/T_R$. Figure 1.16(d) illustrates the actual spectrum for a rather wide band of frequency modulation (compared with the repetition period). The transmitted spectrum is a line spectrum that is almost flat and extends across a range B (from f_1 to f_2). The spectrum of such a frequency modulated wave extends slightly beyond the nominal limits of the FM, as indicated in the figure. The difference-frequency output, instead of consisting of a single line, is the spectrum of the periodic waveform shown in Fig. 1.16(b) and this appears in Fig. 1.16(d) near zero frequency. The maximum of this line spectrum is approximately at the location Δf_R indicated in Fig. 1.16(b) but there are components adjacent to it that remain of finite size. If the duration of the constant frequency in Fig. 1.16(b) is long enough so that many cycles pass at that constant frequency before it switches from positive to negative, the line spectrum of the output (near zero in Fig. 1.16(d)) is very narrow. If only a cycle or two of the output frequency is contained in each of the positive and negative halves of Fig. 1.16(b), the spectrum spreads out more, as indicated in the sketch of Fig. 1.16(d).

Radars that combine the pulse and frequency modulation techniques are called *chirp* radars. Most synthetic-aperture remote-sensing radars fall in this category, and details of this technique are discussed under the topic of synthetic-aperture radars. Pulse radar discussed in this chapter is considered to be a *noncoherent* radar because the relationship between transmitted and received frequency and phase is unimportant; only the modulation is used for determining the range. Both the Doppler speed-measuring radar and the frequency-modulated radar are *coherent* systems because the phase of the transmitted signal is compared with the phase of the received signal in the mixer. Since a chirp radar uses the FM technique, it too must be coherent, and it is often spoken of as a coherent pulsed radar. Pulse radars that are used for measuring speed usually are also coherent so that the Doppler technique can be used for speed determination, although speed determination can also be achieved over a long period of time by tracking the distance indicated by a noncoherent radar. Coherent pulse radars that use the Doppler speed effect to distinguish between fixed and moving targets are known as MTI (moving-target indicator) radars.

1-6.2 Remote-Sensing Radars

Radar systems used for remote sensing fall into three categories: imaging radars, scatterometers, and altimeters. Most remote-sensing applications call for an imaging radar, but specialized applications, such as measuring winds at sea, use scatterometers, and spacecraft-borne altimeters are also used over the oceans. Scatterometers are also widely used for gathering experimental data to be used in aiding in the design and interpretation of outputs from other radars.

SLAR

Most imaging radars used for remote sensing are *side-looking airborne radars* (SLARs). The antenna points to the side with a beam that is wide vertically and narrow horizontally. The image is produced by motion of the aircraft past the area being covered, as illustrated in Fig. 1.18. A short pulse is transmitted from the airborne radar, primarily within the horizontally narrow beam shown. When the pulse strikes a target of some kind, a signal returns to the aircraft. The time delay associated with this received signal, as with other pulse radars, gives the distance between target and radar. The picture illustrates a typical return for a particular instant in the flight, with strong signals coming from clumps of trees and bridges and no signal coming from the radar "shadow" of a stream bed. When a single pulse is transmitted, the return signal can be displayed on an oscilloscope as shown in Fig. 1.13; however, this does not allow the production of an image. Hence, in the imaging radar, the signal return is used to modulate the intensity of the beam on the oscilloscope, rather than to displace it vertically in proportion to the signal strength. Thus, a single intensity-modulated line appears on the oscilloscope, and is transferred by a lens to a film. The film is in the form of a strip that moves synchronously with the motion of the aircraft, so that as the aircraft moves forward the film also moves. When the aircraft has moved one beamwidth forward, the return signals come from a different strip on the ground. These signals intensity-modulate the line on the cathode-ray tube and produce a different image on a

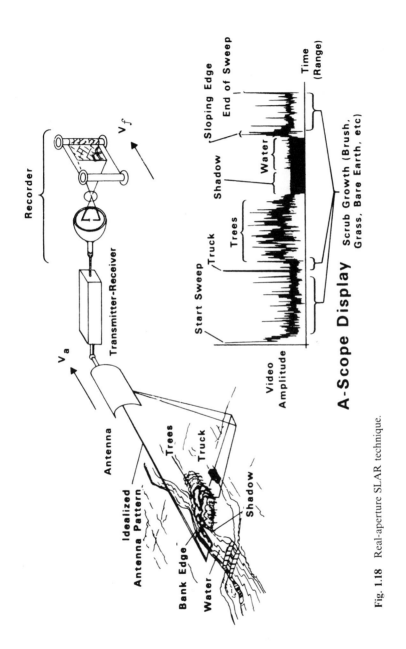

Fig. 1.18   Real-aperture SLAR technique.

line on the film adjacent to the original line. As the aircraft moves forward, a series of these lines is imaged onto the film, and the result is a two-dimensional picture of the radar-return from the surface.

The speed of the film is adjusted so that the scales of the image in the directions perpendicular to and along the flight track are maintained as nearly identical to each other as possible. Because the across-track dimension in the image is determined by a time measurement, and the time measurement is associated with the direct distance (slant range) from the radar to the point on the surface, the map is distorted somewhat by the difference between the slant range and the horizontal distance, or ground range. In some radar systems, this distortion is removed by making the sweep on the cathode-ray tube nonlinear so that the points are mapped in their proper ground-range relationship. This, however, only applies exactly if the points all lie in or close to a plane surface, and this modification can result in excessive distortion in mountainous areas. The subject of image distortion is discussed in Chapter 8 in more detail. An illustration of an image produced by such a system is given in Fig. 1.19.

Side-looking airborne radars normally are divided into two groups: the real-aperture systems that depend on the beamwidth determined by the actual antenna, and the synthetic-aperture systems that depend upon signal processing to achieve a much narrower beamwidth in the along-track direction than that attainable with the real antenna. The customary nomenclature used is "SLAR" for the real-aperture system and "SAR" for the synthetic-aperture system, although the latter is also a side-looking airborne radar.

The real-aperture SLAR normally uses a short pulse to achieve range resolution rather than a chirped (frequency-modulated) pulse. Straightforward FM radars ordinarily are not used for SLAR.

The picture element (pixel) dimensions for the real-aperture radar are established by the antenna beamwidth (see Fig. 1.20):

$$\beta_h \simeq \lambda / l \text{ radians,} \tag{1.10}$$

where β_h is the beamwidth, λ is the wavelength, and l is the horizontal length of the antenna. The resulting along-track resolution is

$$r_a = \beta_h R, \tag{1.11}$$

where R is the slant range. Hence the along-track resolution is a function of the slant range and is not the same in different parts of the image. In the range or across-track dimension, the pixel size is given by

$$r_\rho = \frac{c\tau}{2 \sin \theta} \tag{1.12}$$

where r_ρ is the pixel dimension, c is the velocity of light, τ is the pulse duration and θ is the angle from vertical. Clearly this dimension of the pixel is also a function of distance, for $\sin \theta$ is small near vertical and approaches unity near

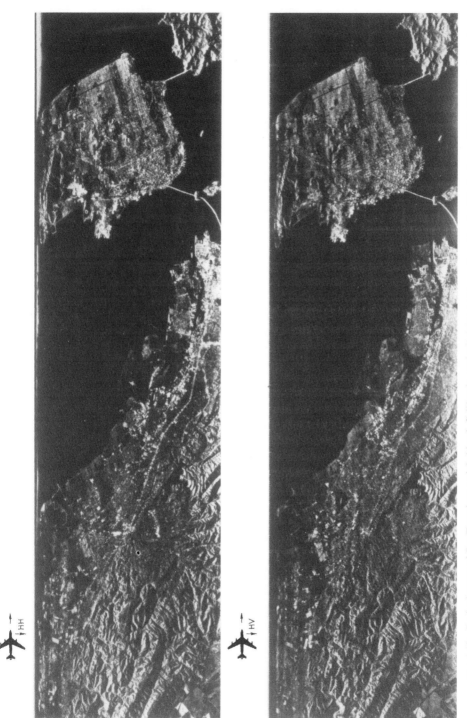

Fig. 1.19 Radar images of San Francisco and Oakland, California, and adjoining areas, produced by the Westinghouse AN/APQ-97 real-aperture SLAR. The polarization mode is HH for the top image and HV for the bottom image.

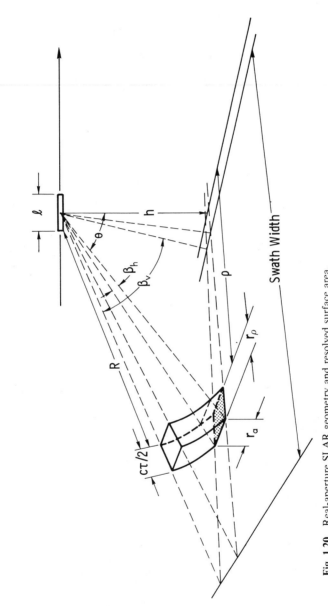

Fig. 1.20 Real-aperture SLAR geometry and resolved surface area.

TABLE 1.11
Some Examples of Real-Aperture Side-Looking Airborne Radars

System	Wavelength (cm)	Pixel dimensions along track $\beta_h R$ (m)	Across-track slant range $c\tau/2$ (m)	Pixel dimensions at 6-km altitude (m) 5 km[a]	20 km[a]
Westinghouse AN/APQ-97	0.86	1.1R$_{km}$	9	8.6×14.1	23.0×9.4
Univ. of Kansas "Inexpensive SLAR"	3.2	6R$_{km}$	12	46.9×18.7	125×12.5
Motorola AN/APS-94D	3.2	7.7R$_{km}$	30	60.1×46.8	161×31.3
EMI P391	0.86	3.5R$_{km}$	15	27.3×23.4	73.1×15.7

[a] Ground range.

grazing. Thus the shape of the pixel changes from being elongated in a cross-track direction near vertical (short) ranges to being elongated in an along-track direction near grazing (long) ranges. Table 1.11 is a summary of some example SLAR systems. The wavelength, the pixel dimensions in general, and the pixel dimensions for a 6-km altitude and ground ranges of 5 and 20 km are shown to allow comparison of the systems. Although some of the pixel dimensions may appear large at first glance, each of these radars has been used successfully in remote-sensing applications, and the Motorola system, which has the largest pixel, has been applied very successfully even to ranges as large as 50 km.

SAR

The synthetic-aperture radar (SAR) system has a major advantage over the real-aperture system in that the resolution in the along-track direction is independent of the distance. Hence, such a system may be used in either an aircraft or a spacecraft without compromising the along-track resolution. The pixel dimension in the along-track direction theoretically can be as small as

$$r_a = l/2, \tag{1.13}$$

where l is the along-track length of the antenna. Thus, for fine resolution the synthetic-aperture system calls for a short antenna, whereas the real-aperture system calls for a very long antenna.

In the acrosstrack direction, (1.12) applies, but it is usually written in the form

$$r_\rho = \frac{c}{2B\sin\theta} \tag{1.14}$$

because synthetic aperture radars ordinarily use a frequency-modulated (chirp)

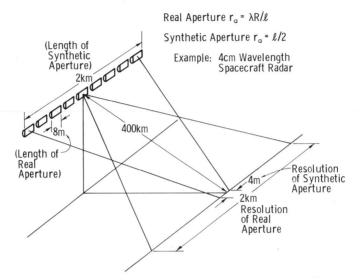

Fig. 1.21 Illustration of advantage of synthetic aperture in a space application.

pulse with bandwidth B to achieve fine resolution in the range direction without resorting to the use of very short pulses. This is because the energy of the pulse determines the signal-to-noise ratio, and a very short pulse requires a very high peak power. The bandwidth B of the transmitted signal can be made quite large without excessive peak power requirements if the chirp technique is used, as discussed in Chapter 7.

The advantages of this method of forming the beam are best illustrated for a spacecraft radar as shown in Fig. 1.21.

Some examples of SAR systems that are in use are shown in Table 1.12. Although the Goodyear GEMS system has a nominal pixel dimension of 15×15 m, in fact its pixels are smaller than the nominal value. An example of a Seasat SAR image is shown in Fig. 1.22, and a GEMS image in Fig. 1.23.

TABLE 1.12
Some Examples of Synthetic-Aperture Side-Looking Radars

System	Wavelength (cm)	Nominal pixel dimensions, Along-track × Across-track (m)
Goodyear GEMS	3	15×15
ERIM X/L band	3/23	2.5×2
Seasat SAR	25	6.25×25

36 km

32 km

Fig. 1.22 Digitally processed Seasat SAR image of the region of Newport Beach (lower center) and Santa Ana, California, with a spatial resolution of 25 m.

Scatterometer

Nonimaging remote-sensing radars are either scatterometers or altimeters. The best-proved application for a scatterometer as an operational tool is for measuring winds at sea, but scatterometers are also widely used for measuring characteristics of the radar return for design and analysis purposes. The spaceborne systems that have been flown include the one aboard Skylab in 1973, which was the first, and a subsequent system that was designed specifically for wind-speed determination on Seasat in 1978. Various types of airborne scatterometers have been used, some of them with relatively narrow beams and with either pulse modulation or no modulation at all. In some continuous-wave systems with long, narrow beams, the separation of different observed points on the ground is achieved by filtering the Doppler frequency

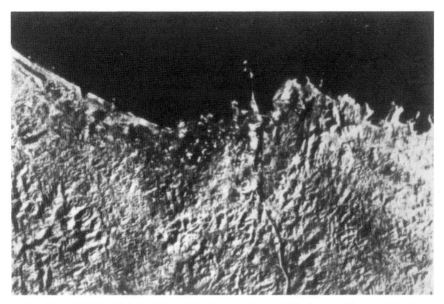

Fig. 1.23   GEMS (Goodyear Electronic Mapping System) SAR image of Panama Canal.

Fig. 1.24   Skylab S-193 radiometer-scatterometer instrument.

Fig. 1.25 Photograph of the MAS (microwave active spectrometer).

of the return signal. Figure 1.24 shows the Skylab radiometer-scatterometer-altimeter.

A class of scatterometer, the spectrometer, has been used since about 1971 for measuring the characteristics of radar return from truck-mounted platforms, transportable structures, and helicopters. The spectrometer is a scatterometer capable of making measurements over a wide band of frequencies, so that the frequency response of the radar return from a particular surface may be established. Figure 1.25 shows a truck-mounted spectrometer.

Altimeter

Radar altimeters also are used for remote sensing, particularly when they are flown aboard spacecraft. The first such system was flown on Skylab, and it demonstrated that one could establish not only the properties of the geoid, but also characteristics of waves and tides by measuring the distance between a spacecraft and the surface of the ocean very accurately. This system led to the development of more precise altimeters in the GEOS series of satellites and the Seasat. Satellite altimeters have a measurement accuracy on the order of 10 cm, which is considerably more precise than the orbit determination, so that the accuracy of the measurements made is primarily limited by the accuracy of knowledge of the satellite orbit.

By examining the shape of the pulse return to a spaceborne radar altimeter over the sea, one also may establish the height of the waves beneath the spacecraft. This technique has been well demonstrated in the series of altimeters flown on satellites. If the altimeter is calibrated accurately for amplitude, it may be used also as a scatterometer, but only over a very restricted range of angles contained within the vertically pointed beam.

1-7 OPERATION OF RADIOMETERS

The signal received by a radar receiving antenna consists of energy scattered back by the target after it has been illuminated by the radar transmitting antenna. For the radiometer, the "transmission source" is the target itself, and the radiometer is merely a passive receiver. The energy received by a radiometer is due to radiation self-emitted and/or reflected by the scene and collected by the antenna. As is shown in Chapter 4, the power P emitted by an object in thermodynamic equilibrium is a function of its physical temperature T, and in the microwave region P is directly proportional to T. For a given value of T, the maximum amount of power that an object can emit is equal to P_{bb}, the power emitted by an ideal blackbody. If a microwave antenna is placed inside a chamber whose walls are made of a perfectly absorbing (and therefore, perfectly emitting) material, the power received by the antenna is

$$P_{bb} = kTB, \qquad (1.15)$$

where k is Boltzmann's constant and B is the radiometer bandwidth. The above correspondence between power and temperature has led to the definition of *radiometric* temperatures to characterize the power emitted by or received from a real scene. Specifically, the term radiometric *brightness* temperature T_B is used to characterize the emission by a material through the expression

$$T_B = \frac{P}{kB}, \qquad (1.16)$$

where P is the power emitted by the material over the bandwidth B. If the material has a constant physical temperature T, the material is said to have an emissivity $e = T_B/T$, and e varies between 0 for a perfectly nonemitting material and 1 for a perfect emitter (blackbody).

Similarly, corresponding to the power P_A received by a radiometer antenna, a radiometric *antenna* temperature T_A is defined by

$$T_A = P_A / k B. \tag{1.17}$$

If the scene observed by the antenna beam is characterized by a uniform brightness temperature T_B (representing radiation in the direction of the antenna), then $T_A = T_B$. In the general case, however, T_A represents all radiation incident upon the antenna, integrated over all possible directions and weighted according to the antenna directional pattern. Additionally, in the real situation, other factors also are involved. These include the effects of the atmosphere and self-emission by the antenna structure. These factors are accounted for in Chapter 4 through a treatment using radiative-transfer theory.

It was stated earlier that a radiometer is merely a passive receiver. A radiometer, however, is different from traditional radar or communications receivers in two respects. First, whereas the input signal that is processed by a traditional receiver may be phase-coherent and nearly monochromatic, the natural radiation emitted by material media is phase-incoherent and extends over the entire electromagnetic spectrum. That is, it is "noiselike" in character and similar to the noise power generated by the receiver components.

The second difference relates to the signal-to-noise ratio, S_n, at the receiver output. In traditional receivers, faithful extraction of the information contained in the received signal necessitates that $S_n \gg 1$ to differentiate the signal from the fluctuating component of the noise. This condition usually is achieved through a combination of amplitude and waveform design of the transmitted signal and the application of signal-processing techniques in the receiver section, although some scatterometers use methods similar to those used in radiometers.

Unlike the situation in traditional receivers, the radiometric signal to be measured, P_A, usually is much smaller than the receiver noise power. Radiometers are highly sensitive receivers that are configured to measure very small input signal levels with a high degree of precision. Several different configurations have been developed, some of which are discussed in Chapter 6. For the purposes of this introductory presentation, we shall discuss briefly the operation of a simple configuration known as the *total-power radiometer*.

The total-power radiometer (Fig. 1.26) consists of an antenna, an amplifying predetection section, a detector, an integrator (low-pass filter) and a display section. For simplicity, square-law detection is assumed, which means that the output voltage V_{out} is proportional to the input power. The power gain of the predetection section is G, and the RF bandwidth of the detected input signal is B. It is customary to refer the internally generated receiver output noise power, P_{no}, to the receiver input by treating the receiver as noise-free and "injecting" an equivalent input noise $P_{ni} = P_{no}/G$ (see Fig. 1.26(b)). Furthermore, using the power-temperature correspondence relation, P_{ni} is char-

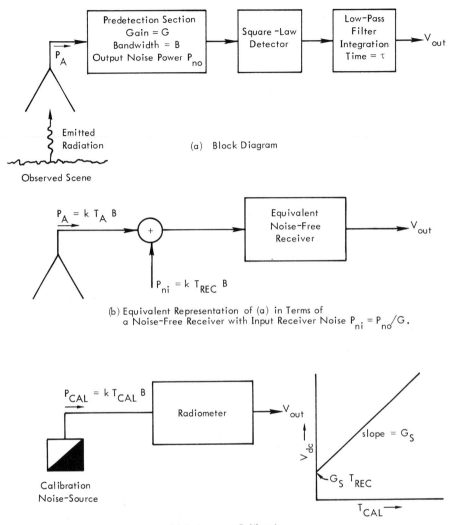

(a) Block Diagram

(b) Equivalent Representation of (a) in Terms of
a Noise-Free Receiver with Input Receiver Noise $P_{ni} = P_{no}/G$.

(c) Radiometer Calibration

Fig. 1.26 Total-power radiometer, (a) block diagram, (b) equivalent representation and (c) calibration.

acterized by an equivalent receiver input noise-temperature T_{REC} as follows:

$$P_{ni} = k T_{REC} B. \tag{1.18}$$

The total input power consists of P_A, due to energy incident upon the antenna, and P_{ni} representing the noise power generated by the receiver. The sum of these two components is sometimes referred to as the system input-noise-power, $P_{SYS} = P_A + P_{ni}$.

The output voltage consists of a dc component corresponding to the mean value of the input power, and an ac component representing the low-frequency portion of the post-detection noise spectrum (high frequencies are removed by the low-pass filter),

$$V_{out}(t) = V_{dc} + V_{ac}(t) \tag{1.19}$$

and

$$V_{dc} = G_S(T_A + T_{REC}) \tag{1.20}$$

where G_S is a system gain factor. For phase incoherent noise, it can be shown (Section 6-7.2) that the rms value of V_{ac} is related to V_{dc} through

$$\frac{(V_{ac})_{rms}}{V_{dc}} = 1/\sqrt{B\tau} \tag{1.21}$$

where τ is the integration time provided by the low-pass filter integrator. The above relation leads to the following expression for the rms radiometric resolution associated with the measurement of T_A,

$$\Delta T = (T_A + T_{REC})/\sqrt{B\tau} . \tag{1.22}$$

That is, ΔT is the precision with which T_A can be recovered from $V(t)$, assuming that a calibration equation relating $V(t)$ to T_A is available and that the receiver gain factor G_S remains absolutely constant over the integration period τ. Both of these points are discussed further below, but before we do so, it will be useful to develop a "feel" for the relative magnitudes of the quantities given in (1.22). Theoretically, T_A may range between 0 K for a scene with an emissivity $e=0$ and a maximum value equal to the physical temperature of the scene (for $e=1$). For terrestrial observations, this maximum value seldom exceeds 320 K. Radiometers usually are designed so that ΔT is of the order of 1 K or less. The RF bandwidth B typically is between 1 and 10 percent of the center frequency, and the receiver noise temperature T_{REC} varies between values of the order of 50 K for very low-noise radiometers and values in excess of 1000 K for most high-microwave-frequency radiometers. As an example, consider a 10-GHz radiometer with $B=100$ MHz and $T_{REC}=700$ K. For $T_A=300$ K and a desired precision $T_A=1$ K, the integration time $\tau \geqslant 0.01$ s.

The procedure used for establishing the receiver transfer function usually consists of two steps. First, the antenna is replaced by a variable noise source with known noise temperature T_{CAL} (Fig. 1.18(c)). Since the output voltage is linearly related to the calibration temperature T_{CAL}, it suffices to measure V_{out} at each of two values of T_{CAL}. In practice, however, it is advisable to perform measurements for more than two points. The equation of the calibration line is of the form

$$V_{dc} = a(T_{CAL} + b),\tag{1.23}$$

where a and b are constants given by $a = G_S$ and $b = T_{REC}$.

The total-power radiometer described above is simple to construct and easy to use. For the example cited in the discussion, a resolution $\Delta T = 1$ K was achievable using an integration time $\tau = 0.01$ s. This result, however, hinges on an important assumption, namely that the fluctuations in the output voltage due to receiver gain variations are much smaller than those due to noise variations. The degree to which this condition can be met is governed by the receiver configuration and by how often the radiometer is calibrated; the general case where both noise and gain variations are important is treated in Chapter 6. An attractive solution to the gain-fluctuation problem is through the use of modulation techniques, which also are treated in Chapter 6.

References

Attema, E. P. W., and F. T. Ulaby (1978), Vegetation Modeled as a Water Cloud, *Radio Science*, 13, pp. 357–364.

Barrett, A. H., and E. Lilley (1963), Mariner-2 Microwave Observations of Venus, *Sky and Telescope*, pp. 192–195.

Barrick, D. E., and J. B. Snider (1977), The Statistics of HF Sea Echo Doppler Spectra, *IEEE J. Oceanic Engineering*, OE-2, pp. 19–28.

Basharinov, A. E., A. S. Gurvich, S. T. Yegorov, A. A. Kurskaya, D. T. Matvyev, and A. M. Shutko (1971), The Results of Microwave Sounding of the Earth's Surface According to Experimental Data from the Satellite Cosmos 243, *Space Research*, 11, Akademie-Verlag, Berlin.

Beal, R. C. (1980), Spaceborne Imaging Radar: Monitoring of Ocean Waves, *Science*, 208, pp. 1373–1375.

Breit, G., and M. Tuve (1926), A Test of the Existence of the Conducting Layer, *Phys. Rev.*, 28, p. 554.

Bush, T. F., and F. T. Ulaby (1978), An Evaluation of Radar as a Crop Classifier, *Rem. Sens. Env.*, 7, pp. 15–36.

Cihlar, J., and F. T. Ulaby (1974), Dielectric Properties of Soils as a Function of Moisture Content, CRES Technical Report 177-47, University of Kansas, Lawrence, Kansas.

Claassen, J. P., R. K. Moore, H. S. Fung, and W. J. Pierson, Jr. (1972), Radar Sea Return and the RADSCAT Satellite Anemometer, *Oceans '72, IEEE International Conference Record: Engineering in the Ocean Environment* (IEEE Publication 72 CHO 660-1 OCC), Newport, Rhode Island, pp. 180–185.

Cosgriff, R. L., W. H. Peake, and R. C. Taylor (1960), Terrain Scattering Properties for Sensor System Design (Terrain Handbook II), Engineering Experiment Station Bulletin 181, Ohio State University.

Cutrona, L. J., W. E. Vivian, E. N. Leith, and G. O. Hall (1961), A High Resolution Radar Combat Surveillance System, *IRE Trans.*, MIL-5, pp. 127–131.

Cutrona, L. J., and G. O. Hall (1962), A Comparison of Techniques for Achieving Fine Azimuth Resolution, *IRE Trans.*, MIL-6, pp. 119–133.

Cutrona, L. J. (1970), Synthetic Aperture Radar, Chapter 23 in *Radar Handbook*, M. I. Skolnik, ed., McGraw-Hill Book Company, Inc., p. 23–3.

Davies, H., and G. G. MacFarlane (1946), Radar Echoes from the Sea Surface at Centimeter Wavelengths, *Proc. Phys. Soc.*, 58, pp. 717–729.

Deitz, P., and J. G. Constantine (1979), Passive MMW Detection in Snow, *NAECON*, pp. 371–381.

Edison, A. R., R. K. Moore, and B. D. Warner (1960), Radar Return Measured at Near Vertical Incidence, *IRE Trans.*, AP-8, pp. 246–254.

Fischer, W. A. (1964), personal communication.

Gedney, R. T., R. J. Schertler, R. A. Mueller, R. J. Jirberg, and H. Mark (1975), An Operational All-Weather Great Lakes Ice Information System, *Proc. 3rd Canadian Symp. Rem. Sens.*, Edmonton, Alberta, Canada, September, pp. 73–82.

Gloersen, P., T. T. Wilheit, A. T. C. Chang, W. Nordberg, and W. J. Campbell (1974), Microwave Maps of the Polar Ice of the Earth, *Bull. Amer. Meteorological Soc.*, 55, pp. 1442–1448.

Gower, J. F. R. (1979), The Computation of Ocean Wave Heights from GEOS-3 Satellite Radar Altimeter Data, *Rem. Sens. Env.*, 8, pp. 97–114.

Grantham, W. L., E. M. Bracalente, W. L. Jones, and J. W. Johnson (1977), The SEASAT-A Satellite Scatterometer, *IEEE J. Oceanic Engineering*, OE-2, pp. 200–206.

57

Guerlac, H. E. (n.d.), *OSRD Long History*, vol. V, division 14, "Radar," available from the Office of Technical Services, U. S. Department of Commerce.

Guinard, N. W., and J. C. Daley (1970), An Experimental Study of a Sea Clutter Model, *Proc. IEEE*, 57, pp. 605–614.

Hall, J. S. (1947), *Radar Aids to Navigation*, MIT Radiation Laboratory Series, 2, McGraw-Hill Book Company, New York.

Harger, R. O. (1970), *Synthetic Aperture Radar Systems: Theory and Design*, Academic Press, New York, pp. 109–128.

Henderson, F. M. (1975), Radar for Small-Scale Land Use Mapping, *Photogram. Eng. and Rem. Sens.*, pp. 307–320.

Hockeborn, H. A. (1971), Extraction of Positional Information from Side-Looking Radar, *Bildmessung und Luftbildwesen*, 39, pp. 55–58.

Hülsmeyer, C. (1904), Hertzian-Wave Projecting and Receiving Apparatus Adapted to Indicate or Give Warning of the Presence of a Metallic Body such as a Ship or a Train, British Patent 13170, 9/22/1904.

Jordan, R. L. (1980), The SEASAT-A Synthetic Aperture Radar System, *IEEE J. Oceanic Engineering*, OE-5, pp. 154–164.

Kerr, D. E., and H. Goldstein (1951), Radar Targets and Echoes, Chapter 6 in *Propagation of Short Radio Waves*, D. E. Kerr, ed., 13, MIT Radiation Laboratory Series, McGraw-Hill Book Company, New York.

Kirk, J. C., Jr. (1975), A Discussion of Digital Processing in Synthetic Aperture Radar, *IEEE Trans.*, AES-11, pp. 326–337.

Kraus, S. P., J. E. Estes, S. G. Atwater, J. R. Jensen, and R. R. Villmers (1977), Radar Detection of Surface Oil Slicks, *Photogram. Eng. and Rem. Sens.*, 43, pp. 1523–1531.

Leitao, C. D., N. E. Huang, and C. G. Perra (1978), Final Report of GEOS-3 Ocean Current Investigation Using Radar Altimeter Profiling, NASA Technical Memorandum 73280, NASA Wallops Flight Center, Wallops Island, Virginia.

Long, A. E., and E. B. Trizna (1973), Mapping of North Atlantic Winds by HF Radar Sea Backscatter Interpretation, *IEEE Trans.*, AP-21, pp. 680–685.

Long, M. W. (1975), *Radar Reflectivity of Land and Sea*, Lexington Books, Lexington, Massachusetts.

MacDonald, F. C. (1956), The Correlation of Radar Sea Clutter on Vertical and Horizontal Polarizations with Wave Height and Slope, *IRE Convention Record*, Part 1, pp. 29–32.

MacDonald, H. C. (1969), Geologic Evaluation of Radar Imagery from Darien Province, Panama, *Modern Geology*, 1, pp. 1–63.

Marconi, S. G. (1922), Radio Telegraphy, *Proc. IRE*, 10, p. 237.

Martin-Kaye, P. (1972), Application of Side-Looking Radar in Earth Resources Survey, Environmental Remote Sensing: Applications and Achievements, *Proc. Bristol Symp. on Remote Sensing*, Department of Geography, University of Bristol, England, pp. 31–48.

Matsuo, S. (1938), A Direct-Reading Radio-Wave-Reflection-Type Absolute Altimeter for Aeronautics, *Proc. IRE*, 6, p. 848.

McCoy, R. M. (1969), Drainage Network Analysis with K-Band Radar Imagery, *Geog. Rev.*, 59, pp. 491–512.

MIT Radiation Laboratory Series (1947–1952), 20 volumes, McGraw-Hill Book Company, New York.

Moncrief, F. J. (1980), Side-Looking Radar Will Spot Oil Slicks, *Microwaves*, 19, March, pp. 25–26.

Moore, R. K. (1966), Radar Scatterometry—An Active Remote Sensing Tool, *Proc. 4th Symp. Rem. Sens. Env.*, University of Michigan, Ann Arbor, pp. 339–375.

Moore, R. K., and J. D. Young (1977), Active Measurement from Space of Sea Surface Winds, *IEEE J. Oceanic Engineering*, OE-2, pp. 309–317.

Page, D. F., and R. O. Ramseier (1975), Application of Radar Techniques to Ice and Snow Studies, *J. Glaciol.*, 15, pp. 171–191.

Patel, J. S. (1979), Backscatter Measurements of Sea Ice with a Helicopter-Borne Scatterometer, Master's Thesis, University of Kansas, Lawrence, Kansas.

Rango, A., A. T. C. Chang, and J. L. Foster (1979), The Utilization of Spaceborne Microwave Radiometers for Monitoring Snowpack Properties, *Nordic Hydrol.*, 10, pp. 25–40.

Rawson, R. F., and F. L. Smith (1974), 4-Channel Simultaneous X-L Imaging SAR Radar, *Proc. 9th Intl. Symp. Rem. Sens. Env.*, 1, University of Michigan, Ann Arbor, pp. 251–270.

Reutov, A. P., and B. A. Mikhaylov (1970), *Side-Looking Radar*, Soviet Radio, Moscow. [*Radiolokatsionnyye Stantsii Bokovogo Obzora*. English translation available from National Technical Information Service, U. S. Department of Commerce, Catalog Number AD-787070.]

Rouse, J. W., Jr. (1969), Arctic Ice Identification by Radar, *Proc. IEEE*, 57, pp. 605–614.

Rowe, A. P. (1948), *One Story of Radar*, Cambridge University Press, New York.

Schaber, G. G., C. Elachi, and T. G. Farr (1980), Remote Sensing of S. P. Mountain and S. P. Lava Flow in North Central Arizona, *Rem. Sens. Env.*, 9, pp. 149–170.

Schmugge, T. (1978), Remote Sensing of Surface Soil Moisture, *J. Appl. Meteorol.*, 17, pp. 1549–1557.

Shahin, M. S. (1980), Traitement d'Images Radar en Vue de l'Étude de Surfaces Agricoles et Forestières par Télédétection, Ph.D. Thesis, L'Université Paul Sabatier de Toulouse, Toulouse, France.

Sherwin, C. W., J. P. Ruina, and R. D. Rawcliffe (1962), Some Early Developments in Synthetic Aperture Radar Systems, *IRE Trans.*, MIL-6, pp. 111–116.

Shilin, B. V., and V. B. Komarov (1974), Aerial Methods in Geological and Geographical Explorations, *Advances in Geophysics*, 17, pp. 263–322. Laboratory of Aeromethods, Ministry of Geology, Leningrad, USSR.

Skolnik, M. I. (1980), *Introduction to Radar Systems*, 2nd edition, McGraw-Hill Book Company, New York.

Staelin, D. H., A. H. Barrett, J. W. Waters, F. T. Barath, E. J. Johnston, P. W. Rosenkranz, N. E. Gant, and W. R. Lenoir (1973), Microwave Spectrometer on the NIMBUS 5 Satellite: Meteorological and Geophysical Data, *Science*, 182, pp. 1339–1341.

Staelin, D. H., and P. W. Rosenkranz, eds. (1978), High Resolution Passive Microwave Satellites, Applications Review Panel Report, Final Report, Research Laboratory of Electronics, Massachusetts Institute of Technology.

Stiles, W. H., and F. T. Ulaby (1980), The Active and Passive Microwave Response to Snow Parameters: Part 1—Wetness; Part 2—Water Equivalent of Dry Snow, *J. Geophys. Res.*, 85, pp. 1037–1049.

Straiton, A. W., C. W. Tolbert, and C. O. Britt (1958), Apparent Temperature Distributions of Some Terrestrial Materials and the Sun at 4.3 mm Wavelength, *J. Appl. Phys.*, 29, pp. 776–782.

Taylor, A. H., L. C. Young, and L. A. Hyland (1934), System for Detecting Objects by Radio, U. S. Patent 1,981,884.

Townsend, W. F. (1980), An Initial Assessment of the Performance Achieved by the SEASAT-1 Radar Altimeter, *IEEE Trans.*, OE-5, pp. 80–92.

Ulaby, F. T., R. K. Moore, R. Moe, and J. Holtzman (1972), On Microwave Remote Sensing of Vegetation, *Proc. 8th Intl. Symp. Rem. Sens. Env.*, University of Michigan, Ann Arbor.

Ulaby, F. T., and T. F. Bush (1976), Corn Growth as Monitored by Radar, *IEEE Trans. Ant. Prop.*, AP-24, pp. 819–828.

Ulaby, F. T., P. P. Batlivala, and M. C. Dobson (1978), Microwave Backscatter Dependence on Surface Roughness, Soil Moisture, and Soil Texture: Part 1—Bare Soil, *IEEE Trans. Geoscience Elect.*, GE-16, pp. 286–295.

Ulaby, F. T., W. H. Stiles, D. Brunfeldt, and E. Wilson (1979a), 1–35 GHz Microwave Scatterometer, *Proc. 1979 IEEE/MTT-S Intl. Microwave Symp.*, Orlando, Florida.

Ulaby, F. T., G. A. Bradley, and M. C. Dobson (1979b), Microwave Backscatter Dependence on Surface Roughness, Soil Moisture, and Soil Texture: Part 2—Vegetation-Covered Soil,

IEEE Trans. Geoscience Electr., GE-17, pp. 33–40.

Ulaby, F. T. (1980), Microwave Response of Vegetation, 23rd Ann. Conf. of the Committee on Space Research (COSPAR), Budapest, Hungary, June 2–14.

van Roessel, J. W., and R. D. de Godoy (1974), SLAR Mosaic for Project RADAM, *Photogram. Eng.*, 40, pp. 583–595.

Viksne, A., T. C. Liston, and C. D. Sapp (1969), SLR Reconnaissance of Panama, *Geophysics*, 34, pp. 54–64.

Waite, W. P. (1970), Broad Spectrum Electromagnetic Backscatter, Ph.D. Thesis, University of Kansas, Lawrence, Kansas.

Watson-Watt, Sir Robert (1957), *Three Steps to Victory*, Odhams Press, London.

Wilheit, T. T., A. T. C. Chang, M. S. V. Rao, E. B. Rodgers, and J. S. Theon (1977), A Satellite Technique for Quantitatively Mapping Rainfall Rates over the Ocean, *J. Appl. Meteorol.*, 16, pp. 551–560.

Wilheit, T. T. (1979), Microwave Radiometric Determination of Oceanographic and Meteorological Parameters, presented at COSPAR, Bangalore, India, June.

Zwally, H., and P. Gloersen (1977), Microwave Emissivity and Accumulation Rate of Polar Firn, *J. Glaciol.*, 18, pp. 195–215.

Chapter 2

Plane Waves

2-1 INTRODUCTION

This chapter deals with some common properties of plane waves in lossless and lossy media. It starts out with the derivation of the wave equation from Maxwell's equations and its simplest solution, the plane wave, in Section 2-2. Section 2-3 discusses the general form of the attenuation and phase constants in homogeneous lossy media together with various special cases of interest. The definitions of plane-wave polarization are given in Section 2-4, where the concept of coherence as applied to the degree of polarization and to scalar waves is explored. The two forms of Poynting vector commonly used are defined and applied to elliptically polarized plane waves in Section 2-5. In Section 2-6 the problem of plane-wave reflection and transmission across a plane dielectric boundary is treated. Expressions for reflectivity and transmissivity are also derived. The phenomena of total transmission and total reflection are treated in Section 2-7. Explicit forms of the transmitted wave in a finitely conducting medium are derived in Section 2-8, starting with the formal expression for the transmitted wave given in Section 2-6. Section 2-9 deals with waves in layered media and Section 2-10 treats media with a permittivity profile.

2-2 WAVE EQUATION AND PLANE WAVES IN HOMOGENEOUS UNBOUNDED MEDIA

In this section we shall derive the wave equations from Maxwell's equations in both the real-time fields and the phasor or complex fields. A simple solution to these wave equations is then examined, leading to the definitions of wavelength, wave number, phase velocity, and plane waves. Specially significant properties of plane waves are also discussed.

In a source-free region characterized by permeability μ and permittivity ε the electromagnetic fields satisfy Maxwell's equations of the form

$$\nabla \times \mathbf{E} = -\mu \frac{\partial \mathbf{H}}{\partial t}, \tag{2.1}$$

$$\nabla \times \mathbf{H} = \varepsilon \frac{\partial \mathbf{E}}{\partial t}. \tag{2.2}$$

Fawwaz T. Ulaby, Richard K. Moore, and Adrian K. Fung,
Microwave Remote Sensing: Active and Passive,
Vol. I: Microwave Remote Sensing Fundamentals and Radiometry　　　ISBN 0-201-10759-7

It is worth noting that the above equations form a dual. That is, (2.1) and (2.2) can be converted back and forth by the following relationships:

$$\mathbf{E} \leftrightarrow \mathbf{H},$$

$$\mu \leftrightarrow \varepsilon,$$

$$\mathbf{H} \leftrightarrow -\mathbf{E}.$$

As a result, when a problem described in terms of the electric field is solved, the analogous problem described in terms of the magnetic field can be obtained from these conversion relations. Further discussion of the dual property of $\mathbf{E}$ and $\mathbf{H}$ will be given in Section 2-6.

To obtain the governing equation for $\mathbf{E}$, we take the curl of (2.1) and then eliminate $\nabla \times \mathbf{H}$ by (2.2). Thus,

$$\nabla \times (\nabla \times \mathbf{E}) = -\mu\varepsilon \frac{\partial^2 \mathbf{E}}{\partial t^2}, \tag{2.3}$$

which is known as the homogeneous vector wave equation. Since the medium has been assumed to be homogeneous and source-free, $\nabla \cdot \mathbf{E}$ is zero and (2.3) simplifies to

$$\nabla^2 \mathbf{E} = \mu\varepsilon \frac{\partial^2 \mathbf{E}}{\partial t^2} \tag{2.4}$$

which is called the homogeneous wave equation.

A simple solution to (2.4) can be obtained by assuming sinusoidal time dependence as follows:

$$\mathbf{E}(\mathbf{r}, t) = \mathrm{Re}\{\mathbf{E}(\mathbf{r})e^{j\omega t}\}, \tag{2.5}$$

where ω is the radian frequency. Hence, the *phasor* or the *complex electric field* satisfies

$$\nabla^2 \mathbf{E}(\mathbf{r}) = -\omega^2 \mu\varepsilon \mathbf{E}(\mathbf{r}). \tag{2.6}$$

Note that in phasor representation the common factor, $e^{j\omega t}$, is usually understood and not written down explicitly. In rectangular coordinates, it can be readily verified that a solution to (2.6) has the form

$$\mathbf{E}(\mathbf{r}) = \mathbf{E}_0 \exp\left[\pm j(k_x x + k_y y + k_z z)\right] \tag{2.7}$$

where $\mathbf{E}_0$ is a constant vector and

$$k_x^2 + k_y^2 + k_z^2 = \omega^2 \mu\varepsilon \equiv k^2. \tag{2.8}$$

A more compact form for (2.7) can be obtained by defining:

$$\mathbf{k} = \hat{\mathbf{x}} k_x + \hat{\mathbf{y}} k_y + \hat{\mathbf{z}} k_z,$$

$$\mathbf{r} = \hat{\mathbf{x}} x + \hat{\mathbf{y}} y + \hat{\mathbf{z}} z,$$

where $\mathbf{k}$ is called the propagation vector (its magnitude k is called the wave number) and $\mathbf{r}$ is the displacement vector. Thus, (2.7) can be written as

$$\mathbf{E}(\mathbf{r}) = \mathbf{E}_0 \exp[\pm j \mathbf{k} \cdot \mathbf{r}].$$

By substituting $\mathbf{E}(\mathbf{r})$ in (2.5), the real-time field becomes

$$\mathbf{E}(\mathbf{r}, t) = \mathbf{E}_0 \cos(\omega t \pm \mathbf{k} \cdot \mathbf{r}). \tag{2.9}$$

This expression is recognized as two waves propagating in directions defined by the unit vectors $\pm \mathbf{k}/k$. For further interpretation of (2.9) it is convenient to rotate the coordinate system so that its z-axis is in the same direction as $\mathbf{k}$. In this case, (2.9) may be written as

$$\mathbf{E}(z, t) = \mathbf{E}_0 \cos(\omega t \pm kz). \tag{2.10}$$

Equation (2.10) represents two waves propagating in opposite directions along the z-axis with time phase ωt and space phase kz. Since

$$\omega = 2\pi f = 2\pi / T,$$

where f is the frequency in hertz and T is the *time period*, it is natural to apply analogy and define

$$k = 2\pi / \lambda,$$

where λ is the space period, or wavelength, in the medium. In view of (2.8), λ can also be expressed as

$$\lambda = 1 / (f\sqrt{\mu\varepsilon}).$$

Consider the positive-traveling wave. The surface on which the phase of the electric field is a constant is defined by

$$\omega t - kz = \text{constant}. \tag{2.11}$$

At any given time, this surface coincides with the plane defined by $z = $ constant. For this reason, (2.10) is said to represent plane waves. In the case considered, the plane of constant phase is also the plane of constant amplitude. Plane waves of this type are called *uniform plane waves*. The velocity of propagation of this constant phase plane, called the *phase velocity*, can be found by differentiating (2.11) with respect to time. Thus, the phase velocity is given by

$$v = \frac{dz}{dt} = \frac{\omega}{k} = \frac{1}{\sqrt{\mu\varepsilon}} . \tag{2.12}$$

The relation between $\mathbf{E}$ and $\mathbf{H}$ for a plane wave is easily found by working with phasor fields. Thus, we write (2.10) as

$$\mathbf{E}(z,t) = \mathrm{Re}\left\{\mathbf{E}_0 e^{j(\omega t \pm kz)}\right\}.$$

For simplicity consider only one component of the electric field, say $E_{x0} e^{j(\omega t - kz)}$. Substitution of this component in (2.1) yields

$$H_y(z) = \frac{k}{\omega\mu} E_{x0} e^{j(\omega t - kz)}.$$

Hence

$$H_y(z,t) = \frac{E_{x0}}{\eta} \cos(\omega t - kz) \tag{2.13}$$

where $\eta = \omega\mu/k = \sqrt{\mu/\varepsilon}$ is called the *intrinsic impedance* of the medium. It follows that the amplitudes of $\mathbf{E}$ and $\mathbf{H}$ (in plane waves) are related by η analogous to Ohm's law for voltage and current in circuit theory. It is interesting to note that the vector directions of $\mathbf{E}$, $\mathbf{H}$, and $\mathbf{k}$ for a uniform plane wave form an orthogonal system. In the case considered above,

$$\mathbf{E} = \hat{\mathbf{x}} E_x,$$
$$\mathbf{H} = \hat{\mathbf{y}} H_y,$$
$$\mathbf{k} = \hat{\mathbf{z}} k.$$

For any uniform plane wave $\mathbf{E} \times \mathbf{H}$ always points in the direction of propagation. Note that although the results (2.10) through (2.13) are derived with a special choice of coordinate, the definitions of wave number, wavelength, and phase velocity and the relation between the amplitudes of $\mathbf{E}$ and $\mathbf{H}$ are not coordinate-dependent and are valid in general (Durney and Johnson, 1969; Hoyt, 1974; Jordan and Balmain, 1968; Kraus and Carver, 1973).

2-3 PLANE WAVES IN A LOSSY HOMOGENEOUS MEDIUM

For a lossy medium characterized by μ, ε, and conductivity σ, Maxwell's equations become

$$\nabla \times \mathbf{E} = -\mu \frac{\partial \mathbf{H}}{\partial t},$$
$$\nabla \times \mathbf{H} = \sigma \mathbf{E} + \varepsilon \frac{\partial \mathbf{E}}{\partial t}.$$

Assuming harmonic time dependence as defined by (2.5), we obtain

$$\nabla \times \mathbf{E}(\mathbf{r}) = -j\omega\mu\mathbf{H}(\mathbf{r}), \tag{2.14}$$

$$\nabla \times \mathbf{H}(\mathbf{r}) = (\sigma + j\omega\varepsilon)\mathbf{E}(\mathbf{r})$$

$$\equiv j\omega\varepsilon_c\mathbf{E}(\mathbf{r}), \tag{2.15}$$

$$\varepsilon_c = \varepsilon - j\sigma/\omega \tag{2.16a}$$

$$\stackrel{\triangle}{=} \varepsilon' - j\varepsilon'', \tag{2.16b}$$

where ε_c is called the complex permittivity (or dielectric constant). It is a common practice to use ε' and ε'' to represent the real and imaginary parts of ε_c. Note that the definition of ε_c is dependent on the assumed form for the time dependence. In view of (2.6), the wave equation for **E** becomes

$$\nabla^2\mathbf{E}(\mathbf{r}) = -\omega^2\mu\varepsilon_c\mathbf{E}(\mathbf{r}). \tag{2.17}$$

When the direction of propagation of the plane-wave solution to (2.17) is chosen to be along the z-axis, (2.17) simplifies to

$$\frac{d^2\mathbf{E}(z)}{dz^2} = -\omega^2\mu\varepsilon_c\mathbf{E}(z). \tag{2.18}$$

From Section 2-2, the **E** and **H** fields have been shown to be transverse to their propagation direction. Hence, $\mathbf{E}(z)$ may have an $E_x(z)$ or $E_y(z)$ component. For the purpose of discussion consider the $E_x(z)$ component traveling along the positive z-axis. Since (2.18) is a special form of (2.6), (2.7) indicates that

$$E_x(z) = E_{x0}\exp\left(-j\omega\sqrt{\mu\varepsilon_c}\,z\right). \tag{2.19}$$

2-3.1 Low-Loss Medium

Under the assumption of a low-loss medium (i.e., $\omega\varepsilon \gg \sigma$),

$$j\omega\sqrt{\mu\varepsilon_c} \simeq j\omega\sqrt{\mu\varepsilon}\,(1 - j\sigma/2\omega\varepsilon)$$

$$= \eta\sigma/2 + j\omega\sqrt{\mu\varepsilon}\,. \tag{2.20}$$

The expression for $E_x(z)$ may be approximated as

$$E_x(z) \simeq E_{x0}\exp\left[-\eta\sigma z/2 - j\omega\sqrt{\mu\varepsilon}\,z\right]$$

$$\equiv E_{x0}\exp\left[-\alpha z - j\beta z\right], \tag{2.21}$$

where $\alpha = \eta\sigma/2$ is known as the *attenuation constant* and $\beta = \omega\sqrt{\mu\varepsilon}$ is called the *phase constant*. Again we can recover the real time expression for $E_x(z,t)$ by taking the real part of (2.21) multiplied by exp($j\omega t$):

$$E_x(z,t) = E_{x0} e^{-\alpha z} \cos(\omega t - \beta z). \tag{2.22}$$

It follows from (2.9) and (2.22) that the plane-wave solution to the wave equation in a lossless and a slightly lossy medium differs by an exponential factor of the form $e^{-\alpha z}$ which accounts for the attenuation present in the lossy medium. Note that the phase constant is equal to the wave number in the lossless medium. This is not generally true for media with larger loss.

2-3.2 High-Loss Medium

For a conducting medium (i.e., highly lossy medium with $\sigma \gg \omega \varepsilon$),

$$j\omega\sqrt{\mu\varepsilon_c} \simeq \sqrt{j\omega\mu\sigma} = \sqrt{\omega\mu\sigma/2} + j\sqrt{\omega\mu\sigma/2}.$$

Equation (2.19) reduces to

$$E_x(z) = E_{x0} \exp\left[-\sqrt{\omega\mu\sigma/2}\, z - j\sqrt{\omega\mu\sigma/2}\, z\right]. \tag{2.23}$$

The real time expression can again be written in the form given by (2.22). However, the values for α and β in (2.22) are now given by

$$\beta = \alpha = \sqrt{\omega\mu\sigma/2}. \tag{2.24}$$

Hence, the phase constant is now different from the lossless case. The characteristic medium parameter $(2/\omega\mu\sigma)^{1/2}$, which represents the distance over which the field amplitude decreases by a factor of $1/e$, is called the *skin depth*. It is used as an effective depth of penetration for the electromagnetic wave as it impinges upon a conducting medium.

2-3.3 A General Lossy Medium

For a lossy medium which is neither conducting nor only slightly lossy, the values of both the phase constant and the attenuation constant can no longer be approximated. In this case

$$j\omega\sqrt{\mu\varepsilon_c} = j\omega(\mu\varepsilon - j\mu\sigma/\omega)^{1/2}$$

$$\equiv j\omega\sqrt{\mu\varepsilon}(1 - j\tan\delta)^{1/2}$$

$$= jk(1 - j\tan\delta)^{1/2}. \tag{2.25a}$$

An alternative representation of (2.25a) is to write it in terms of the wave number in air, k_0, and the relative permittivity, $\varepsilon_r = \varepsilon_c/\varepsilon_0 = \varepsilon_r' - j\varepsilon_r''$. Thus,

$$
\begin{aligned}
j\omega\sqrt{\mu\varepsilon_c} &= jk_0(\varepsilon_r' - j\varepsilon_r'')^{1/2} \\
&= jk_0\sqrt{\varepsilon_r'}\,(1 - j\tan\delta)^{1/2},
\end{aligned}
\tag{2.25b}
$$

where $\tan\delta = \sigma/\omega\varepsilon = \varepsilon''/\varepsilon'$ is known as the loss tangent. From (2.25) α and β can be shown to be

$$
\alpha = k_0|\operatorname{Im}\{\sqrt{\varepsilon_r}\}| = k\left[\tfrac{1}{2}\left(\sqrt{1+\tan^2\delta}-1\right)\right]^{1/2},
\tag{2.26}
$$

$$
\beta = k_0\operatorname{Re}\{\sqrt{\varepsilon_r}\} = k\left[\tfrac{1}{2}\left(\sqrt{1+\tan^2\delta}+1\right)\right]^{1/2}.
\tag{2.27}
$$

Since the above results for α and β are the most general, it is possible to obtain the special cases discussed earlier in terms of k and $\tan\delta$. Thus, for the low-loss case where $1 \gg \tan^2\delta$,

$$
\begin{aligned}
\alpha &\simeq \tfrac{1}{2}k\tan\delta, \\
\beta &\simeq k,
\end{aligned}
\tag{2.28}
$$

and for conducting media where $\tan^2\delta \gg 1$, we get

$$
\alpha \simeq \beta = k\left(\tfrac{1}{2}\tan\delta\right)^{1/2}.
\tag{2.29}
$$

For related discussions see Plonus (1978), Ramo et al. (1967), and Stratton (1941).

In many studies particularly those related to the atmosphere it is common practice to speak of the *refractive index* instead of the permittivity or dielectric property of the medium. The standard notation for the refractive index is n, and

$$
\begin{aligned}
n^2 &= \varepsilon_r = \varepsilon_r' - j\varepsilon_r'', \\
n &= n' - jn'' \\
&= (\beta - j\alpha)/k_0.
\end{aligned}
$$

2-4 POLARIZATION OF PLANE WAVES AND COHERENCE

For a uniform plane wave traveling in the positive z-direction, the electric field vector must lie in the xy-plane perpendicular to the z-axis. At any fixed point in space the electric field vector is a function of time. As time changes, the tip of the **E** vector traces a curve in the xy-plane. When this curve is a straight line, the plane wave is said to be *linearly polarized*. When this curve is a circle, the wave is *circularly polarized*, and when it forms an ellipse, the wave is *elliptically*

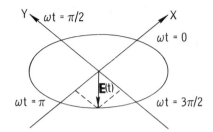

Fig. 2.1 A right-hand, elliptically polarized **E** field with sinusoidal time dependence.

polarized (see Fig. 2.1). In the case of circular or elliptic polarization, the tip may move either clockwise or counterclockwise. To distinguish the two, the wave is said to be *right-hand polarized* when the right-hand thumb points in the direction of propagation while the other fingers point in the direction of the tip motion. Similarly, if that description fits the left-hand thumb and fingers, the wave is *left-hand polarized* (Jordan and Balmain, 1968; Kong, 1975; Kraus and Carver, 1973; Ramo et al., 1967).

A mathematical description of the linearly polarized wave can be written

$$E_x(z,t) = E_{x0}\cos(\omega t - \beta z).$$

For a fixed value of z the electric field varies with time in magnitude along the x-axis. An elliptically polarized wave is the sum of two linearly polarized waves separated 90° in space and θ degrees in time:

$$\mathbf{E}(z,t) = \hat{\mathbf{x}} E_x(z,t) + \hat{\mathbf{y}} E_y(z,t)$$
$$= \hat{\mathbf{x}} E_{x0} \cos(\omega t - \beta z) + \hat{\mathbf{y}} E_{y0} \cos(\omega t - \beta z + \theta). \qquad (2.30)$$

To show that the above equation describes in general an ellipse at all times for a fixed z, let us set z equal to zero. It follows that

$$E_x = E_{x0} \cos \omega t, \qquad (2.31)$$
$$E_y = E_{y0} \cos(\omega t + \theta). \qquad (2.32)$$

Equations (2.31) and (2.32) constitute, in general, a parametric representation for an ellipse centered at the origin of the xy-plane. The following special cases are of interest:

1. When $E_{x0} = 0$ or $E_{y0} = 0$, the wave becomes linearly polarized along y- or x-directions respectively. The wave is also linearly polarized along the direction 45° from the x-axis when $\theta = 0$ and $E_{x0} = E_{y0}$.
2. When $E_{x0} = E_{y0}$ and $\theta = \pm 90°$, the wave is circularly polarized. At $\omega t = 0$, $z = 0$, and $\theta = 90°$, (2.31) and (2.32) yield

$$E_x = E_{x0},$$
$$E_y = 0,$$

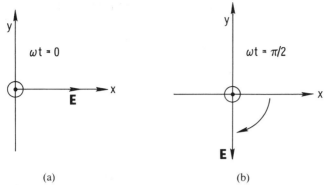

(a)   (b)

Fig. 2.2 (a) **E** location at $z=0$, $\omega t=0$, and $\theta=90°$; (b) **E** location at $z=0$, $\omega t=\pi/2$, and $\theta=90°$. Since the wave advances along the positive z-axis, this figure shows that $\theta=90°$ gives rise to a left-hand polarized wave. Similarly, if $\theta=-90°$, the wave is right-hand polarized.

as shown in Fig. 2.2(a). When ωt increases to $\pi/2$, the equations become

$$E_x=0,$$
$$E_y=-E_{y0},$$

as shown in Fig. 2.2(b). Thus, the **E** vector goes through a clockwise rotation in Fig. 2.2(b) and corresponds to a left-hand polarized wave.

In the above discussions only completely polarized plane waves have been considered. Signals transmitted from single-frequency or multifrequency transmitters are of this type. On the other hand, electromagnetic signals emitted by physical objects, irregular terrains, or inhomogeneous media usually cover a wide frequency band and consist of a superposition of many statistically independent waves of different polarizations. There is no correlation between the component waves of such a signal, and therefore it is said to be an *incoherent* or *unpolarized wave*. Between these two extremes there exist also the partially polarized waves which may arise when polarized signals are scattered by statistical targets. To identify the *state of polarization* or *degree of coherence* of a plane wave, the magnitude of the normalized cross-correlation between the x- and y-components in phasor representation has been introduced by Born and Wolf (1964) and others (Ko, 1962; Kraus and Carver, 1973). It is defined as follows:

$$\rho_{xy}=\left|\frac{\langle E_x E_y^* \rangle}{\left(\langle|E_x|^2\rangle\langle|E_y|^2\rangle\right)^{1/2}}\right|, \tag{2.33}$$

where $\langle\cdots\rangle$ denotes an average operator which is needed when the amplitudes or phases of the field components are functions of time:

$$\langle\cdots\rangle=\lim_{T\to\infty}\frac{1}{T}\int_0^T\cdots dt.$$

In the case of completely polarized waves the amplitudes and phases of the wave components are constants in time, and therefore no averaging is necessary. As an example, let us write (2.30) in phasor form:

$$\mathbf{E}(z) = \hat{\mathbf{x}} E_{x0} e^{-j\beta z} + \hat{\mathbf{y}} E_{y0} e^{-j\beta z + j\theta} \tag{2.34}$$

and substitute the field components in (2.33):

$$\rho_{xy} = \frac{|E_{x0} E_{y0} e^{-j\theta}|}{|E_{x0}||E_{y0}|} = 1. \tag{2.35}$$

It follows that $\rho_{xy} = 1$ for completely polarized waves.

Natural radiation received by an antenna operating at radian frequency ω with a narrow bandwidth $\Delta\omega$ can be viewed as a *quasimonochromatic plane wave*. That is, the received signal can be treated as a single-frequency plane wave whose amplitude and phase are slowly varying time functions. In other words the signal actually has a finite bandwidth, $\Delta\omega$, but its spectral components are appreciable only near the mean radian frequency, ω. Mathematically, such a signal in phasor form is analogous to (2.34) and can be written as

$$\mathbf{E}(z) = \hat{\mathbf{x}} E_{x0}(t) e^{-j\beta z + j\theta_x(t)} + \hat{\mathbf{y}} E_{y0}(t) e^{-j\beta z + j\theta_y(t)}, \tag{2.36}$$

where for natural radiation $E_{x0}(t), E_{y0}(t), \theta_x(t), \theta_y(t)$ are statistically independent random time functions. To compute ρ_{xy} using (2.36), note that

$$E_x = E_{x0}(t) e^{-j\beta z + j\theta_x(t)},$$
$$E_y = E_{y0}(t) e^{-j\beta z + j\theta_y(t)}.$$

Hence, the numerator in (2.33) becomes

$$\langle E_x E_y^* \rangle = \langle E_{x0}(t) E_{y0}(t) e^{j(\theta_x - \theta_y)} \rangle \tag{2.37}$$

$$= \langle E_{x0}(t) \rangle \langle E_{y0}(t) \rangle \langle e^{j\theta_x} \rangle \langle e^{-j\theta_y} \rangle. \tag{2.38}$$

Equation (2.38) is zero if one of the random amplitude functions has zero mean or if one of the phase functions is randomly distributed over $(0, 2\pi)$, which is the case for natural radiation. For this reason natural radiation has $\rho_{xy} = 0$ and is said to be incoherent or unpolarized.

When a plane wave is scattered from a statistical target and is propagating along an axis of a chosen coordinate, the scattered wave can also be represented by (2.36). However, in general $E_{x0}(t)$, $E_{y0}(t)$, $\theta_x(t)$, and $\theta_y(t)$ are not statistically independent and the cross-correlation given by (2.37) is not zero. By applying Schwartz's inequality to (2.33), it follows that

$$\rho_{xy} \leq 1$$

in this case. Since this case falls between the completely polarized and unpolarized cases, this type of wave is referred to as a *partially polarized wave* or *partially coherent wave*.

The concept of coherence has also been used for scalar waves containing more than one component. For instance, a scalar wave containing two components is said to be a coherent wave if the substitution of its two components in (2.33) results in $\rho_{xy} = 1$. Similarly, the wave is said to be incoherent when $\rho_{xy} = 0$. Since ρ_{xy} is proportional to the cross terms in power calculation, it follows that the power of an incoherent wave is the algebraic sum of the powers of its component waves.

2-5 POYNTING VECTOR FOR PLANE WAVES

In phasor or complex representation, the *complex Poynting vector*, $\mathbf{S}_c$, is

$$\mathbf{S}_c = \tfrac{1}{2}\mathbf{E}(\mathbf{r}) \times \mathbf{H}^*(\mathbf{r}), \tag{2.39}$$

where * denotes the complex conjugate.

The *time-average Poynting vector*, $\mathbf{S}_a$, is the real part of $\mathbf{S}_c$, or

$$\mathbf{S}_a = \tfrac{1}{2}\mathrm{Re}\{\mathbf{E}(\mathbf{r}) \times \mathbf{H}^*(\mathbf{r})\}. \tag{2.40}$$

The dimensions of $\mathbf{S}_a$ are power per unit area. To find $\mathbf{S}_a$ for an elliptically polarized plane wave given by (2.30), note that in complex form the plane wave is

$$\mathbf{E}(z) = \hat{\mathbf{x}} E_{x0} e^{-j\beta z} + \hat{\mathbf{y}} E_{y0} e^{-j\beta z + j\theta}. \tag{2.41}$$

From Maxwell's equations, the corresponding complex $\mathbf{H}$ field is

$$\mathbf{H}(z) = -\hat{\mathbf{x}} \frac{E_{y0}}{\eta} e^{-j\beta z + j\theta} + \hat{\mathbf{y}} \frac{E_{x0}}{\eta} e^{-j\beta z}, \tag{2.42}$$

where η is the intrinsic impedance of the medium in which the plane wave is propagating. The expression for the complex Poynting vector becomes

$$\begin{aligned}
\mathbf{S}_c &= \tfrac{1}{2}\mathbf{E}(z) \times \mathbf{H}^*(z) \\
&= \frac{\hat{\mathbf{z}}}{2\eta^*} \left\{ |E_{x0}|^2 + |E_{y0}|^2 \right\}.
\end{aligned} \tag{2.43}$$

The time-average Poynting vector is

$$\mathbf{S}_a = \frac{\hat{\mathbf{z}}}{2} \left(|E_{x0}|^2 + |E_{y0}|^2 \right) \mathrm{Re}\left\{ \frac{1}{\eta^*} \right\}. \tag{2.44}$$

Since η is a function of the permittivity of the medium, which is in general complex, it is a good practice not to write η outside the real-part operator. Additional and more detailed discussions on the Poynting vector can be found in Durney and Johnson (1969), Hayt (1974), Jordan and Balmain (1968), Kraus and Carver (1973), Plonus (1978), and Ramo et al. (1967).

2-6 REFLECTION AND TRANSMISSION AT A PLANE INTERFACE

As mentioned in previous sections, the field vectors of a uniform plane wave always lie in a plane perpendicular to its direction of propagation. Since any two-dimensional vector can be decomposed into two orthogonal components, it is convenient to consider each of these linearly polarized components independently. The selection of these orthogonal components for a reflection or transmission problem is usually done with respect to the plane of incidence, which is defined as the plane containing the normal vector to the interface and the propagation vector of the plane wave. When the incident **E** vector is perpendicular to the plane of incidence, it is said to be perpendicularly polarized, horizontally polarized, or a TE wave. When the incident **E** vector is parallel to the plane of incidence, it is said to be parallel polarized, vertically polarized, or a TM wave. Both TE and TM waves are linearly polarized (Kong, 1975; Kraus and Carver, 1973; Plonus, 1978).

Figure 2.3 depicts the case of a TE wave incident upon the interface at $z=0$ between two media characterized by ε_1, μ_1 and ε_2, μ_2 respectively. For simplicity the law of reflection has been assumed in Figure 2.3, although it

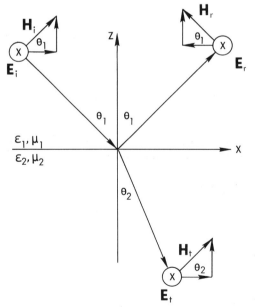

Fig. 2.3   Reflection and transmission of a horizontally polarized wave.

follows later from the matching of boundary conditions. The phasor forms of the incident, reflected, and transmitted waves, with the time factor $e^{j\omega t}$ understood, are as follows:

$$\mathbf{E}_i = \hat{y} E_0 \exp\left[-j(k_{1x}x - k_{1z}z)\right], \tag{2.45}$$

$$\mathbf{E}_r = \hat{y} R_\perp E_0 \exp\left[-j(k_{1x}x + k_{1z}z)\right], \tag{2.46}$$

$$\mathbf{E}_t = \hat{y} T_\perp E_0 \exp\left[-j(k_{2x}x - k_{2z}z)\right], \tag{2.47}$$

where $k_{1x} = k_1 \sin\theta_1$, $k_{1z} = k_1 \cos\theta_1$, $k_{2x} = k_2 \sin\theta_2$, and $k_{2z} = k_2 \cos\theta_2$. In (2.45)–(2.47), the angle of transmission θ_2, the reflection coefficient $R_\perp$, and the transmission coefficient $T_\perp$ are the only unknowns. The magnetic fields corresponding to (2.45) through (2.47) can be found from (2.1):

$$\mathbf{H}_i = \frac{E_0}{\eta_1}(\hat{x}\cos\theta_1 + \hat{z}\sin\theta_1)\exp\left[-j(k_{1x}x - k_{1z}z)\right], \tag{2.48}$$

$$\mathbf{H}_r = \frac{R_\perp E_0}{\eta_1}(-\hat{x}\cos\theta_1 + \hat{z}\sin\theta_1)\exp\left[-j(k_{1x}x + k_{1z}z)\right], \tag{2.49}$$

$$\mathbf{H}_t = \frac{T_\perp E_0}{\eta_2}(\hat{x}\cos\theta_2 + \hat{z}\sin\theta_2)\exp\left[-j(k_{2x}x - k_{2z}z)\right]. \tag{2.50}$$

To find θ_2, $R_\perp$, and $T_\perp$ the expressions for $\mathbf{E}$ and $\mathbf{H}$ may be substituted into the boundary conditions, which require the tangential $\mathbf{E}$ and $\mathbf{H}$ fields to be continuous across the plane interface at $z=0$. Hence, the equality of the phases leads to Snell's law:

$$k_2 \sin\theta_2 = k_1 \sin\theta_1, \tag{2.51}$$

and the equality of the tangential field amplitudes yields

$$1 + R_\perp = T_\perp, \tag{2.52a}$$

$$\eta_2(1 - R_\perp)\cos\theta_1 = \eta_1 T_\perp \cos\theta_2. \tag{2.52b}$$

From (2.51), θ_2 is determined in terms of θ_1, and from (2.52), $R_\perp$ and $T_\perp$ are found as follows:

$$R_\perp = \frac{\eta_2 \cos\theta_1 - \eta_1 \cos\theta_2}{\eta_2 \cos\theta_1 + \eta_1 \cos\theta_2}, \tag{2.53}$$

$$T_\perp = \frac{2\eta_2 \cos\theta_1}{\eta_2 \cos\theta_1 + \eta_1 \cos\theta_2}. \tag{2.54}$$

The above coefficients are for the $\mathbf{E}$ fields. To find the power reflection coefficient or reflectivity Γ, and transmissivity Υ, note that these coefficients are defined with respect to the normal components of the time-average

Poynting's vectors as follows:

$$\Gamma = \frac{\hat{z} \cdot \mathbf{S}_{ar}}{-\hat{z} \cdot \mathbf{S}_{ai}}, \tag{2.55}$$

$$\Upsilon = \frac{\hat{z} \cdot \mathbf{S}_{at}}{\hat{z} \cdot \mathbf{S}_{ai}}. \tag{2.56}$$

For the TE wave, the *reflectivity* is

$$\Gamma_{\perp} = \frac{\text{Re}\{|R_{\perp} E_0|^2 (\cos\theta_1)/\eta_1\}}{\text{Re}\{|E_0|^2 (\cos\theta_1)/\eta_1\}} = |R_{\perp}|^2 \tag{2.57}$$

and the *transmissivity* is

$$\Upsilon_{\perp} = \frac{\text{Re}\{|T_{\perp} E_0|^2 (\cos\theta_2)/\eta_2\}}{\text{Re}\{|E_0|^2 (\cos\theta_1)/\eta_1\}} = \frac{\text{Re}\{(\cos\theta_2)/\eta_2\}}{\text{Re}\{(\cos\theta_1)/\eta_1\}} |T_{\perp}|^2. \tag{2.58}$$

It is worthwhile to note that the field coefficients satisfy

$$1 + R_{\perp} = T_{\perp},$$

while the power coefficients satisfy

$$\Gamma_{\perp} + \Upsilon_{\perp} = 1,$$

which is a statement of energy conservation.

Due to the dual nature of the electromagnetic fields and the analogy which exists between the TE and TM waves (i.e., Fig. 2.3 also depicts the vertically polarized case, if we replace $\mathbf{E}$ by $\mathbf{H}$ and $\mathbf{H}$ by $-\mathbf{E}$), it is possible to obtain the reflection and transmission coefficients for the $\mathbf{H}$ fields in the vertically polarized case from (2.53) and (2.54) by interchanging μ and ε:

$$R_{\parallel} = \frac{\eta_1 \cos\theta_1 - \eta_2 \cos\theta_2}{\eta_1 \cos\theta_1 + \eta_2 \cos\theta_2}, \tag{2.59}$$

$$T_{\parallel} = \frac{2\eta_1 \cos\theta_1}{\eta_1 \cos\theta_1 + \eta_2 \cos\theta_2}. \tag{2.60}$$

Similarly, the reflectivity and transmissivity for the vertically polarized case are

$$\Gamma_{\parallel} = |R_{\parallel}|^2, \tag{2.61}$$

$$\Upsilon_{\parallel} = \frac{\text{Re}\{\eta_2 \cos\theta_2\}}{\text{Re}\{\eta_1 \cos\theta_1\}} |T_{\parallel}|^2. \tag{2.62}$$

Equations (2.58) and (2.62) are formally valid also for lossy media where the intrinsic impedance and the cosine of the polar angle are complex. The explicit form of the complex cosine may be found from the results in Section 2-8. Note that the real-part operators in (2.58) and (2.62) are essential not only for lossy media but also for cases of total reflection in lossless media, where $\cos\theta_2$ becomes purely imaginary. In checking energy conservation η_1 and $\cos\theta_1$ should be taken to be real. The reason is that any loss of energy in the incident wave before it reaches the boundary does not enter into reflection or transmission.

2-7 TOTAL REFLECTION AND BREWSTER ANGLE

In considering the plane-wave transmission problem in the previous section, the *angle of transmission* is found from Snell's law:

$$\sin\theta_2 = \frac{k_1 \sin\theta_1}{k_2}. \tag{2.63}$$

If the wave is incident from a dense to a less dense medium (i.e., $k_1 > k_2$), it is possible for the right-hand side of (2.63) to be greater than one. In this case no real angle of transmission exists and the wave is said to be totally reflected. The smallest incidence angle at which this phenomenon occurs is called the *critical angle*, θ_c, and it is defined by

$$\sin\theta_c = k_2/k_1. \tag{2.64}$$

Thus, all waves incident at angles greater than θ_c suffer total reflection (Durney and Johnson, 1969; Plonus, 1978; Ramo et al., 1967). Since

$$\begin{aligned}
\cos\theta_2 &= \left(1 - \sin^2\theta_2\right)^{1/2} \\
&= \left(1 - \frac{k_2^2 \sin^2\theta_2}{k_2^2}\right)^{1/2} \\
&= \left(1 - \frac{k_1^2 \sin^2\theta_1}{k_2^2}\right)^{1/2} \\
&= j\left(\frac{k_1^2 \sin^2\theta_1}{k_2^2} - 1\right)^{1/2},
\end{aligned} \tag{2.65}$$

it follows that for $\theta_1 > \theta_c$, $\cos\theta_2$ is purely imaginary. Upon substituting (2.65) in (2.57), and (2.61), it follows that

$$\Gamma_\parallel = \Gamma_\perp = 1$$

for lossless media. Under the same condition, (2.58) and (2.62) yield

$$\Upsilon_\perp = \Upsilon_\parallel = 0,$$

which indicates that no average energy can be transmitted into the lower medium. This phenomenon of total reflection holds for either TE or TM waves.

Another phenomenon of interest which relates to plane-wave transmission across a plane boundary between lossless media is that there exists an angle at which total transmission occurs for the vertically polarized wave. This angle is called the *Brewster angle*, θ_B, and it can be obtained by setting (Hayt, 1974; Jordan and Balmain, 1968; Kraus and Carver, 1973)

$$R_\parallel = 0.$$

In dielectric media, $R_\parallel = 0$ leads to

$$\sqrt{\varepsilon_2}\cos\theta_B = \sqrt{\varepsilon_1}\cos\theta_2$$

$$= \sqrt{\varepsilon_1}\left(1 - \frac{\varepsilon_1\sin^2\theta_B}{\varepsilon_2}\right)^{1/2},$$

or

$$\tan\theta_B = (\varepsilon_2/\varepsilon_1)^{1/2}. \tag{2.66}$$

Since $T_\parallel = R_\parallel + 1$, it is clear that at Brewster angle $T_\parallel = 1$. Note that the phenomenon of total transmission does not occur for horizontal polarization.

2-8 REFRACTION IN A CONDUCTING MEDIUM

When a plane wave is incident upon a finitely conducting medium, the laws of Fresnel and Snell are still valid in a purely formal way. Since the medium permittivity is complex, the Fresnel reflection 'coefficients are now complex, indicating that an incident wave will be modified in both amplitude and phase upon reflection. The problem of using Snell's law to find the angle of transmission is more involved. However, a direct application of Snell's law is still possible and leads to a transmitted wave which is attenuated in amplitude (Stratton, 1941).

Assume a horizontally polarized plane wave incident upon a plane boundary from a lossless dielectric medium on a lossy medium. From Section 2-6, Eq. (2.47), the transmitted wave is given formally by

$$\mathbf{E}_t = \hat{\mathbf{y}}T_\perp E_0\exp\left[-j(k_{2x}x - k_{2z}z)\right].$$

Since $k_{1x} = k_{2x} = k_1 \sin \theta_1$, only $k_{2z} = k_2 \cos \theta_2$ need be determined for the lossy-medium case where both k_2 and θ_2 are now complex. Formally,

$$k_2 \cos \theta_2 = k_2 (1 - \sin^2 \theta_2)^{1/2}.$$

By Snell's law,

$$\sin \theta_2 = \frac{k_1 \sin \theta_1}{k_2}.$$

Hence,

$$k_2 \cos \theta_2 = (k_2^2 - k_1^2 \sin^2 \theta_1)^{1/2}.$$

From (2.21) and (2.25), $k_2 = \beta - j\alpha$, where α, β are given by (2.26) and (2.27). Thus,

$$k_2 \cos \theta_2 = \left[(\beta - j\alpha)^2 - k_1^2 \sin^2 \theta_1 \right]^{1/2}$$
$$= \left[(\beta^2 - \alpha^2 - k_1^2 \sin^2 \theta_1)^2 + (2\alpha\beta)^2 \right]^{1/4} e^{-j\gamma/2}, \qquad (2.67)$$

where

$$\gamma = \tan^{-1} \left[\frac{2\alpha\beta}{\beta^2 - \alpha^2 - k_1^2 \sin^2 \theta_1} \right].$$

In view of the trigonometric identities

$$\cos \tfrac{1}{2}\gamma = \left[\tfrac{1}{2}(1 + \cos \gamma) \right]^{1/2},$$
$$\sin \tfrac{1}{2}\gamma = \left[\tfrac{1}{2}(1 - \cos \gamma) \right]^{1/2},$$

(2.67) can be written as

$$k_2 \cos \theta_2 = \frac{1}{\sqrt{2}} \left\{ \left[(p^2 + q^2)^{1/2} + q \right]^{1/2} - j \left[(p^2 + q^2)^{1/2} - q \right]^{1/2} \right\}, \qquad (2.68)$$

where

$$p = 2\alpha\beta,$$
$$q = \beta^2 - \alpha^2 - k_1^2 \sin^2 \theta_1.$$

With $k_2 \cos \theta_2$ expressed in terms of α, β, and θ_1, the transmitted wave is known. It has an attenuation factor given by

$$\exp\left\{2^{-1/2}\left[(p^2+q^2)^{1/2}-q\right]^{1/2}z\right\}$$

and a phase factor given by

$$\exp\left\{-jk_{2x}x+j2^{-1/2}\left[(p^2+q^2)^{1/2}+q\right]^{1/2}z\right\}.$$

The *real angle of transmission*, χ, can be found from the phase

$$\tan\chi=\frac{k_{2x}}{2^{-1/2}\left[(p^2+q^2)^{1/2}+q\right]^{1/2}}. \tag{2.69}$$

2-9 LAYERED MEDIA

The problem of reflection and transmission at a plane boundary can be generalized to a multilayer case by evaluating the fields existing within a layer and then using a matrix technique to sum the effects of all the layers. A method to compute the reflection coefficient R and the transmission coefficient T for an n-layer medium follows (Kong, 1975).

Figure 2.4 depicts an n-layer medium. Assume a horizontally polarized incident field of the form

$$\mathbf{E}^i=\hat{\mathbf{y}}E_y=\hat{\mathbf{y}}\exp[j\omega t-jk_0x\sin\theta_0+jk_0z\cos\theta_0].$$

Then, from (2.6) the governing equation for the electric field in any layer is

$$\left(\frac{\partial^2}{\partial x^2}+\frac{\partial^2}{\partial z^2}+\omega^2\mu\varepsilon\right)E_y=0. \tag{2.70}$$

Hence, with the time factor $e^{j\omega t}$ understood, the solution to (2.70) for the mth layer is

$$E_{ym}=\left(A_me^{jk_{zm}z}+C_me^{-jk_{zm}z}\right)e^{-jk_0x\sin\theta_0}. \tag{2.71}$$

From Maxwell's equations, the corresponding magnetic fields are

$$H_{xm}=\frac{k_{zm}}{\omega\mu_m}\left(A_me^{jk_{zm}z}-C_me^{-jk_{zm}z}\right)e^{-jk_0x\sin\theta_0}, \tag{2.72}$$

$$H_{zm}=\frac{k_0\sin\theta_0}{\omega\mu_m}\left(A_me^{jk_{zm}z}+C_me^{-jk_{zm}z}\right)e^{-jk_0x\sin\theta_0}. \tag{2.73}$$

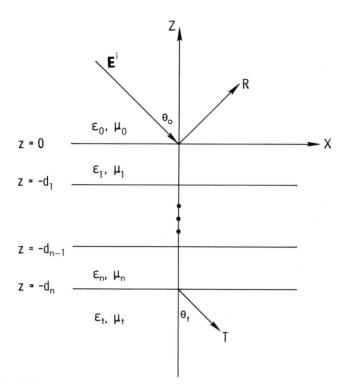

Fig. 2.4 Reflection and transmission for an *n*-layer medium.

To find k_{zm} we can substitute (2.71) in (2.70) and obtain

$$k_{zm} = \left(\omega^2 \mu_m \varepsilon_m - k_0^2 \sin^2 \theta_0\right)^{1/2}. \tag{2.74}$$

To relate the amplitudes A_m, C_m to the amplitudes A_{m+1}, C_{m+1}, we apply the boundary conditions at $z = -d_m$. From the continuity of the tangential electric fields, we get

$$A_m e^{-jk_{zm}d_m} + C_m e^{jk_{zm}d_m} = A_{m+1} e^{-jk_{z(m+1)}d_m} + C_{m+1} e^{jk_{z(m+1)}d_m}. \tag{2.75}$$

From the continuity of tangential magnetic fields, we get in view of (2.72)

$$\mu_{m+1} k_{zm} \left(A_m e^{-jk_{zm}d_m} - C_m e^{jk_{zm}d_m}\right)$$
$$= \mu_m k_{z(m+1)} \left(A_{m+1} e^{-jk_{z(m+1)}d_m} - C_{m+1} e^{jk_{z(m+1)}d_m}\right). \tag{2.76}$$

In matrix form (2.75) and (2.76) can be combined in one equation as

$$\begin{bmatrix} A_m e^{-jk_{zm}d_m} \\ C_m e^{jk_{zm}d_m} \end{bmatrix} = B_{m(m+1)} \begin{bmatrix} A_{m+1} e^{-jk_{z(m+1)}d_{m+1}} \\ C_{m+1} e^{jk_{z(m+1)}d_{m+1}} \end{bmatrix}, \tag{2.77}$$

where

$$B_{m(m+1)} = \frac{1}{2}\left(1 + \frac{\mu_m k_{z(m+1)}}{\mu_{m+1}k_{zm}}\right)$$

$$\times \begin{bmatrix} e^{jk_{z(m+1)}(d_{m+1}-d_m)} & R_{m(m+1)}e^{-jk_{z(m+1)}(d_{m+1}-d_m)} \\ R_{m(m+1)}e^{jk_{z(m+1)}(d_{m+1}-d_m)} & e^{-jk_{z(m+1)}(d_{m+1}-d_m)} \end{bmatrix},$$

$$R_{m(m+1)} = \frac{\mu_{m+1}k_{zm} - \mu_m k_{z(m+1)}}{\mu_{m+1}k_{zm} + \mu_m k_{z(m+1)}}.$$

It is seen that $R_{m(m+1)}$ is the Fresnel reflection coefficient for horizontal polarization at the boundary $z = -d_m$ within the medium defined by ε_m. The matrix $B_{m(m+1)}$, is called the *backward propagation matrix*, since it permits A_m, C_m to be expressed in terms of A_{m+1}, C_{m+1}. Similarly, we can also express A_{m+1}, C_{m+1} in terms of A_m, C_m, as

$$\begin{bmatrix} A_{m+1}e^{-jk_{z(m+1)}d_{m+1}} \\ C_{m+1}e^{jk_{z(m+1)}d_{m+1}} \end{bmatrix} = F_{(m+1)m}\begin{bmatrix} A_m e^{-jk_{zm}d_m} \\ C_m e^{jk_{zm}d_m} \end{bmatrix}, \tag{2.78}$$

where

$$F_{(m+1)m} = \frac{1}{2}\left(1 + \frac{\mu_{m+1}k_{zm}}{\mu_m k_{z(m+1)}}\right)$$

$$\times \begin{bmatrix} e^{-jk_{z(m+1)}(d_{m+1}-d_m)} & -R_{m(m+1)}e^{-jk_{z(m+1)}(d_{m+1}-d_m)} \\ -R_{m(m+1)}e^{jk_{z(m+1)}(d_{m+1}-d_m)} & e^{jk_{z(m+1)}(d_{m+1}-d_m)} \end{bmatrix}.$$

The matrix $F_{(m+1)m}$ is called the *forward propagation matrix*. It allows the field amplitudes in the $(m+1)$th layer to be expressed in terms of those in the mth layer. Upon substituting (2.77) into (2.78) or vice versa, it follows that

$$B_{m(m+1)}F_{(m+1)m} = I,$$

where I is the identity matrix. Since $B_{m(m+1)}$ and $F_{(m+1)m}$ are not independent of each other, either one may be used to compute the reflection and transmission coefficients of the n-layer medium.

To use the backward propagation matrix to compute R and T, note that the amplitudes for the incident and reflected fields are E_y and RE_y. From (2.77) these amplitudes can be related to those in layer 1 by B_{01} and to those in layer 2 by $B_{01}B_{12}$ etc. In the semiinfinite medium below layer n there is only a transmitted field amplitude. The value for d_t in (2.77) can be an arbitrary finite number when we reach the boundary $z = -d_n$, since the d_t in the transmitted field will cancel with that in B_{nt}. Hence, the incident and the reflected field amplitudes are related to the transmitted field amplitudes by

$$\begin{bmatrix} 1 \\ R \end{bmatrix} = B_{01} B_{12} \cdots B_{nt} \begin{bmatrix} Te^{-jk_{zt}d_t} \\ 0 \end{bmatrix} \tag{2.79}$$

Since (2.79) represents two equations with two unknowns R and T, expressions for R, T can be found.

As an example, the one interface problem considered in Section 2-6 corresponds to $t = 1$. Then $B_{0t} = B_{01}$, where

$$B_{01} = \frac{1}{2} \left(1 + \frac{\mu_0 k_{z1}}{\mu_1 k_{z0}} \right) \begin{bmatrix} e^{jk_{z1}d_1} & R_{01}e^{-jk_{z1}d_1} \\ R_{01}e^{jk_{z1}d_1} & e^{-jk_{z1}d_1} \end{bmatrix},$$

$$B_{01} \begin{bmatrix} Te^{-jk_{z1}d_1} \\ 0 \end{bmatrix} = \frac{1}{2} \left(1 + \frac{\mu_0 k_{z1}}{\mu_1 k_{z0}} \right) \begin{bmatrix} T \\ R_{01}T \end{bmatrix}.$$

From (2.79), we get

$$\begin{bmatrix} 1 \\ R \end{bmatrix} = \frac{1}{2} \left(1 + \frac{\mu_0 k_{z1}}{\mu_1 k_{z0}} \right) \begin{bmatrix} T \\ R_{01}T \end{bmatrix},$$

$$\therefore \quad T = \frac{2 k_{z0} \mu_1}{\mu_1 k_{z0} + k_{z1}\mu_0}, \tag{2.80}$$

$$R = R_{01}, \tag{2.81}$$

where

$$k_{z0} = \left(\omega^2 \mu_0 \varepsilon_0 - k_0^2 \sin^2 \theta_0 \right)^{1/2} = k_0 \cos \theta_0,$$

$$k_{z1} = \left(\omega^2 \mu_1 \varepsilon_1 - k_0^2 \sin^2 \theta_0 \right)^{1/2} = k_1 \cos \theta_t,$$

$\theta_t = $ angle of transmission in accordance with Snell's law.

As another example, let $t = 2$. Then

$$B_{01} B_{12} \begin{bmatrix} Te^{-jk_{z2}d_2} \\ 0 \end{bmatrix} = \frac{1}{2} \left(1 + \frac{\mu_0 k_{z1}}{\mu_1 k_{z0}} \right) \begin{bmatrix} e^{jk_{z1}d_1} & R_{01}e^{-jk_{z1}d_1} \\ R_{01}e^{jk_{z1}d_1} & e^{-jk_{z1}d_1} \end{bmatrix}$$

$$\times \frac{1}{2} \left(1 + \frac{\mu_1 k_{z2}}{\mu_2 k_{z1}} \right) \begin{bmatrix} Te^{-jk_{z2}d_1} \\ R_{12}Te^{-jk_{z2}d_1} \end{bmatrix}.$$

From (2.79), we get

$$\begin{bmatrix} 1 \\ R \end{bmatrix} = \frac{Te^{-jk_{z2}d_1}}{4}\left(1+\frac{\mu_0 k_{z1}}{\mu_1 k_{z0}}\right)\left(1+\frac{\mu_1 k_{z2}}{\mu_2 k_{z1}}\right)\begin{bmatrix} e^{jk_{z1}d_1}+R_{01}R_{12}e^{-jk_{z1}d_1} \\ R_{01}e^{jk_{z1}d_1}+R_{12}e^{-jk_{z1}d_1} \end{bmatrix},$$

$$\therefore \quad T = \frac{4k_{z0}k_{z1}\mu_1\mu_2 e^{j(k_{z2}-k_{z1})d_1}}{(\mu_1 k_{z0}+\mu_0 k_{z1})(\mu_2 k_{z1}+\mu_1 k_{z2})(1+R_{01}R_{12}e^{-j2k_{z1}d_1})}, \qquad (2.82)$$

$$R = \frac{R_{01}+R_{12}e^{-j2k_{z1}d_1}}{1+R_{01}R_{12}e^{-j2k_{z1}d_1}}. \qquad (2.83)$$

If we use forward propagation matrix for the n-layer medium, we get

$$\begin{bmatrix} Te^{-jk_{zt}d_t} \\ 0 \end{bmatrix} = F_{tn}F_{n(n-1)}\cdots F_{10}\begin{bmatrix} 1 \\ R \end{bmatrix}. \qquad (2.84)$$

In (2.84), d_t is again an arbitrary constant which will cancel out with the d_t in F_{tn}. As an example, let $t=1$. Then

$$\begin{bmatrix} Te^{-jk_{z1}d_1} \\ 0 \end{bmatrix} = \frac{1}{2}\left(1+\frac{\mu_1 k_{z0}}{\mu_0 k_{z1}}\right)\begin{bmatrix} e^{-jk_{z1}d_1}-RR_{01}e^{-jk_{z1}d_1} \\ -R_{01}e^{jk_{z1}d_1}+Re^{jk_{z1}d_1} \end{bmatrix},$$

$$\therefore \quad R = R_{01}, \qquad (2.85)$$

$$T = 1+R_{01}, \qquad (2.86)$$

Since we have kept both μ and ε in our solutions to the horizontally polarized case, the corresponding vertically polarized solutions can be obtained by duality, i.e., replacing $\mathbf{E}, \mathbf{H}, \varepsilon, \mu$ by $\mathbf{H}, -\mathbf{E}, \mu, \varepsilon$ respectively.

2-10 REFLECTION FROM A LAYER WITH KNOWN PERMITTIVITY PROFILE

Consider a medium with permittivity profile $\varepsilon(z)$ which approaches constant values ε_0 at $z=+\infty$ and ε_1 at $z=-\infty$. At $z=+\infty$ there is an incident plane wave propagating in the negative z-direction making an angle θ_0 with the negative z-axis. The problem is to find the ratio of the complex amplitudes of the reflected and the incident waves, i.e., the magnitude and phase of the reflection coefficient at any point inside the medium. This can be accomplished by first deriving and then solving the governing equation for the reflection coefficient.

2-10.1 Derivation of the Reflection-Coefficient Equation

Consider a horizontally polarized incident wave polarized in the y-direction. With the time factor $\exp(j\omega t)$ understood, the incident and reflected waves at any point inside the medium are taken to be of the following form:

$$E_y^i = A(z)\exp(-jk_0 nx\sin\theta),$$

$$H_x^i = \frac{nA(z)}{\eta_0}\cos\theta\exp(-jk_0 nx\sin\theta),$$

$$H_z^i = \frac{nA(z)}{\eta_0}\sin\theta\exp(-jk_0 nx\sin\theta),$$

$$E_y^r = R(z)\exp(-jk_0 nx\sin\theta),$$

$$H_x^r = -\frac{nR(z)\cos\theta}{\eta_0}\exp(-jk_0 nx\sin\theta),$$

$$H_z^r = \frac{nR(z)\sin\theta}{\eta_0}\exp(-jk_0 nx\sin\theta),$$

where

$$n = [\varepsilon(z)]^{1/2} \text{ is the refractive index,}$$

$$\theta = \theta(z),$$

$$\eta_0 = (\mu_0/\varepsilon_0)^{1/2},$$

$$k_0 = \omega(\mu_0\varepsilon_0)^{1/2},$$

and

$$n\sin\theta = \sin\theta_0 \qquad \text{due to Snell's law.}$$

The sum of the incident and the reflected waves must satisfy Maxwell's equations. Hence, from

$$-j\omega\mu_0 H_x = -\frac{\partial E_y}{\partial z}$$

we get

$$\frac{d}{dz}(A+R) = j\beta(A-R), \tag{2.87}$$

where for simplicity we have dropped the argument of A and R, and $\beta = k_0 n\cos\theta$. From $j\omega\varepsilon_0 n^2 E_y = \partial H_x/\partial z - \partial H_z/\partial x$, we obtain

$$\frac{d}{dz}(A-R) - j\beta(A+R) + \frac{\beta'}{\beta}(A-R) = 0, \tag{2.88}$$

where β' is the derivative of β with respect to z. The sum of (2.87) and (2.88) yields

$$\frac{dA}{dz} - j\beta A + \frac{\beta'}{2\beta}(A - R) = 0, \tag{2.89}$$

while the difference between (2.87) and (2.88) gives

$$\frac{dR}{dz} + j\beta R - \frac{\beta'}{2\beta}(A - R) = 0. \tag{2.90}$$

Multiply (2.89) by R and (2.90) by A, and take the difference between the two products. Divide the difference by A^2, and denote the ratio R/A, which is the reflection coefficient, by R_n. We get

$$\frac{dR_n}{dz} = -j2\beta R_n + \frac{\beta'}{2\beta}(1 - R_n^2), \tag{2.91}$$

which is the equation governing the reflection coefficient. It can be shown similarly that the governing equation for the vertically polarized case is also given by (2.91) except that the coefficient for the $(1 - R_n^2)$ term becomes

$$\left(\frac{\beta}{n^2}\right)' \frac{n^2}{2\beta} \quad \text{instead of} \quad \frac{\beta'}{2\beta}.$$

This governing equation for the reflection coefficient is known as the *Riccati equation*.

2-10.2 A Solution of the Riccati Equation

When the reflection coefficient of a layer is weak, a useful method of solving the Riccati equation is by iteration. For this method to work it is required that the permittivity profile be continuous and that there be no total reflection at any point along the profile.

Let $\gamma(z) = q'/2q$ and $q = \beta/m$, where $m = 1$ for horizontal polarization and $m = \varepsilon(z)$ for vertical polarization. Then, (2.91) can be written for either polarization in terms of $\gamma(z)$ as

$$\frac{dR_n}{dz} + j2\beta R_n = \gamma(z)(1 - R_n^2). \tag{2.92}$$

Multiplying both sides of (2.92) by $\exp(2j\int_{z_0}^{z} \beta \, dz)$ and integrating from $-\infty$ to z, we get

$$R_n(z) = \exp\left(-2j\int_{z_0}^{z} \beta \, dz\right)\left[\int_{-\infty}^{z} \gamma(z)\left[1 - R_n^2(z)\right]\exp\left(2j\int_{z_0}^{z} \beta \, dz\right) dz\right], \tag{2.93a}$$

or

$$R_n(z_0) = \int_{-\infty}^{z_0} \gamma(z)(1 - R_n^2) \exp\left(2j \int_{z_0}^{z} \beta \, dz\right) dz, \tag{2.93b}$$

where z_0 is an arbitrary point in the medium where the reflection coefficient is desired, and $R_n(-\infty)$ is zero. For small R_n the first approximate solution is obtained by ignoring R_n^2 in comparison with unity:

$$R_{n1}(z_0) = \int_{-\infty}^{z_0} \gamma(z) \exp\left(2j \int_{z_0}^{z} \beta \, dz\right) dz. \tag{2.94}$$

The second approximation is obtained by substituting the first approximation into the right-hand side of (2.93), yielding

$$R_{n2}(z_0) = \int_{-\infty}^{z_0} \gamma(z)\left[1 - R_{n1}^2(z)\right] \exp\left(2j \int_{z_0}^{z} \beta \, dz\right) dz.$$

Similarly, higher-order approximations can be obtained by continuing the iterative process.

To visualize the physical meaning of (2.94) let us split the entire imhomogeneous medium into a collection of very thin layers:

$$R_{n1}(z_0) = \left(\int_{z_1}^{z_0} + \int_{z_2}^{z_1} + \cdots + \int_{z_{n+1}}^{z_n} + \cdots\right) \gamma(z) \exp\left(2j \int_{z_0}^{z} \beta \, dz\right) dz.$$

Consider the layer between z_n and z_{n+1}. This integral contribution can be approximated as follows:

$$\int_{z_{n+1}}^{z_n} \gamma(z) \exp\left(2j \int_{z_0}^{z} \beta \, dz\right) \simeq \exp\left(2j \int_{z_0}^{z_{n+1}} \beta \, dz\right) \int_{z_{n+1}}^{z_n} \gamma(z) \, dz$$

$$= \exp\left(2j \int_{z_0}^{z_{n+1}} \beta \, dz\right) \int_{z_{n+1}}^{z_n} \frac{dq}{2q}, \tag{2.95}$$

where

$$\int_{z_{n+1}}^{z_n} \frac{dq}{2q} = \tfrac{1}{2} \ln(q_n/q_{n+1}) \simeq \frac{1}{2}\left(\frac{q_n}{q_{n+1}} - 1\right) \simeq \frac{q_n - q_{n+1}}{q_n + q_{n+1}},$$

since the value of q_n is very close to that of q_{n+1}. Thus, (2.95) can be approximated as

$$\frac{q_n - q_{n+1}}{q_n + q_{n+1}} \exp\left(2j \int_{z_0}^{z_{n+1}} \beta \, dz\right). \tag{2.96}$$

If we assume that the layers are homogeneous and that the properties of the medium change at the boundaries between layers, then the ratio in (2.96) is recognized as the well-known Fresnel reflection coefficient (Brekhovskikh, 1960) and the exponential factor accounts for the phase change of the direct wave as it travels from z_0 to z_{n+1}.

2-10.3 An Application of (2.94)

Consider the medium with permittivity profile defined as follows:

$$\varepsilon(z) = \begin{cases} 1, & z \geq 0, \\ 1 + \alpha z, & z \leq 0, \end{cases}$$

where α is a small number representing the slope of the profile. A horizontally polarized plane wave is assumed to incident at an angle θ_0 from the homogeneous region, and the problem is to compute the reflection coefficient at the $z=0$ plane. Hence, $z_0 = 0$ in (2.94), and

$$\beta = k_0 n \cos\theta(z)$$
$$= k_0 \left[\varepsilon(z) - \varepsilon(z) \sin^2\theta(z) \right]^{1/2}$$
$$= k_0 \left[\varepsilon(z) - \sin^2\theta_0 \right]^{1/2}$$
$$= k_0 \left[\cos^2\theta_0 + \alpha z \right]^{1/2},$$
$$\gamma = \frac{\beta'}{2\beta} = \frac{\alpha}{4(\cos^2\theta_0 + \alpha z)},$$
$$\int_0^z \beta\, dz = k_0 \int_0^z \left[\cos^2\theta_0 + \alpha z \right]^{1/2} dz$$
$$= \frac{2k_0}{3\alpha} \left[(\cos^2\theta_0 + \alpha z)^{3/2} - \cos^3\theta_0 \right].$$

From (2.94)

$$R_{n1}(0) = \int_{-\infty}^0 \frac{\alpha}{4(\cos^2\theta_0 + \alpha z)}$$
$$\times \exp\left(j \frac{4k_0}{3\alpha} \left[(\cos^2\theta_0 + \alpha z)^{3/2} - \cos^3\theta_0 \right] \right) dz.$$

Let

$$j\xi = \frac{4k_0}{3\alpha} \left[(\cos^2\theta_0 + \alpha z)^{3/2} - \cos^3\theta_0 \right],$$
$$j\, d\xi = 2k_0 (\cos^2\theta_0 + \alpha z)^{1/2} dz.$$

With this change of variable, we get

$$R_{n1}(0) = \frac{j\alpha}{8k_0} \int_\infty^0 \frac{e^{-\xi} d\xi}{\cos^3 \theta_0 + j(3\alpha/4k_0)\xi} \tag{2.97}$$

Since the integrand is significant only for small values of ξ, we can expand the denominator in powers of ξ,

$$\left[\cos^3 \theta_0 + j\frac{3\alpha}{4k_0}\xi\right]^{-1} = \cos^{-3} \theta_0 \left[1 + j\frac{3\alpha}{4k_0\cos^3\theta_0}\xi\right]^{-1}$$

$$= \cos^{-3} \theta_0 \left[1 - j\frac{3\alpha}{3k_0\cos^3\theta_0}\xi\right.$$

$$\left. - \left(\frac{3\alpha}{4k_0\cos^3\theta_0}\right)^2 \xi^2 - \cdots\right],$$

and make use of the definite integral

$$\int_0^\infty e^{-\xi}\xi^{m-1} d\xi = (m-1)!,$$

where m is a positive integer. Then the integral in (2.97) can be evaluated, yielding

$$R_{n1}(0) = \frac{\alpha}{j8k_0\cos^3\theta_0}\left[1 - j\frac{3\alpha}{4k_0\cos^3\theta_0} - 2\left(\frac{3\alpha}{4k_0\cos^3\theta_0}\right)^2 - \cdots\right]. \tag{2.98}$$

For (2.98) to be valid it is necessary that

$$\frac{3\alpha}{4k_0\cos^3\theta_0} \ll 1.$$

The above-described method is applicable to a continuous permittivity profile if it does not cause total reflection at any point.

PROBLEMS

2.1. Show all the steps necessary to go from (2.4) to (2.6). Which operation is removed to obtain your final answer?

2.2. Show that (2.7) satisfies (2.6).

2.3. Show that any plane wave of the form (2.9) in an unbounded medium can always be rewritten as (2.10) by a change of coordinates.

2.4. The time domain representation of an electric field is

$$\mathbf{E}(z,t) = \hat{\mathbf{x}} 5\cos(10^8 t + 0.5z)$$

Find

(a) its complex representation,
(b) the corresponding $\mathbf{H}$ field,
(c) the phase velocity,
(d) the wavelength,
(e) the frequency.

2.5. What is the direction of propagation of the wave

$$E(\mathbf{r},t) = \cos(100t + 4x + 2y + 4z)?$$

2.6. The electrical parameters of sea water are given approximately by $\mu/\mu_0 \simeq 1$, $\varepsilon/\varepsilon_0 \simeq 81$ and a conductivity $\simeq 4.0$ Sm^{-1} at a frequency of $f = 4 \times 10^8$ Hz.

(a) Find the attenuation and phase constants of a plane wave at the above frequency.
(b) Can sea water be treated as a low-loss medium?
(c) Can it be treated as a conducting medium?

2.7. Assume the conductivities of fresh water, wet earth, and dry earth are 10^{-3}, 10^{-3}, and 10^{-5} Sm^{-1} respectively and the corresponding relative permittivities are 81, 15, and 2.5. In each case the relative permeability is taken to be 1. Do these media act like conducting materials at (a) $f = 10$ kHz, (b) $f = 1$ GHz?

2.8. In Problem 2.7, what are the values of the skin depth for each medium at $f = 1$ kHz?

2.9. The attenuation constant α represents loss in nepers per meter. It can be converted to the dB scale by the relation

$$\text{attenuation in dB} = 20\alpha \log e.$$

Compute the loss in dB per meter for a plane wave propagating in the media given in Problem 7 at $f = 10$ kHz.

2.10. Derive (2.26) and (2.27) from (2.25). *Hint:* Use the trigonometric identity $\cos \frac{1}{2}\theta = [\frac{1}{2}(1 + \cos\theta)]^{1/2}$.

2.11. In (2.30) an elliptically polarized wave is written in terms of two linearly polarized waves. Show that this equation can be rewritten as the sum of a right-hand and a left-hand circularly polarized wave.

2.12. In (2.30) choose $E_{x0} = E_{y0}$, $z = 0$, and $\theta = 90°$. Plot $\mathbf{E}(\theta, t)$ as a function of ωt. Is it a right-handed or left-handed wave?

2.13. Determine the state of polarization of the following waves given in complex form:

(a) $\mathbf{E}(z) = \hat{\mathbf{x}} 10 e^{-j\beta z} + \hat{\mathbf{y}} 15 e^{-j\beta z + j\theta}$, where θ is uniformly distributed between $(0, 2\pi)$.

(b) Same as (a) except that θ is distributed between $(0, 2\pi)$ with the probability density function

$$p(\theta) = \tfrac{1}{4} |\sin \theta|.$$

(c) $\mathbf{E}(z) = \hat{\mathbf{x}} E_x e^{-j\beta z} + \hat{\mathbf{y}} E_y e^{-j\beta z + j\pi/4}$, where E_x and E_y follow the joint probability density function

$$p(E_x, E_y) = (2\pi\sigma^2)^{-1} \exp\left[-\left(E_x^2 + E_y^2\right)/2\sigma^2\right].$$

2.14. A plane wave propagating within an unbounded lossy medium has the form

$$E_x(z, t) = E_0 e^{-\alpha z + j(\omega t - \beta z)}.$$

(a) Find the expression for the magnetic field.

(b) Show that the time-average Poynting vector is

$$\mathbf{S}_a = \frac{\hat{\mathbf{z}}}{2} E_0^2 e^{-2\alpha z} \frac{\cos \theta_2}{|\eta|},$$

where η is the intrinsic impedance of the lossy medium and θ_2 is its phase angle.

2.15. A 10-W, 10-GHz transmitter has an antenna with aperture diameter 0.57 m. It is situated on the earth's surface, pointing at the moon. The radius of the moon is 1.74×10^3 km, and the distance between the surfaces of the earth and the moon is 3.84×10^5 km. (a) What is the power density at the surface of the moon? (b) What is the power intercepted by the moon? Assume that the antenna beamwidth can be estimated as the ratio of the wavelength to the width of the antenna aperture.

2.16. In Problem 15, what is the amplitude of the electric field on the surface of the moon? What is the amplitude of the corresponding magnetic field? Recall $\mu_0 = 4\pi \times 10^{-7}$ henry m^{-1} and $\varepsilon_0 \simeq 10^{-9}/36\pi$ farad m^{-1}.

2.17. A TE wave is incident from air upon a dielectric half space at $z = 0$.

(a) If the relative dielectric constant is 6, relative magnetic permeability $\mu_r = 1$, and the angle of incidence is 60°, what are the magnitude of the transmission coefficient and the angle of transmission?

(b) Find $\Gamma_\perp$ and $\Upsilon_\perp$. Do they satisfy energy conservation?

2.18. What are the Brewster angles at an air-water ($\varepsilon_r = 81$) interface? Consider both the case of incidence from air and from water.

2.19. Since at the Brewster angle only the vertically polarized wave is totally transmitted, an arbitrarily oriented linearly polarized (or circularly polarized) wave becomes horizontally polarized upon reflection if it is incident upon an interface at the Brewster angle. For this reason, the Brewster angle is also called the polarizing angle. Find the reflected wave at the interface, $z = 0$, between air and a dielectric of $\varepsilon_r = 2.25$, if the circularly polarized incident wave,

$$\mathbf{E} = (\hat{\mathbf{v}} + j\hat{\mathbf{h}}) \exp(-jkx \sin\theta + jkz \cos\theta)$$

$$\hat{\mathbf{h}} = \hat{\mathbf{y}}$$

$$\hat{\mathbf{v}} = \hat{\mathbf{x}} \cos\theta + \hat{\mathbf{z}} \sin\theta,$$

is incident at the polarizing angle.

2.20. When a wave in a denser medium is incident upon a less dense medium at an incident angle larger than the critical angle, the wave is totally reflected but there is a highly attenuated transmitted wave in the transmitted medium also. Let the incident wave be

$$\mathbf{E} = \hat{\mathbf{y}} \exp(-jk_1 x \sin\theta + jk_1 z \cos\theta)$$

In terms of the geometry of Fig. 2.3, $\varepsilon_1/\varepsilon_2 = 81$, $\mu_1/\mu_2 = 1$, and $\theta = 30°$. Find (a) the transmission coefficient, (b) the transmitted field as a function of θ, k_1, $\varepsilon_1/\varepsilon_2$, x, and z, and (c) the magnitude of the transmitted field at a distance of one wavelength into medium 2.

2.21. The form of the transmitted wave in Problem 2.20 is

$$E_y = T_\perp e^{\alpha z - jk_1 x \sin\theta},$$

where $\alpha = k_2(\varepsilon_1 \sin^2\theta/\varepsilon_2 - 1)^{1/2}$. This wave decreases in magnitude very rapidly as it leaves the boundary surface at $z = 0$, and can travel along the boundary without attenuation. Since it is confined to the boundary surface, it is called a surface wave. Find the corresponding magnetic field and the time-average Poynting vector.

2.22. A plane wave of unit amplitude with $f = 10$ kHz is incident upon sea water from air at $30°$. The relative permittivity and conductivity of sea water are assumed to be 81 and $4 \, \mathrm{S\,m^{-1}}$ respectively.

(a) Find the expression for the transmitted wave and the real angle of transmission.

(b) What is the wavelength of the wave in sea water?

(c) What is the velocity of propagation in sea water?

2.23. An incident plane wave impinges from air normally on a perfectly conducting boundary at $z=0$. Show that the total magnetic field on the surface is twice the incident magnetic field, i.e., $2\mathbf{H}^i$.

2.24. Two semiinfinite media of intrinsic impedances η_1 and η_3 are separated by a plane layer of thickness d and of intrinsic impedance η_2. Find the reflection coefficient for a plane wave incident normally from medium 1, if d is a quarter wavelength long and $\eta_2 = (\eta_1\eta_3)^{1/2}$.

2.25. A radome is a dome-shaped dielectric shell used to protect antennas. It should be transparent to the antenna's radiation at the operating frequency of interest. That is, no reflection should occur due to its presence. The geometry of this problem is like Problem 2.24 except that $\eta_1 = \eta_3 =$ intrinsic impedance of free space. We assume that the wave radiated from the antenna is incident normally on the radome. If the radome is made of polystyrene ($\varepsilon_r = 2.55$), how thick must the radome wall be at an operating frequency of 5 GHz?

2.26. A dielectric panel of thickness d and relative permittivity $\varepsilon_r = 4$ is placed in air. Find the magnitude squared of its reflection coefficient for a plane wave normally incident upon it. Plot this power reflection coefficient (reflectivity) as a function of kd, where k is the wave number in the dielectric.

2.27. A plane wave is normally incident in air upon a layer, extending from $z=l/2$ to $z=-l/2$, in which the index of refraction varies as

$$[\varepsilon(z)]^{1/2} = \frac{A}{A+(0.5-z/l)},$$

where $A = n_1/(1-n_1)$. Outside this layer the refractive index is 1 (air) for $z>l/2$ and n_1 for $z<-l/2$. Calculate $|R_{n2}(l/2)|$ for $n_1 = 2$ and $k_0 l = 0.2$, 0.5, 1.0, 2.0, 4.0, and 6.0.

References

Born, M., and E. Wolf (1964), *Principles of Optics*, MacMillan Company, New York.

Brekhovskikh, L. M. (1960), *Waves in Layered Media*, Academic Press, New York.

Durney, C. H. and C. C. Johnson (1969), *Introduction to Modern Electromagnetics*, McGraw Hill, New York.

Hayt, W. H. (1974), *Engineering Electromagnetics*, 3rd edition, McGraw-Hill, New York.

Jordan, E. C., and K. G. Balmain (1968), *Electromagnetic Waves and Radiating Systems*, Prentice-Hall, Englewood Cliffs, New Jersey.

Ko, H. C. (1962), On the Reception of Quasi-monochromatic Partially Polarized Radio Waves, *Proc. IRE*, 50, pp. 1950–1957.

Kong, J. A. (1975), *The Theory of Electromagnetic Waves*, John Wiley & Sons, Inc., New York.

Kraus, J. D., and K. R. Carver (1973), *Electromagnetics*, McGraw-Hill, New York.

Plonus, M. A. (1978), *Applied Electromagnetics*, McGraw-Hill, New York.

Ramo, S., J. R. Whinnery, and T. Van Duzer (1967), *Fields and Waves in Communication Electronics*, John Wiley & Sons, Inc., New York.

Stratton, J. A. (1941), *Electromagnetic Theory*, McGraw-Hill, New York.

Chapter 3

Antenna Systems in Microwave Remote Sensing

3-1 INTRODUCTION

An *antenna* may be defined as the region of transition between an electromagnetic wave propagating in free space and a guided wave propagating in a transmission line, or vice versa. It acts as a coupler between the two media, performing the same function that a lens does in optical sensors. The function of a microwave radiometer antenna is to receive electromagnetic energy radiated by the scene under observation. In radar systems, separate antennas may be used for transmission and reception, or the same antenna may serve both functions.

An *isotropic* antenna is a hypothetical antenna that radiates equally in all directions. Due to the vector nature of electromagnetic fields, such an antenna cannot exist (Mathis, 1951). However, the isotropic antenna often is used in antenna engineering as a reference radiator. In transferring energy from a transmission line into space, a real antenna radiates the energy nonuniformly in direction. The directional function describing the relative distribution of energy is known as the *antenna radiation pattern*. Most antennas are reciprocal devices exhibiting the same radiation pattern for transmission as for reception. Exceptions are some solid-state antennas composed of nonlinear semiconductors or ferrite materials, which may not obey the reciprocity law. Such nonreciprocal antennas are beyond the scope of this chapter; reciprocity will be assumed throughout. Therefore, no distinction will be made between the transmission and reception modes.

In this chapter, we shall examine the factors affecting the radiation characteristics of antenna types commonly used in microwave remote sensing (Fig. 3.1). To this end we shall review the techniques used in calculating the radiation pattern of an antenna, define the basic antenna parameters, and introduce the concepts of pattern synthesis, antenna arrays, and electronic scanning.

Fawwaz T. Ulaby, Richard K. Moore, and Adrian K. Fung,
Microwave Remote Sensing: Active and Passive,
Vol. I: Microwave Remote Sensing Fundamentals and Radiometry   ISBN 0-201-10759-7

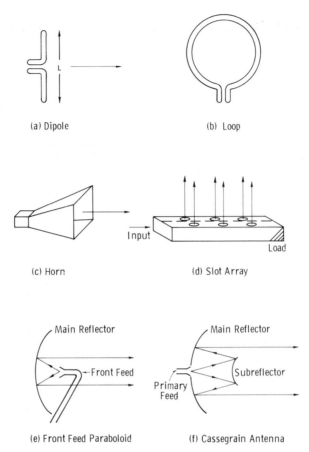

(a) Dipole   (b) Loop

(c) Horn   (d) Slot Array

(e) Front Feed Paraboloid   (f) Cassegrain Antenna

Fig. 3.1 Antenna types commonly used in microwave remote sensing.

3-2 BASIC ANTENNA PARAMETERS

The phenomenon of electromagnetic radiation by means of antenna systems is first introduced in Section 3-3, followed by more detailed considerations of the basic techniques used to determine the radiative properties of antennas. Specifically, the objective of these techniques is to relate the electric and magnetic field vectors, **E** and **H**, at a given point in space to the source of the radiation. Associated with the electric and magnetic fields is a Poynting vector describing the direction of propagation of the electromagnetic wave. For an $\exp(j\omega t)$ time dependence, the time-average Poynting vector, which frequently is referred to as the *power density* $\mathbf{S}_a$, is given by

$$\mathbf{S}_a = \tfrac{1}{2}\mathrm{Re}(\mathbf{E}\times\mathbf{H}^*). \tag{3.1}$$

As will be shown below, the directional dependence of the magnitude of $\mathbf{S}_a$ defines most of the parameters commonly used to describe the radiation properties of antennas, including *directivity*, *beamwidth*, and *effective area*. To facilitate discussion of these properties, it will be assumed that the antenna is matched to the transmission line connected to its terminals (to avoid reflections).

The spatial distribution of energy radiated by an antenna as a function of position or direction in space is characterized by the *antenna pattern*. Because of the spherical nature of the radiation, the spherical coordinate system shown in Fig. 3.2(a) is usually used in the presentation of antenna pattern plots, with the variables, r, θ, and ϕ referred to as *range*, *elevation angle*, and *azimuth angle*, respectively. The *directional pattern* of a transmitting antenna is a plot of the relative amplitude of the electromagnetic field or, more commonly, the power density, $|\mathbf{S}_a|$, as a function of direction $\hat{\mathbf{r}}$ with the distance from the radiation source, r, held constant. By the use of the reciprocity theorem, this definition is also applicable in the receiving condition.

Consider a transmitting antenna placed at the origin of the observation sphere shown in Fig. 3.2(b). If r is sufficiently large that the wavefront across the receiving aperture may be considered a plane wave (Fig. 3.2(c)), the observation point is said to be in the *far-field* (or *far-zone*) region of the transmitting antenna. This region, whose inner limit is defined later by (3.80), is of particular interest because in most applications, the observation region of interest is in the far-field region of the antenna. As will be shown in later sections, the far-field plane-wave approximation allows the use of certain mathematical approximations which simplify the computation of the radiated field and, conversely, provide convenient techniques for synthesizing the appropriate antenna structure that would give rise to the desired far-field antenna directional pattern.

Related as in a plane wave, the far-zone electric and magnetic field vectors are mutually perpendicular and lie in a plane normal to the unit vector $\hat{\mathbf{r}}$. Consequently, the power density $\mathbf{S}_a(\hat{\mathbf{r}})$ has only a radial component, S_r, and no components in either the $\hat{\boldsymbol{\theta}}$ or the $\hat{\boldsymbol{\phi}}$ direction. Thus,

$$\mathbf{E} = \hat{\boldsymbol{\theta}} E_\theta + \hat{\boldsymbol{\phi}} E_\phi, \tag{3.2a}$$

$$\mathbf{H} = \frac{1}{\eta}(\hat{\mathbf{r}} \times \mathbf{E}) = \frac{1}{\eta}\left(\hat{\boldsymbol{\phi}} E_\theta - \hat{\boldsymbol{\theta}} E_\phi\right), \tag{3.2b}$$

$$\mathbf{S}_a = \frac{1}{2}\operatorname{Re}(\mathbf{E} \times \mathbf{H}^*) = \hat{\mathbf{r}} \frac{1}{2\eta}\left(|E_\theta|^2 + |E_\phi|^2\right), \tag{3.3}$$

or

$$S_r = \frac{1}{2\eta}\left(|E_\theta|^2 + |E_\phi|^2\right). \tag{3.4}$$

At a large distance from the antenna, the radiated field E_θ (and similarly E_ϕ) may be described by the spherical propagation function e^{-jkr}/r character-

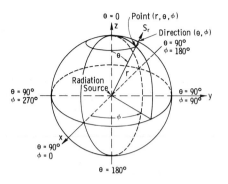

(a) Spherical Coordinate System

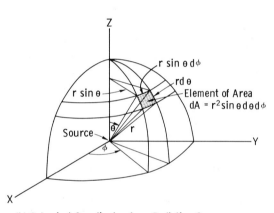

(b) Spherical Coordinates for a Radiation Source

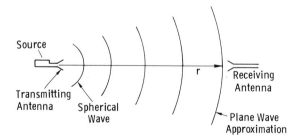

(c) Far-zone Plane Wave Approximation

Fig. 3.2   Radiation geometry.

istic of a point source, multiplied by a directional function $f(\theta, \phi)$:

$$E_\theta = \frac{e^{-jkr}}{r} f_1(\theta, \phi), \tag{3.5a}$$

$$E_\phi = \frac{e^{-jkr}}{r} f_2(\theta, \phi), \tag{3.5b}$$

where $k = 2\pi/\lambda$. The power flow in the far field is then given by

$$S_r = \frac{1}{2\eta r^2} \left(|f_1(\theta, \phi)|^2 + |f_2(\theta, \phi)|^2 \right). \tag{3.6}$$

Instead of using the power density $S_r(r, \theta, \phi)$ to describe the directional properties of an antenna, it is usually more convenient to use an r-independent function known as the *radiation intensity*, or *radiation pattern*, $F(\theta, \phi)$. This function is given by

$$F(\theta, \phi) = r^2 S_r = \frac{1}{2\eta} \left(|f_1(\theta, \phi)|^2 + |f_2(\theta, \phi)|^2 \right), \tag{3.7}$$

where $F(\theta, \phi)$ is now expressed in watts per unit solid angle (watts per steradian). It is customary to normalize the maximum value of $F(\theta, \phi)$ to unity, in which case the pattern is referred to as the *normalized radiation pattern*, $F_n(\theta, \phi)$. Thus,

$$F_n(\theta, \phi) = \frac{F(\theta, \phi)}{F(\theta, \phi)_{max}} = \frac{S_r(r, \theta, \phi)}{S_r(r, \theta, \phi)_{max}}, \tag{3.8}$$

with the understanding that r is held constant.

An example of a normalized radiation pattern is shown in Fig. 3.3(a), where $F_n(\theta, \phi)$ is plotted on a decibel scale in polar coordinates, along with contours of constant intensity versus angle. This format permits a convenient visual interpretation of the spatial distribution of the *radiation lobes*. Another format commonly used for inspecting the pattern of a narrow-beam antenna is the rectangular display shown in Fig. 3.3(b), which permits the pattern to be easily expanded by changing the scale of the horizontal axis. These plots represent the variation in only one plane in the observation circle, namely the $\phi = 0$ plane. Unless the pattern is symmetrical in ϕ, additional patterns are required to define the variation of $F_n(\theta, \phi)$ with θ and ϕ. If the antenna is linearly polarized and the coordinate system is defined so that the electric field lies in one of the two *principal planes*, $\theta = 90°$ and $\phi = 0$, then measurements of the principal-plane patterns may suffice. In the case of an elliptically polarized antenna or an antenna whose polarization vector changes direction at angles away from the principal planes, it may be necessary to make radiation-pattern measurements in several planes, in addition to polarization patterns in several

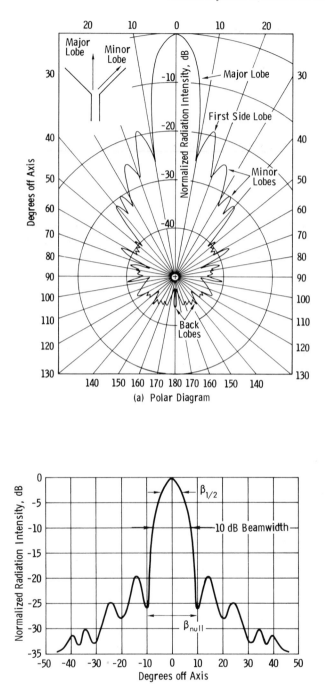

(a) Polar Diagram

(b) Rectangular Plot

Fig. 3.3   Representative plots of the normalized radiation pattern of a microwave antenna in (a) polar form and (b) rectangular form.

different directions. These cases are discussed in detail in Kraus (1950, Chapter 15), Hickman et al. (1970), and the IEEE *Standard Test Procedures for Antennas* (1979).

The pattern shown in Fig. 3.3(a) indicates that the antenna is fairly directive, since most of the energy is radiated through a narrow angular range called the *main lobe*. In addition to the main lobe, several *side lobes* and *back*

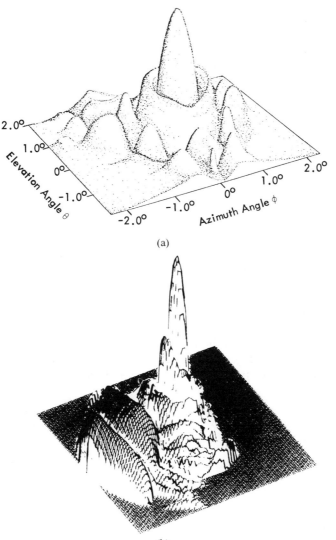

(a)

(b)

Fig. 3.4 Three-dimensional antenna patterns. (a) Three-dimensional pencil-beam pattern of the AN/FPQ-6 radar antenna. Base is at −40 dB relative to the peak (from Skolnik, 1970). (b) Three-dimensional pattern of the 22.235-GHz Scanning Microwave Spectrometer (SCAMS) antenna flown on Nimbus 6. Plot is ±100° from axis and the base is at −50 dB relative to the peak (from Sissala, 1975).

lobes are also shown, which for most applications are considered undesirable. If the intended application calls for an assessment of the general configuration of the radiation pattern over a selected region in the $\theta-\phi$ space, such as the vicinity of the main beam, $F_n(\theta,\phi)$ can be displayed in the form of a three-dimensional pattern (Fig. 3.4). To generate these types of displays, a single-plane pattern of $F_n(\theta,\phi)$ versus θ (or ϕ) has to be recorded for each of many values of ϕ (or θ) over the region of interest.

We shall now define the terms commonly used in numerically specifying the radiation pattern of an antenna.

3-2.1 Solid Angles

The *pattern solid angle* Ω_p, *main-beam* (or *main-lobe*) solid angle Ω_M, and *minor-lobe* solid angle Ω_m, are solid angles describing, in different ways, the effective width of the main lobe of the antenna pattern. They are given by

$$\Omega_p = \iint_{4\pi} F_n(\theta,\phi)\,d\Omega, \tag{3.9}$$

$$\Omega_M = \iint_{main\ lobe} F_n(\theta,\phi)\,d\Omega, \tag{3.10}$$

$$\Omega_m = \Omega_p - \Omega_M, \tag{3.11}$$

where Ω_p, Ω_M and Ω_m are in steradians (sr), and $d\Omega$ is an elemental solid angle given by

$$d\Omega = \sin\theta\,d\theta\,d\phi. \tag{3.12}$$

The only difference between the three solid angles is the region of integration; whereas for Ω_p the integration is carried out over 4π, for Ω_M it is limited to the main lobe (down to the first minimum) and for Ω_m to the solid angle excluding the main lobe.

The *main-beam efficiency* η_M of an antenna and its *stray factor* η_m characterize the fraction of power emitted (or received) by the main lobe and the minor lobes, respectively:

$$\eta_M = \frac{\Omega_M}{\Omega_p}, \tag{3.13}$$

$$\eta_m = \frac{\Omega_m}{\Omega_p} = 1 - \eta_M. \tag{3.14}$$

An isotropic antenna is a hypothetical directionless antenna whose radiation pattern $F_n(\theta,\phi)=1$ in all directions. For such an antenna, $\Omega_p = \Omega_M = 4\pi$ sr, $\Omega_m = 0$, $\eta_M = 1$, and $\eta_m = 0$.

3-2.2 Beam Dimensions

The solid angles defined above characterize the directional properties of the two-dimensional radiation pattern $F_n(\theta, \phi)$. To characterize the width of the main lobe in a given plane, the term used is *beamwidth*. The definitions in common use are given below, with Fig. 3.3(b) used as reference.

Half-Power Beamwidth, $\beta_{1/2}$

The *half-power beamwidth $\beta_{1/2}$* is defined as the angular width of the main lobe between the two angles at which the magnitude of $F_n(\theta, \phi)$ is equal to half of its peak value (or -3 dB on a decibel scale). For example, in the *xz*-plane ($\phi=0$), $\beta_{1/2}$ of a symmetrical pattern is given by

$$\beta_{1/2} = 2\theta_{1/2}, \tag{3.15}$$

where $\theta_{1/2}$ is the angle at which

$$F_n(\theta_{1/2}, 0) = 0.5. \tag{3.16}$$

$\beta_{1/2}$ is also known as the 3-dB beamwidth.

Beamwidth Between First Nulls, β_{null}

The spacing between the first nulls on the two sides of the peak is sometimes used to describe the total width of the main lobe. Thus, for a symmetrical pattern,

$$\beta_{null} = 2\theta_{null}, \tag{3.17}$$

where θ_{null} is the angle at which the first minimum of $F_n(\theta, \phi)$ occurs. In a given plane (say $\phi=0$), the solution of

$$\frac{dF_n}{d\theta}(\theta, 0) = 0 \tag{3.18}$$

may provide θ_{null}, as well as all the other minima and maxima of $F_n(\theta, 0)$.

Beamwidth at a Specific Level of $F_n(\theta, \phi)$

In some applications, the angular width of the pattern at a specified level of $F_n(\theta, \phi)$ may be of interest. For example, the beamwidth at the -10-dB level is shown in Fig. 3.3b.

3-2.3 Directivity

The *directivity $D(\theta, \phi)$* of an antenna in a given direction is the ratio of its normalized radiation pattern $F_n(\theta, \phi)$ in that direction to the average value of

$F_n(\theta, \phi)$,

$$D(\theta, \phi) = \frac{F_n(\theta, \phi)}{\dfrac{1}{4\pi} \displaystyle\iint_{4\pi} F_n(\theta, \phi)\, d\Omega}. \tag{3.19}$$

Alternatively, through the use of (3.7), the directivity may be defined in terms of the power density $S_r(\theta, \phi)$,

$$D(\theta, \phi) = \frac{S_r(\theta, \phi)}{\dfrac{1}{4\pi} \displaystyle\iint_{4\pi} S_r(\theta, \phi)\, d\Omega}. \tag{3.20}$$

Of particular importance in antenna design is the *maximum directivity* D_0, which is given by (3.19) with $F_n = 1$ in the numerator:

$$D_0 = \frac{4\pi}{\displaystyle\iint_{4\pi} F_n(\theta, \phi)\, d\Omega} = \frac{4\pi}{\Omega_p}, \tag{3.21}$$

where use has been made of (3.9). In terms of D_0, the directivity D in any direction (θ, ϕ) may then be written in the form

$$D(\theta, \phi) = D_0 F_n(\theta, \phi). \tag{3.22}$$

For an antenna with a single main lobe pointing in the z-direction as shown in Fig. 3.5, the pattern solid angle Ω_p is approximately equal to the product of the half-power beamwidths β_{xz} and β_{yz} (in radians):

$$\Omega_p \simeq \beta_{xz}\beta_{yz},$$

and therefore,

$$D_0 = \frac{4\pi}{\Omega_p} \simeq \frac{4\pi}{\beta_{xz}\beta_{yz}}. \tag{3.23}$$

Although approximate, the above relation provides a useful method for estimating the antenna maximum directivity from measurements of the half-power beamwidths in the two orthogonal planes whose intersection is the axis of the main lobe. As will be shown later, D_0 of a rectangular aperture (see (3.108)) is equal to the right-hand side of (3.23) multiplied by the factor 0.77. For a circular aperture, the multiplying factor is 0.78. In general, (3.23) provides an estimate of D_0 within about 3 dB of its true value, provided the radiation pattern consists of only one major lobe.

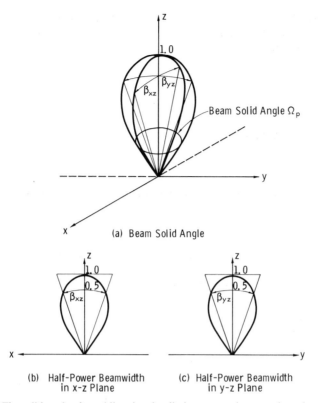

(a) Beam Solid Angle

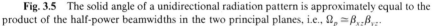

(b) Half-Power Beamwidth in x-z Plane

(c) Half-Power Beamwidth in y-z Plane

Fig. 3.5 The solid angle of a unidirectional radiation pattern is approximately equal to the product of the half-power beamwidths in the two principal planes, i.e., $\Omega_p \cong \beta_{xz}\beta_{yz}$.

3-2.4 Effective Area

As will be shown in Section 3.12, the maximum directivity D_0 of an antenna is related to an *effective area* (or *effective aperture*) of the antenna, A_{eff}, by

$$D_0 = \frac{4\pi}{\lambda^2} A_{eff} = \frac{4\pi}{\lambda^2} \eta_a A_p,$$ (3.133)

where A_p is the physical aperture of the antenna and $\eta_a = A_{eff}/A_p$ is the *aperture efficiency* $(0 \le \eta_a \le 1)$.

Equating (3.23) to (3.133) leads to the relation

$$A_{eff} = \frac{\lambda^2}{\Omega_p} \simeq \frac{\lambda^2}{\beta_{xz}\beta_{yz}},$$ (3.24)

which states that the main lobe becomes more directive (narrower beamwidths) as the aperture area increases. For a rectangular aperture with dimensions l_x

and l_y along the x- and y-axes, respectively, and an aperture efficiency $\eta_a = 1$, we may divide the above expression into two parts, corresponding to two linear antennas of lengths l_x and l_y:

$$\beta_{xz} \simeq \frac{\lambda}{l_x} \text{ radians,} \tag{3.25a}$$

$$\beta_{yz} \simeq \frac{\lambda}{l_y} \text{ radians.} \tag{3.25b}$$

Thus, the half-power beamwidth in the plane containing the linear antenna is inversely proportional to its length, measured in wavelength units.

3-2.5 Gain

Of the total power P_t supplied to the antenna, a part P_o is radiated out into space, and the remainder P_l is dissipated as heat in the antenna structure. The *radiation efficiency* η_l is defined as the ratio of P_o to P_t,

$$\eta_l = \frac{P_o}{P_t}. \tag{3.26}$$

The *gain* $G(\theta, \phi)$ of an antenna in a specified direction is defined as the ratio of the power density radiated by the subject antenna, $S_r(\theta, \phi)$, to the power density radiated by a lossless isotropic antenna, S_{ri}, provided both antennas are supplied with the same amount of power, P_t:

$$G(\theta, \phi) = \frac{S_r(\theta, \phi)}{S_{ri}}. \tag{3.27}$$

The total power radiated by the subject antenna can be evaluated by integrating $S_r(\theta, \phi)$ over a spherical surface of radius r:

$$P_o = \iint_{4\pi} S_r(\theta, \phi) r^2 \, d\Omega = r^2 \iint_{4\pi} S_r(\theta, \phi) \, d\Omega, \tag{3.28}$$

while the total power radiated by the lossless nondirectional isotropic antenna is given by

$$P_{oi} = 4\pi r^2 S_{ri}. \tag{3.29}$$

Since $P_t = P_{oi} = P_o / \eta_l$, the two previous equations can be combined to give

$$S_{ri} = \frac{1}{4\pi \eta_l} \iint_{4\pi} S_r(\theta, \phi) \, d\Omega, \tag{3.30}$$

and upon substitution in (3.27), the latter becomes

$$G(\theta,\phi)=\frac{4\pi\eta_l S_r(\theta,\phi)}{\displaystyle\iint_{4\pi} S_r(\theta,\phi)\,d\Omega}.$$ (3.31)

In terms of the directivity $D(\theta,\phi)$ defined by (3.20),

$$G(\theta,\phi)=\eta_l D(\theta,\phi),$$ (3.32)

and in the direction of maximum radiation, the *maximum gain is* $G_0=\eta_l D_0$. *Thus, the antenna gain accounts for ohmic losses in the antenna material, while the directivity does not.*

Another useful formula relating the power density S_r to the input power P_t is

$$S_r=\frac{P_t G(\theta,\phi)}{4\pi r^2}.$$ (3.33)

3-2.6 Friis Transmission Formula

The two antennas shown in Fig. 3.6 are in free space and are far enough away from one another for each to be in the far-field region of the other. Initially, we shall consider the case where the two antenna apertures are oriented so that the peak of the radiation pattern of each antenna points in the direction of the other. At a fixed distance R from the transmitting antenna, the power intercepted by the receiving antenna with effective aperture A_r is

$$P_i=S_r A_r=\frac{P_t}{4\pi R^2}G_t A_r,$$ (3.34)

where use has been made of (3.33) and G_t is the maximum gain of the transmitting antenna. If the radiation efficiency η_l of the receiving antenna is designated η_r, the power received at the output terminals of the receiving

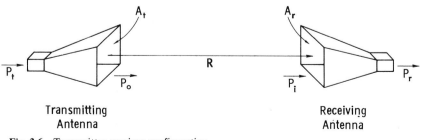

Transmitting   Receiving
Antenna   Antenna

Fig. 3.6   Transmitter-receiver configuration.

antenna is

$$P_r = \eta_r P_i = \frac{P_t}{4\pi R^2} G_t \eta_r A_r. \tag{3.35}$$

Through the use of (3.32), the above formula may be expressed in the equivalent forms

$$\frac{P_r}{P_t} = \left(\frac{\lambda}{4\pi R}\right)^2 G_t G_r = \eta_r \eta_t \frac{A_t A_r}{\lambda^2 R^2}. \tag{3.36}$$

This is known as Friis's transmission formula, and P_r/P_t is sometimes called the power transfer ratio. Another notion in common use is the *free-space transmission loss* L_{FS}, which is the propagation loss experienced in transmission between two lossless isotropic antennas. L_{FS} is given by

$$L_{FS} = \left(\frac{4\pi R}{\lambda}\right)^2, \tag{3.37}$$

and the power transfer ratio becomes

$$\frac{P_r}{P_t} = \frac{G_t G_r}{L_{FS}}. \tag{3.38}$$

If the two antennas are not oriented in the direction of maximum power transfer, (3.38) can be written in the general form

$$\frac{P_r}{P_t} = \frac{1}{L_{FS}} G_t(\theta_t, \phi_t) G_r(\theta_r, \phi_r), \tag{3.39}$$

where (θ_t, ϕ_t) is the direction of the receiving antenna in the transmitting-antenna coordinates, and vice versa for the direction (θ_r, ϕ_r).

3-3 SOURCES OF RADIATION

An antenna connected to a radio-frequency oscillator can radiate electromagnetic energy. The radiation process, or launching of a free-space wave, may be viewed in several different ways, which lead to different approaches for calculating the radiated field. In this chapter, we shall consider the following three basic approaches:

1. *Radiation from Current Sources.* In the case of the *dipole* and *loop* antennas (Fig. 3.1(a) and (b)), the time-varying current elements give rise to the radiated electromagnetic field. Expressions for the electric- and magnetic-field intensities at a given distance and in a given direction from such a wire

antenna excited by a given voltage can be obtained by first regarding the antenna as consisting of a series of infinitesimal dipoles and then integrating the fields from all of the dipoles making up the antenna. The fields from an infinitesimal dipole, or *Hertzian* dipole, can be obtained through the use of the scalar and vector potentials. This approach may be generalized to compute the fields radiated by any current distribution, including two- and three-dimensional configurations.

2. *Radiation from Apertures—Scalar Approach.* The *electromagnetic horn* antenna (Fig. 3.1(c)) usually is designed to match an electromagnetic traveling wave from a guiding system, such as a waveguide, to a large radiating aperture by properly shaping the transition. The radiated field may be viewed as emanating from the horn opening. Hence, the fields or wavefronts over the aperture now may be considered the sources of radiation. The aperture electric and magnetic fields may be determined through a solution of Maxwell's equations (for the region inside the horn) subject to the appropriate boundary conditions. To compute the radiated field in space in terms of the aperture fields, two types of approaches are available. The first approach is based on *Kirchhoff's scalar diffraction theory*. By *scalar*, we mean that each component of the aperture fields is treated separately, without regard to the coupling between the electric- and magnetic-field vectors as mandated by Maxwell's equations. Thus, using scalar diffraction theory, the radiated field would have the same polarization as the aperture field, which is not always the case. Despite its theoretical limitations, however, this theory has been found to be very useful for calculating the radiated field, usually with acceptable accuracy, provided the aperture is large compared to a wavelength. If this condition is not satisfied, the second approach, *vector diffraction*, should be employed. Its basis is discussed next.

3. *Radiation from Apertures—Vector Approach.* The vector diffraction formulation is derived from Maxwell's equations. In its most general form, the electric- and magnetic-field vectors at a point in space are each given by a surface integral involving both the electric and magnetic fields at the aperture. Through the application of the field equivalence principle (Collin, 1969), the general form may be modified to more convenient forms requiring knowledge of either the electric or the magnetic field across the aperture, rather than both. The vector approach is particularly suitable for apertures with dimensions of the order of a wavelength or smaller, such as small horns and slot antennas (Section 3-23).

Next, we shall proceed to examine each of the above radiation approaches in more detail.

3-4 THE SHORT DIPOLE

By regarding a linear antenna as consisting of a series of a large number of short conducting elements, each of which is so short that current may be considered uniform over its length, the field of the entire antenna may be

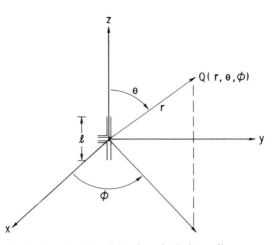

Fig. 3.7 Short dipole placed at the origin of a spherical coordinate system.

obtained by integrating the fields from all these differential antennas with the proper magnitudes and phases taken into account. We shall examine first the radiation properties of such a differential antenna (*short dipole*), and then proceed to use the results to compute the fields for a linear antenna of an arbitrary length.

A thin, linear conductor of length *l* very small compared to the wavelength λ is often called a *short dipole* (or Hertzian dipole). The current is assumed to vary sinusoidally as

$$I = I_0 e^{j\omega t}, \tag{3.40}$$

where I_0 is the peak value.

The customary approach for finding the electric and magnetic fields at a point Q in space (Fig. 3.7) is through the retarded vector potential $\mathbf{A}$, which points in the same direction as the current vector (the z-direction) and is given by (Ramo, et al., 1965)

$$A_z = \frac{\mu l I_0}{4\pi r} e^{-jkr} \tag{3.41}$$

where $k = 2\pi/\lambda$ is the wave number and the $e^{j\omega t}$ factor is implied (that is, the current $I_0 e^{j\omega t}$ is now represented by its peak value, I_0). In spherical coordinates, A_z has two components:

$$A_r = A_z \cos\theta = \frac{\mu l I_0}{4\pi r} e^{-jkr} \cos\theta, \tag{3.42a}$$

$$A_\theta = -A_z \sin\theta = -\frac{\mu l I_0}{4\pi r} e^{-jkr} \sin\theta. \tag{3.42b}$$

The electric- and magnetic-field components may be obtained by applying the relations

$$H = \frac{1}{\mu} \nabla \times A, \tag{3.43a}$$

$$E = \frac{-j\omega}{k^2} \nabla (\nabla \cdot A) - j\omega A, \tag{3.43b}$$

which yield the expressions

$$H_\phi = \frac{I_0 l}{4\pi} e^{-jkr} \left(\frac{jk}{r} + \frac{1}{r^2} \right) \sin \theta$$

$$E_r = \frac{I_0 l \eta}{4\pi} e^{-jkr} \left(\frac{2}{r^2} - \frac{2j}{kr^3} \right) \cos \theta \tag{3.44}$$

$$E_\theta = \frac{I_0 l \eta}{4\pi} e^{-jkr} \left(\frac{jk}{r} + \frac{1}{r^2} - \frac{j}{kr^3} \right) \sin \theta.$$

The remaining components (H_r, H_θ, and E_ϕ) are everywhere zero. As previously defined, η is the intrinsic impedance of the medium,

$$\eta = \sqrt{\mu/\varepsilon}, \tag{3.45}$$

and has the value of 377 ohms ($\simeq 120\pi$ ohms) in free space.

3-4.1 Far-Field Approximation

At great distances from the source such that $kr \gg 1$, the terms varying as $1/r^2$ and $1/r^3$ in (3.44a) to (3.44c) can be neglected in favor of the terms varying as $1/r$. This approximation yields the far-field components, which are given by

$$E_\theta = \frac{jkI_0 l}{4\pi r} \sin \theta \, e^{-jkr}, \tag{3.46a}$$

$$H_\phi = \frac{jkI_0 l}{4\pi r} \sin \theta \, e^{-jkr} = \frac{E_\theta}{\eta}, \tag{3.46b}$$

and E_r is negligible. At the observation point Q (Fig. 3.7), the wave now appears to be similar to a uniform plane wave with its electric and magnetic fields in time phase, related by the impedance of the medium η, and orthogonal to each other and to the direction of propagation. Both fields are proportional to $\sin \theta$ and independent of ϕ.

Since E_θ and H_ϕ vary sinusoidally with time, the time-average Poynting vector, or power density, is given by

$$S_a = \tfrac{1}{2} \text{Re}(E \times H^*) \tag{3.47}$$

which, in this case, is in the radial direction and its magnitude is given by

$$S_r = \left(\frac{\eta k^2 I_0^2 l^2}{32\pi^2 r^2} \right) \sin^2 \theta \qquad \mathrm{W\,m}^{-2}. \tag{3.48}$$

3-4.2 Radiation Pattern

According to (3.48), S_r is maximum at $\theta = \pi/2$. The normalized radiation pattern $F_n(\theta)$ is then given by

$$F_n(\theta) = \frac{S_r(\theta)}{S_r(\pi/2)} = \sin^2 \theta. \tag{3.49}$$

As shown in Fig. 3.8, no energy is radiated in the direction of the dipole axis

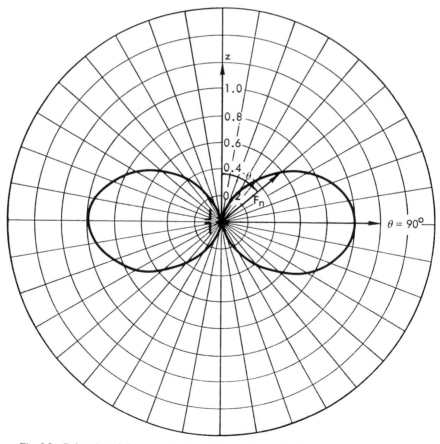

Fig. 3.8   Polar plot of the normalized radiation pattern of a short dipole antenna.

($\theta = 0$ and $180°$), and maximum radiation is in the broadside direction ($\theta = 90°$). Since F_n is independent of ϕ, as would be expected from symmetry considerations, the pattern is doughnut-shaped in $\theta - \phi$ space.

3-4.3 Radiation Resistance

To the transmission line connected to its terminals, an antenna is merely an impedance. If the transmission line is matched to this antenna impedance, part of the energy supplied by the generator is radiated out into space, and the remainder is dissipated as heat in the antenna. Thus the resistance part of the antenna impedance may be defined as consisting of a radiation resistance R_r and a loss resistance R_l. The corresponding time-average radiated power P_o and dissipated power P_l are

$$P_o = \tfrac{1}{2} I_0^2 R_r, \tag{3.50a}$$

$$P_l = \tfrac{1}{2} I_0^2 R_l. \tag{3.50b}$$

As defined earlier in Section 3.2, the radiation efficiency η_l is the ratio of the power radiated to the power input of the antenna. Thus,

$$\eta_l = \frac{P_o}{P_o + P_l} = \frac{R_r}{R_r + R_l}. \tag{3.51}$$

The radiation resistance of the Hertzian dipole can be calculated by integrating the power density of the far-zone field over a large sphere to obtain an expression for P_o. Thus,

$$P_o = \int_A \mathbf{S} \cdot \mathbf{dA} = \iint_{4\pi} S_r r^2 \, d\Omega, \tag{3.52}$$

where A is the surface area of the sphere at range r. Upon substituting (3.48) into (3.52) and integrating, we obtain

$$P_o = 40\pi^2 I_0^2 \left(\frac{l}{\lambda} \right)^2. \tag{3.53}$$

R_r can now be obtained by equating (3.50a) to (3.53):

$$R_r = 80\pi^2 \left(\frac{l}{\lambda} \right)^2. \tag{3.54}$$

Since, by definition, $l \ll \lambda$ for a short dipole, its radiation resistance is always small; for $l = \lambda/10$, $R_r = 7.9$ ohms.

3-4.4 Directivity

The maximum directivity D_0 of the Hertzian dipole can be computed using (3.21) with $F_n(\theta, \phi) = F_n(\theta) = \sin^2 \theta$. Such a computation yields $D_0 = 1.5$.

3-5 THE LONG LINEAR ANTENNA

Consider a thin linear antenna of arbitrary length l, with no restrictions on l compared with the wavelength λ. The antenna, shown in Fig. 3.9, is fed at its center with a sinusoidal current distribution,

$$I = I_0 \sin \left[k \left(l/2 - |z| \right) \right]. \tag{3.55}$$

From (3.46a) and (3.46b) the far-zone fields from an infinitesimal dipole of length dz at a distance s are

$$dE_\theta = \frac{jk\eta I}{4\pi s} dz\, e^{-jks} \sin \theta_s, \tag{3.56a}$$

$$dH_\phi = \frac{1}{\eta} dE_\theta. \tag{3.56b}$$

The far fields of the entire antenna now may be obtained by integrating the fields from all of the Hertzian dipoles making up the antenna:

$$E_\theta = \int_{-L/2}^{L/2} dE_\theta. \tag{3.57}$$

Before we evaluate the above integral, we shall make the following two approximations. The first approximation relates to the magnitude of dE_θ. The distance s between the current element and the observation point Q is considered so large in comparison to l that the difference between s and r may

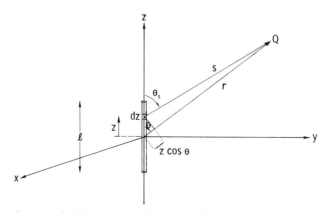

Fig. 3.9 Geometry for linear, center-fed antenna of length l.

be neglected in its effect on the magnitude of dE_θ. Hence,

$$s \simeq r, \tag{3.58}$$

and by the same argument,

$$\theta_s \simeq \theta. \tag{3.59}$$

The second approximation, which relates to the phase part of dE_θ, is

$$s = \sqrt{r^2 + z^2 - 2rz\cos\theta} \simeq r - z\cos\theta. \tag{3.60}$$

Substituting (3.58) and (3.59) into the amplitude factor and (3.60) into the phase factor of (3.56a), the latter becomes

$$dE_\theta = \frac{jk\eta I}{4\pi r} dz\, e^{-jkr} \sin\theta\, e^{jkz\cos\theta}. \tag{3.61}$$

Upon inserting (3.61) into (3.57) and carrying out the integration, the following expressions for the far-zone fields of the long linear antenna are obtained:

$$E_\theta = \frac{j\eta I_0}{2\pi r}\left[\frac{\cos(\tfrac{1}{2}kl\cos\theta) - \cos(\tfrac{1}{2}kl)}{\sin\theta}\right] e^{-jkr}, \tag{3.62a}$$

$$H_\phi = \frac{1}{\eta} E_\theta. \tag{3.62b}$$

As with the short dipole of the previous section, **E** and **H** of the long linear antenna are in time phase, and orthogonal to each other and to the direction of propagation. Using (3.62a) and (3.62b), the time-average Poynting vector can be obtained by applying (3.47). The resulting expression for S_r can then be used to calculate the radiation resistance R_r of the long antenna, following the same procedure employed earlier in connection with the short Hertzian dipole. Details of the mathematical steps are available in Kraus (1950, Chapter 5).

3-6 THE HALF-WAVE DIPOLE

Of particular interest in antenna engineering is the center-fed half-wave dipole. For $l = \lambda/2$, (3.62a) and (3.62b) provide the expressions

$$E_\theta = \frac{j60I_0}{r}\left[\frac{\cos(\tfrac{1}{2}\pi\cos\theta)}{\sin\theta}\right] e^{-jkr} \quad (\text{V m}^{-1}), \tag{3.63}$$

$$S_r = \frac{15I_0^2}{\pi r^2}\left[\frac{\cos(\tfrac{1}{2}\pi\cos\theta)}{\sin\theta}\right]^2 \quad (\text{W m}^{-2}), \tag{3.64}$$

where $\eta \simeq 120\pi$ has been used. Following the procedure outlined in the previous section, the radiation resistance of the half-wave dipole can be shown to be $R_r = 73$ ohms, which is considerably larger than the radiation resistance of the short dipole discussed in Section 3.4.

The far-field radiation pattern of the half-wave dipole exhibits the same doughnut-like shape shown earlier in Fig. 3.8 for the short dipole. Its directivity, however, is slightly larger: 1.64 compared to 1.5 for the short dipole.

In the preceding sections, the far-zone field intensities of the long antenna were obtained by integrating the field contributions of all the short infinitesimal dipoles making up the antenna. This approach may be generalized to include any antenna configuration with a known current distribution $I(x, y)$, as shown by Schelkunoff (1939), who provides a step-by-step procedure for calculating the electric and magnetic field vectors, along with a discussion of the mathematical approximations that may be employed.

3-7 SCALAR FORMULATION

In the previous sections, the field intensities of the electromagnetic wave radiated by wire antennas were related to the antenna current distribution. Thus, the infinitesimal currents were considered the sources of radiation. In considering radiation from aperture-type antennas (Fig. 3.10) such as the slot antenna, the electromagnetic horn, or the parabolic reflector, the radiated fields can be related to the field distribution across the aperture, in which case the latter becomes the radiation source. Two types of formulations may be used to compute the radiated fields of aperture antennas. The first type is a scalar formulation based on Kirchhoff's work and is used commonly in optical diffraction problems and for large-aperture antennas. The second type is a vector formulation based on Maxwell's equations. Although theoretically superior, the vector approach generally is more difficult to apply. Hence, it is

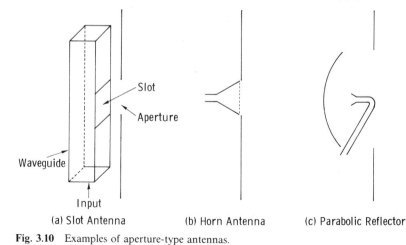

(a) Slot Antenna   (b) Horn Antenna   (c) Parabolic Reflector

Fig. 3.10 Examples of aperture-type antennas.

used mostly in connection with antenna apertures whose dimensions are comparable to or smaller than a wavelength, since in this case the scalar approach is inapplicable.

Because of its inherent simplicity, the scalar formulation will be considered first and will be used to introduce the concepts of *pattern synthesis* and *beam steering*. The vector formulation will be presented in Section 3-16 and applied to slot antennas in Section 3-23.

3-7.1 Scalar Diffraction Integral

The principle proposed by Christian Huygens in 1678 states that (a) *each point on the wavefront of a light disturbance can be considered to be a new source of a secondary spherical wave* and (b) *the wavefront at any other point in space can be found by constructing the envelope of the secondary wavelets.* In his 1818 memoir, Augustin Jean Fresnel extended Huygens's ideas by formulating the *wave theory of light*, which he then combined with the concept of interference proposed earlier by Young to explain the phenomenon known as *diffraction.* Further development of Fresnel's work on diffraction came in 1882 through the efforts of Gustav Kirchhoff, who provided a firmer mathematical foundation for the wave theory of light and formulated the problem of diffraction by an infinite opaque screen. In so doing, he adopted two fundamental assumptions about the boundary conditions of the field distribution and its derivative across the aperture and across the opaque screen. Although Kirchhoff's assumptions were later proved to be inconsistent with each other, his theory has been found to yield remarkably accurate results provided the diffracting aperture is large compared with a wavelength; that is, it is assumed that the *Fresnel-Kirchhoff diffraction integral* (introduced below) may be used to relate the radiated electric field to the aperture electric field by applying it to each field component separately, and then combining the results to obtain the vector field. The same procedure would similarly apply to the magnetic field. In the presentation below, the scalar field E represents one component of the vector field $\mathbf{E}$.

Consider the situation illustrated in Fig. 3.11a, where $E_a(x_a, y_a)$ is the distribution of the scalar electric field across the aperture in the $z=0$ plane. With E_a varying as $e^{j\omega t}$, the objective is to relate the radiated field $E(x, y, z)$ at the point $Q(x, y, z)$ to $E_a(x_a, y_a)$.

Starting with Green's theorem and the Helmholtz wave equation, and then applying the Kirchhoff boundary conditions, we obtain a formula known as the *Fresnel-Kirchhoff diffraction integral* (Silver, 1949; Goodman, 1968a),

$$
E(x, y, z) = \frac{1}{4\pi} \iint_{\text{aperture}} E_a(x_a, y_a) \frac{e^{-jks}}{s}
$$

$$
\times \left[\left(\frac{1}{s} + jk \right) \cos \theta_1 + jk \cos \theta_2 \right] dx_a \, dy_a, \qquad (3.65)
$$

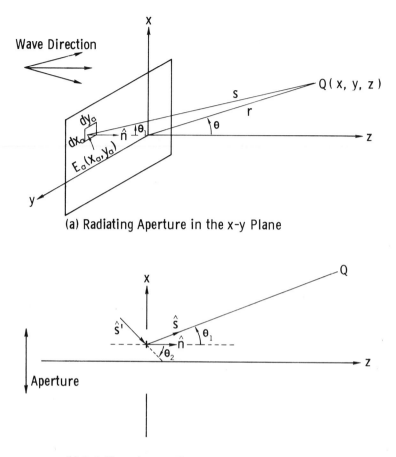

(a) Radiating Aperture in the x-y Plane

(b) Relations for an Elemental Aperture Area $dx_a\, dy_a$

Fig. 3.11 Geometry for the aperture diffraction problem.

where θ_1 (Fig. 3.11(b)) is the angle between the normal $\hat{n}$ to the aperture and the vector $\hat{s}$ joining the elemental aperture area $dx_a\, dy_a$ to the observation point $Q(x, y, z)$, and θ_2 is similarly defined; $\hat{s}'$ is the vector defining the direction of propagation of the wave illuminating the aperture at (x_a, y_a). In most antenna-design cases, the direction of propagation of the aperture illumination is confined to a narrow angular region around the z-axis. Thus $\theta_2 \simeq 0$, and hence $\cos \theta_2 \simeq 1$.

In computing the integral of (3.65), certain approximation may be used to simplify the mathematical manipulations. The validity of these approximations, usually referred to as the Fresnel and Fraunhofer approximations, depends on the range r between the antenna and the observation point. Associated with these approximations, three regions may be defined for r, as discussed next.

3-7.2 Near-Field Region

The immediate vicinity of the aperture is called the near-field (or near-zone) region. In this region, no approximations may be employed in computing the integral of (3.65). Furthermore, because of the invalid Kirchhoff boundary conditions incorporated in the derivation of (3.65), the near-field calculation may be in error, in which case vector diffraction theory should be used.

3-7.3 Fresnel Region

This is an intermediate region extending between the near field region and the Fraunhofer (or far-field) region. Its limits in terms of distance from the aperture are defined later.

Based on the assumption that the distance z between aperture and observation plane (Fig. 3.12(a)) is substantially larger than the longest linear

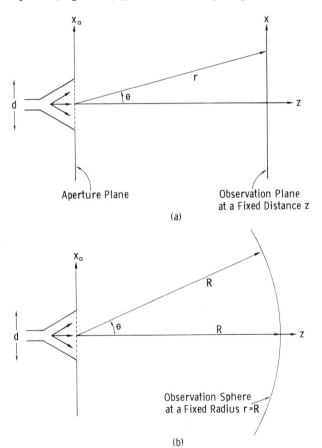

Fig. 3.12 Far-zone observation regions: (a) plane at a fixed distance z, and (b) sphere at a fixed radius $r = R$.

dimension of the aperture d, (whence $z \gg \lambda$, since scalar diffraction is valid only for $d \gg \lambda$), the following approximations can be used in (3.65):

$$\left(\frac{1}{s} + jk \right) = \left(\frac{1}{s} + \frac{j2\pi}{\lambda} \right) \simeq \frac{j2\pi}{\lambda} = jk, \tag{3.66}$$

$$\cos \theta_1 \simeq \cos \theta. \tag{3.67}$$

Furthermore, so far as the magnitude of the spherical propagation factor e^{-jks}/s is concerned, s may be replaced with r (in the denominator).

From Fig. 3.11(a), the distance s between the aperture point $(x_a, y_a, 0)$ and the observation point (x, y, z) is given by

$$s = \left[z^2 + (x - x_a)^2 + (y - y_a)^2 \right]^{1/2}$$

$$= z \left[1 + \left(\frac{x - x_a}{z} \right)^2 + \left(\frac{y - y_a}{z} \right)^2 \right]^{1/2}. \tag{3.68}$$

If the region of interest in the observation plane is restricted to a narrow region about the z-axis such that the condition

$$\frac{(x - x_a)^2 + (y - y_a)^2}{z^2} \ll 1 \tag{3.69}$$

is valid, s may be approximated by the first two terms of the binomial expansion of (3.68),

$$s \simeq z \left[1 + \frac{1}{2} \left(\frac{x - x_a}{z} \right)^2 + \frac{1}{2} \left(\frac{y - y_a}{z} \right)^2 \right], \tag{3.70}$$

which is known as the *Fresnel approximation*. Replacing s in the phase term e^{-jks} with the above approximation and incorporating the approximations discussed earlier, (3.65) becomes

$$E(x, y, z) = \frac{j(1 + \cos \theta)}{2\lambda} \frac{e^{-jkz}}{r} \exp \left[\frac{-jk}{2z} (x^2 + y^2) \right] h(x, y, z), \tag{3.71}$$

where

$$h(x, y, z) = \int_{-\infty}^{\infty} E_a(x_a, y_a) \exp \left[\frac{-jk}{2z} (x_a^2 + y_a^2) \right]$$

$$\times \exp \left[\frac{jk}{z} (xx_a + yy_a) \right] dx_a \, dy_a. \tag{3.72}$$

The function $h(x, y, z)$ will be referred to as the form factor of $E(x, y, z)$. Its integral is written with infinite limits, it being understood that $E_a(x_a, y_a)$ is identically zero outside the aperture.

The formulation given by (3.71) and (3.72) is useful for computing the Fresnel field $E(x, y, z)$ when the objective is to evaluate its variation in the xy-plane at a fixed value of z (Fig. 3.12(a)). In most antenna applications, however, the parameter of interest is the directivity of the antenna, i.e. the shape of the radiation pattern when plotted as a function of direction (and hence θ and ϕ) at a constant radius R from the antenna (Fig. 3.12(b)). Expressions equivalent to (3.71) and (3.72) may be developed for the above purpose by converting the coordinates of the observation point to spherical coordinates:

$$x = R \sin \theta \cos \phi,$$
$$y = R \sin \theta \sin \phi, \tag{3.73}$$
$$z = R \cos \theta,$$

and repeating the steps represented by (3.68) through (3.72) with z replaced by R. Thus,

$$s = \left[z + (x - x_a) + (y - y_a) \right]^{1/2}$$
$$= R \left[1 + \frac{(x_a^2 + y_a^2) - 2(xx_a + yy_a)}{R^2} \right]^{1/2}$$
$$\simeq R \left[1 + \frac{x_a^2 + y_a^2}{2R^2} - \frac{(xx_a + yy_a)}{R^2} \right], \tag{3.74}$$

and therefore $E(R, \theta, \phi)$ is given by

$$E(R, \theta, \phi) = j \frac{1 + \cos \theta}{2\lambda} \frac{e^{-jkR}}{R} h(R, \theta, \phi), \tag{3.75}$$

where

$$h(R, \theta, \phi) = \iint_{-\infty}^{\infty} E_a(x_a, y_a) \exp \left[\frac{-jk}{2R} (x_a^2 + y_a^2) \right]$$
$$\times \exp \left[jk \sin \theta (x_a \cos \phi + y_a \sin \phi) \right] dx_a dy_a. \tag{3.76}$$

So far, the aperture coordinates are still in the Cartesian system; they may be converted to other systems of coordinates to suit the aperture geometry.

3-7.4 Fraunhofer Region

The quantity $(1 + \cos \theta)/2$ in (3.75) frequently is referred to as the *obliquity factor*. If the observation region of interest is limited to a narrow angular range about the z-axis so that $\cos\theta \simeq 1$, the obliquity factor may be set equal to unity. If, additionally, the observation point is far enough from the aperture so that

$$R \gg \left(\frac{k}{2}\right)\left(x_a^2 + y_a^2\right)_{max}, \qquad (3.77)$$

where $(x_a^2 + y_a^2)_{max}^{1/2}$ is the maximum linear distance between the origin and the edge of the aperture, then the quadratic phase factor $\exp[-(jk/2R)(x_a^2 + y_a^2)]$ in (3.76) is approximately unity over the entire aperture. With these approximations, (3.75) and (3.76) simplify to

$$E(R,\theta,\phi) = \frac{je^{-jkR}}{\lambda R} h(\theta,\phi) \qquad (3.78)$$

and

$$h(\theta,\phi) = \iint_{-\infty}^{\infty} E_a(x_a, y_a)\exp\left[jk\sin\theta(x_a\cos\phi + y_a\sin\phi)\right]dx_a\,dy_a. \qquad (3.79)$$

In practice, the above Fraunhofer diffraction equations are used to compute

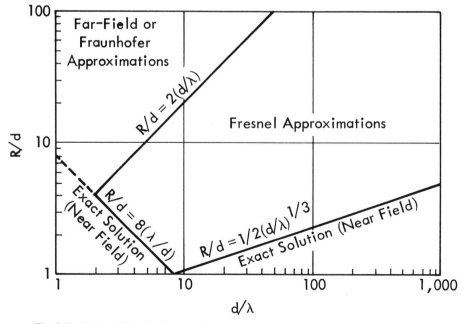

Fig. 3.13   Scalar diffraction-integral approximations for uniformly illuminated apertures (from Sherman, 1970).

the far-field $E(R, \theta, \phi)$ provided

$$R \geqslant 2d^2/\lambda \qquad (3.80)$$

where d is the maximum linear dimension of the radiating aperture. The above constraint, known as the *far-field condition*, is obtained by requiring that the exponent of the quadratic phase factor not exceed $\pi/8$ radians. Thus,

$$\left(\frac{k}{2R}\right)(x_a^2 + y_a^2)_{max} \leqslant \pi/8. \qquad (3.81)$$

By choosing the origin to be midpoint of the longest dimension of the aperture — that is $[(x_a^2 + y_a^2)_{max}]^{1/2} = d/2$ — the far-field condition (3.80) is obtained.

For further discussion of the validity of the Fresnel and Fraunhofer diffraction formulas, the reader is referred to Born and Wolf (1965), Silver (1949), and Hansen (1964). An excellent summary also is available in Sherman (1970), along with a sketch illustrating the regions over which the approximations are applicable. The sketch is reproduced here as Fig. 3.13.

3-8 FOURIER-TRANSFORM RELATIONS

The Fourier transform $\mathcal{F}\{g\}$ of a complex function g of two independent variables, u and v, is defined by

$$G(x_a, y_a) = \mathcal{F}\{g\} = \iint_{-\infty}^{\infty} g(u, v) \exp\left[-j2\pi(x_a u + y_a v)\right] du\, dv, \quad (3.82)$$

and similarly, the inverse Fourier transform of G is defined by

$$g(u, v) = \mathcal{F}^{-1}\{G\} = \iint_{-\infty}^{\infty} G(x_a, y_a) \exp\left[j2\pi(x_a u + y_a v)\right] dx_a\, dy_a.$$

$$(3.83)$$

Now, let us consider the far-field form factor defined by (3.79). If, for a fixed value of $r = R$, we define

$$u = \frac{x}{\lambda R} = \frac{\sin\theta \cos\phi}{\lambda}, \qquad (3.84a)$$

$$v = \frac{y}{\lambda R} = \frac{\sin\theta \sin\phi}{\lambda}, \qquad (3.84b)$$

(3.79) becomes

$$h(u, v) = \iint_{-\infty}^{\infty} E_a(x_a, y_a) \exp\left[j2\pi(x_a u + y_a v)\right] dx_a\, dy_a$$

$$= \mathcal{F}^{-1}\{E_a(x_a, y_a)\}. \qquad (3.85)$$

Thus, $h(\theta, \phi)$ is the inverse Fourier transform of the aperture distribution $E_a(x_a, y_a)$, evaluated at $u = (\sin\theta\cos\phi)/\lambda$ and $v = (\sin\theta\sin\phi)/\lambda$. In the far-zone region, the power density associated with the field E is $S_r = \frac{1}{2}\eta|E|^2$, which leads to

$$S_r(u, v) = \frac{1}{2\eta\lambda^2 R^2} \left| \mathcal{F}^{-1}\{ E_a(x_a, y_a) \} \right|^2. \tag{3.86}$$

Some treatments of the scalar diffraction problem derive the Fresnel-Kirchhoff integral assuming a Green's function of the form e^{jks}/s, instead of the alternative form e^{-jks}/s assumed in the derivation of (3.65). When the form with the positive exponent is used, the resulting expression for $E(x, y, z)$ would be identical to those derived in this section if j were replaced with $-j$. Consequently, $S_r(u, v)$ must be defined in terms of the Fourier transform of $E_a(x_a, y_a)$ rather than its inverse. This must be noted in order to avoid confusion should the reader consult references using the positive-exponent form.

In summary, given an aperture electric-field distribution $E_a(x_a, y_a)$, the far-zone electric field $E(\theta, \phi)$ with the same polarization and the power density $S_r(\theta, \phi)$ can be computed from

$$E(\theta, \phi) = \frac{j}{\lambda R} \left(\frac{1 + \cos\theta}{2} \right) e^{-jkR} h(\theta, \phi), \tag{3.87}$$

$$S_r(\theta, \phi) = \frac{1}{2\eta\lambda^2 R^2} \left(\frac{1 + \cos\theta}{2} \right)^2 |h(\theta, \phi)|^2, \tag{3.88}$$

where

$$h(u, v) = \mathcal{F}^{-1} E_a(x_a, y_a) \tag{3.89}$$

with u and v as defined in (3.84). For completeness, the obliquity factor, $(1 + \cos\theta)/2$, which was previously set equal to unity, has been reintroduced in (3.87) and (3.88).

3-9 POLARIZATION

As was stated earlier, the scalar diffraction formulation does not incorporate the polarization properties of the radiated field. If the aperture field $\mathbf{E}_a(x_a, y_a)$ is given by

$$\mathbf{E}_a(x_a, y_a) = \hat{\mathbf{x}} E_{ax}(x_a, y_a) + \hat{\mathbf{y}} E_{ay}(x_a, y_a), \tag{3.90}$$

the scalar formulation treats the scalar quantities E_{ax} and E_{ay} separately, without regard to the change in the direction of the polarization vector that the radiated wave experiences as it propagates into the far zone. That is, the far-zone field is polarized in the same direction as the aperture field:

$$\mathbf{E}(\theta,\phi)=\hat{\mathbf{x}}E_x(\theta,\phi)+\hat{\mathbf{y}}E_y(\theta,\phi),\tag{3.91}$$

where

$$E_x(\theta,\phi)=\frac{j}{\lambda R}\left(\frac{1+\cos\theta}{2}\right)e^{-jkR}h_x(\theta,\phi),\tag{3.92a}$$

$$E_y(\theta,\phi)=\frac{j}{\lambda R}\left(\frac{1+\cos\theta}{2}\right)e^{-jkR}h_y(\theta,\phi),\tag{3.92b}$$

and $h_x(\theta,\phi)$ and $h_y(\theta,\phi)$ are the inverse Fourier transforms of $E_{ax}(x_a,y_a)$ and $E_{ay}(x_a,y_a)$, respectively, with the proper scaling of variables as indicated in (3.89). According to (3.91), the far-zone electric field at a point in space in a direction away from the z-axis (Fig. 3.14) lies in the xy-plane, which means that it has a component in the $\hat{\mathbf{r}}$-direction (except when the observation point is on the z-axis). This is obviously inconsistent with the far-zone plane-wave representation. For apertures with dimensions that are large compared to the wavelength, however, the radiation pattern is highly directive with most of the energy radiated in a narrow angular region centered along the z-axis. Thus, for large apertures, the use of scalar diffraction is applicable.

The power density $S_r(\theta,\phi)$ associated with $\mathbf{E}(\theta,\phi)$ of (3.91) is

$$\begin{aligned}S_r(\theta,\phi)&=\frac{1}{2\eta}\left(|\mathbf{E}(\theta,\phi)|^2\right)\\&=\frac{1}{2\eta\lambda^2R^2}\left(\frac{1+\cos\theta}{2}\right)^2\left(|h_x(\theta,\phi)|^2+|h_y(\theta,\phi)|^2\right).\end{aligned}\tag{3.93}$$

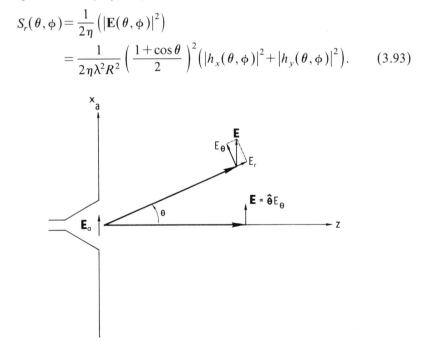

Fig. 3.14 Scalar diffraction does not take account of changes in the wave polarization as the wave propagates away from the aperture. In the broadside direction (z-axis), however, it predicts the correct polarization.

Since scalar diffraction treats each component of the aperture field separately, the material presented in succeeding sections will be confined to consideration of aperture fields with uniform polarization direction across the aperture, or equivalently, to one component of the aperture field.

3-10 RECTANGULAR APERTURE WITH UNIFORM ILLUMINATION

In the general case, $E_a(x_a, y_a)$ is a complex function consisting of an amplitude distribution as well as a phase distribution over the aperture. To demonstrate the utility of the Fourier-transform relations, we consider the case of a rectangular aperture in this section and that of a circular aperture in the next section, both with uniform amplitude and phase illuminations, and then proceed to discuss more complicated illuminations in succeeding sections.

For a rectangular aperture with dimensions a and b and an illumination

$$E_a(x_a, y_a) = \begin{cases} E_0 & |x_a| \leqslant a/2 \text{ and } |y_a| \leqslant b/2, \\ 0 & \text{otherwise,} \end{cases} \tag{3.94}$$

$h(u, v)$ is given by

$$h(u, v) = \mathcal{F}^{-1}\{E_a(x_a, y_a)\}$$

$$= E_0 \int_{-a/2}^{a/2} e^{j2\pi x_a u} \, dx_a \int_{-b/2}^{b/2} e^{j2\pi y_a v} \, dy_a$$

$$= E_0 ab \, \text{sinc}(au) \, \text{sinc}(bv), \tag{3.95}$$

where

$$\text{sinc}(x) \triangleq \frac{\sin \pi x}{\pi x}. \tag{3.96}$$

With $h(u, v)$ given by (3.95), and the obliquity factor set equal to unity, we have

$$E(u, v) = \frac{jE_0 A_p e^{-jkr}}{\lambda R} \text{sinc}(au) \, \text{sinc}(bv), \tag{3.97}$$

$$S_r(u, v) = S_0 \text{sinc}^2(au) \, \text{sinc}^2(bv), \tag{3.98}$$

where $A_p = ab$ is the aperture area, $S_0 = S_r(0,0) = E_0^2 A_p^2 (2\eta \lambda^2 R^2)$, and u and v are as defined previously by (3.84a) and (3.84b), respectively.

Since S_0 is the maximum value of S_r, the normalized radiation pattern of the rectangular aperture is

$$F_n(\theta, \phi) = S_r(\theta, \phi)/S_0$$

$$= \mathrm{sinc}^2(au)\, \mathrm{sinc}^2(bv)$$

$$= \left[\frac{\sin[(\pi a/\lambda)\sin\theta\cos\phi]}{(\pi a/\lambda)\sin\theta\cos\phi} \cdot \frac{\sin[(\pi b/\lambda)\sin\theta\sin\phi]}{(\pi b/\lambda)\sin\theta\sin\phi} \right]^2. \quad (3.99)$$

Figure 3.15 shows a cross-section of $F_n(\theta, \phi)$ in the xz-plane ($\phi = 0$), plotted as a function of $v = (a/\lambda)\sin\theta$. The magnitude of the sinc function is zero when its argument is an integer. Hence, the width of the main lobe in the xz-plane, measured between the first nulls, is

$$\beta_{null} = 2\sin^{-1}(\lambda/a) \simeq 2\lambda/a, \quad (3.100)$$

where it is assumed that $\lambda/a \ll 1$, so that the approximation $\sin x \simeq x$ is applicable. Similarly, $\beta_{null} \simeq 2\lambda/b$ in the yz-plane. The half-power beamwidth in the xz-plane can be obtained by solving for $\beta_{1/2}$ from

$$F_n(\theta) = \left[\frac{\sin[(\pi a\sin\theta_{1/2})/\lambda]}{(\pi a\sin\theta_{1/2})/\lambda} \right]^2 = 0.5.$$

The above equation can be shown to yield

$$\frac{\pi a\sin\theta_{1/2}}{\lambda} = 1.39.$$

Hence, the half-power beamwidth in the xz-plane is

$$\beta_{1/2} = 2\theta_{1/2} = 2\sin^{-1}(1.39\lambda/\pi a) \simeq 0.88\lambda/a \quad (3.101)$$

and similarly, $\beta_{1/2} \simeq 0.88\lambda/b$ in the yz-plane.

With $F_n(\theta, \phi)$ given by (3.99), the maximum directivity D_0 of the rectangular aperture can be computed using (3.21). Alternatively, and mathematically simpler, D_0 can be determined through an evaluation of the total power P_o radiated by the physical aperture. At the aperture,

$$P_o = \frac{1}{2\eta} \iint_{A_p} |E_a(x_a, y_a)|^2 \, dx_a \, dy_a. \quad (3.102)$$

For the uniform illumination defined by (3.94),

$$P_o = \frac{E_0^2 A_p}{2\eta}. \quad (3.103)$$

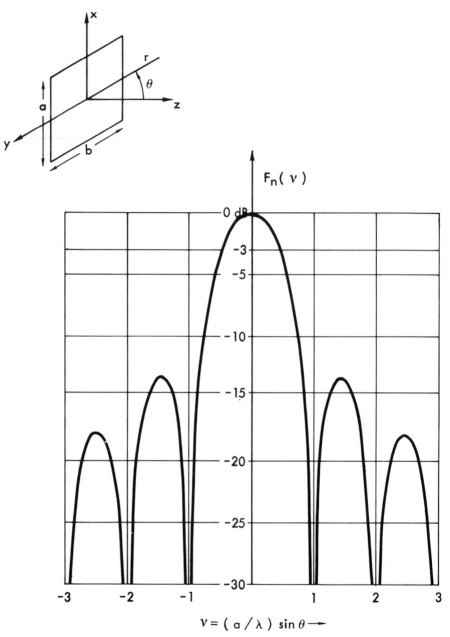

Fig. 3.15 Normalized radiation pattern of a uniformly illuminated rectangular aperture ($\phi = 0$).

Because of energy conservation, P_o is also given by the far-field power density integrated over a spherical surface of radius R,

$$P_o = \iint_{4\pi} S_r(\theta,\phi) R^2 \, d\Omega = R^2 \iint_{4\pi} S_r(\theta,\phi) \, d\Omega. \tag{3.104}$$

Hence,

$$\iint_{4\pi} S_r(\theta,\phi) \, d\Omega = \frac{E_0^2 A_p}{2\eta R^2} = \frac{S_0 \lambda^2}{A_p}. \tag{3.105}$$

From (3.20), D_0 is given by

$$D_0 = \frac{4\pi S_0}{\displaystyle\iint_{4\pi} S_r(\theta,\phi) \, d\Omega}. \tag{3.106}$$

Upon replacing the denominator of (3.106) with the result given in (3.105), we obtain

$$D_0 = \frac{4\pi A_p}{\lambda^2}. \tag{3.107}$$

Using (3.101), D_0 can be expressed in terms of β_{xz} and β_{yz}, respectively the half-power beamwidths (in radians) in the xz- and yz-planes,

$$D_0 = 0.77 \left(\frac{4\pi}{\beta_{xz}\beta_{yz}} \right). \tag{3.108}$$

Before we move on to the circular aperture, let us briefly consider the significance of the far-zone constraint, $R \geqslant 2d^2/\lambda$, where for the rectangular aperture d is the larger of the two dimensions a and b. According to (3.98), the far-zone power density varies with distance as $1/R^2$. Figure 3.16 shows the variation of the on-axis power density, $S_r(0,0)$, for a square aperture ($a=b=d$) as a function of the parameter Δ, which is the range R normalized to the far-zone distance $2d^2/\lambda$. The vertical axis in Fig. 3.16 is the power density normalized to unity at $\Delta=1$. The power-density plot was calculated using the Fresnel expression for the radiated electric field (see (3.76)), which includes a quadratic phase factor inside the integral. This factor is responsible for the oscillatory behavior depicted in Fig. 3.16 for $\Delta<0.2$. Also shown in Fig. 3.16 is a curve representing the $1/R^2$ far-zone dependence, which merges with the exact solution above $\Delta=0.5$.

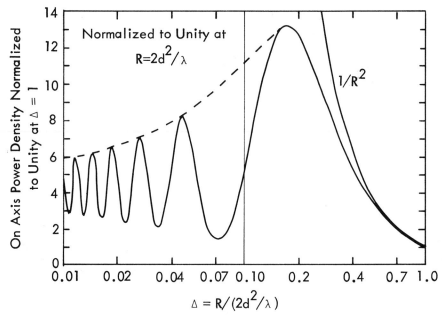

Fig. 3.16 On-axis power density $S_r(0,0)$ normalized to unity at $\Delta = 1$, where Δ is the range from the antenna normalized to the far-zone distance $2d^2/\lambda$. The aperture is a square with $a = b = d$ (from Hansen, 1964).

3-11 CIRCULAR APERTURE WITH UNIFORM ILLUMINATION

For circularly symmetric aperture illuminations, the far-field patterns can be found more conveniently if we first express x_a and y_a in terms of the polar coordinates ρ_a and ϕ_a as follows:

$$x_a = \rho_a \cos \phi_a, \tag{3.109a}$$

$$y_a = \rho_a \sin \phi_a. \tag{3.109b}$$

Substituting the above equations in (3.79) and replacing the elemental area $dx_a \, dy_a$ with its polar-coordinate equivalent $\rho_a \, d\rho_a \, d\phi_a$, the form factor $h(\theta, \phi)$ becomes

$$h(\theta, \phi) = \int_0^{2\pi} \int_0^\infty E_a(\rho_a)$$
$$\times \exp\left[jk\rho_a \sin \theta \left(\cos \phi \cos \phi_a + \sin \phi \sin \phi_a\right)\right] \rho_a \, d\rho_a \, d\phi_a, \tag{3.110}$$

or equivalently,

$$h(\theta, \phi) = \int_0^{2\pi} \int_0^\infty E_a(\rho_a) \exp\left[jk\rho_a \sin \theta \cos(\phi - \phi_a)\right] \rho_a \, d\rho_a \, d\phi_a. \tag{3.111}$$

Using the Bessel-function identity

$$J_0(x) = \frac{1}{2\pi} \int_0^{2\pi} \exp[jx\cos(\phi - \phi_a)]\, d\phi_a,$$
(3.112)

where J_0 is a Bessel function of the first kind, zero order, the expression given by (3.111), can be simplified. Substituting (3.112) into (3.111), we have

$$h(\theta, \phi) = h(\theta) = 2\pi \int_0^\infty E_a(\rho_a) J_0(k\rho_a \sin\theta)\rho_a\, d\rho_a.$$
(3.113)

It is noted that because of the circular symmetry, the dependence on the angles ϕ and ϕ_a has disappeared. The expression (3.113) is of the form of the Hankel transform, also known as the Bessel-Fourier transform, defined as

$$\mathcal{H}\{q\} = 2\pi \int_0^\infty E_a(\rho_a) J_0(2\pi\rho_a q)\rho_a\, d\rho_a.$$
(3.114)

Hence, $h(\theta)$ can be defined in terms of the Hankel transform of the aperture distribution,

$$h(\theta) = \mathcal{H}\{E_a(\rho_a)\}$$
(3.115)

evaluated at $q = (\sin\theta)/\lambda$.

To illustrate the above technique with an example, let us consider the simple case of a uniformly illuminated circular aperture of radius a,

$$E_a(\rho_a, \phi_a) = \begin{cases} E_0, & \rho_a \leq a, \\ 0 & \text{otherwise.} \end{cases}$$
(3.116)

The Hankel transform of the above function is

$$\mathcal{H}\{q\} = 2\pi \int_0^a E_0 J_0(2\pi\rho_a q)\rho_a\, d\rho_a.$$
(3.117)

Using a change of variables $t = 2\pi\rho_a q$, and the identity

$$\int_0^x t J_0(t)\, dt = x J_1(x),$$
(3.118)

the Hankel transform can be rewritten as

$$\mathcal{H}\{q\} = \frac{E_0}{2\pi q^2} \int_0^{2\pi aq} t J_0(t)\, dt = \frac{a}{q} E_0 J_1(2\pi aq).$$
(3.119)

In terms of $q = (\sin\theta)/\lambda$ and the aperture area $A_p = \pi a^2$, the far-field expressions for $E(q)$ and $S_r(q)$ are

$$E(q) = j\frac{E_0 A_p}{\lambda R} e^{-jkR}\left[\frac{2J_1(2\pi a q)}{2\pi a q}\right], \tag{3.120}$$

$$S_r(q) = S_0\left[2\frac{J_1(2\pi a q)}{2\pi a q}\right]^2, \tag{3.121}$$

where $S_0 = S_r(0) = E_0^2 A_p^2/(2\eta\lambda^2 R^2)$. This power density distribution is known as the *Airy pattern*, after G. B. Airy, who was the first to derive it (in a

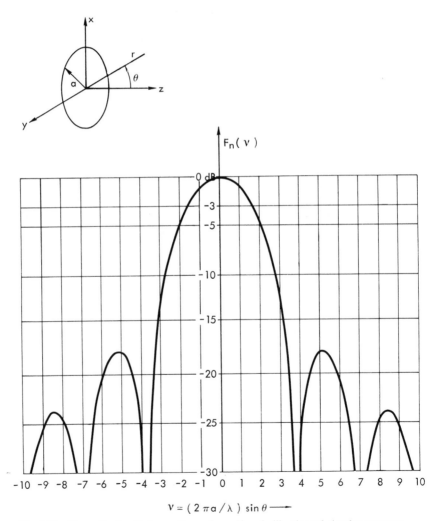

Fig. 3.17 Normalized radiation pattern of a uniformly illuminated circular aperture.

somewhat different form) in 1835. The normalized radiation pattern $F_n(q)=S_r(q)/S_0$ is of the form $[2J_1(\nu)/\nu]^2$, where $\nu=(2\pi a/\lambda)\sin\theta$. It is plotted in Fig. 3.17 on a logarithmic scale as a function of ν. The width of the main lobe between first nulls can be shown to be

$$\beta_{null}=2\left[\sin^{-1}(0.61\lambda/a)\right]\simeq1.22\lambda/a=2.44\lambda/d,\qquad(3.122)$$

where $d=2a$ is the aperture diameter. The first null of $F_n(\nu)$ occurs at $\nu=3.83$.

In a similar fashion, the half-power beamwidth can be obtained by setting $F_n(\nu)=0.5$, which leads to $\nu=1.57$ and

$$\beta_{1/2}=2\left[\sin^{-1}(0.25\lambda/a)\right]\simeq0.5\lambda/a=\lambda/d.\qquad(3.123)$$

Following the same procedure used earlier in connection with the rectangular aperture, the maximum directivity of the circular aperture can be shown to be once more given by

$$D_0=\frac{4\pi A_p}{\lambda^2}\qquad(3.124)$$

and in terms of $\beta_{1/2}$,

$$D_0=0.78\frac{4\pi}{\beta_{1/2}^2}.\qquad(3.125)$$

3-12 DEFINITION OF EFFECTIVE AREA

The two cases covered thus far, the rectangular aperture and the circular aperture, were each characterized by a uniform illumination over the aperture, $E_a(x_a,y_a)=E_0$. In both cases, the maximum directivity was related to the aperture area by (3.124). Now let us consider the more general case of a nonuniform amplitude distribution. We shall assume the phase distribution to be constant over the aperture, although the treatment is equally valid for linear phase. Recall that the maximum directivity D_0 is given, from (3.20), by

$$D_0=\frac{4\pi S_0}{\displaystyle\iint_{4\pi}S_r(\theta,\phi)\,d\Omega}\qquad(3.126)$$

where S_0 is the maximum value of $S_r(\theta,\phi)$, which is in the direction $\theta=0$ for an amplitude distribution that is symmetric with respect to the z-axis. Hence, from (3.85) and (3.86), for $u=v=0$,

$$S_0 = \frac{1}{2\eta\lambda^2 R^2} \left| \iint_{A_p} E_a(x_a, y_a) \, dx_a \, dy_a \right|^2, \tag{3.127}$$

where the integration is carried over the aperture area A_p. Also, by equating (3.102) to (3.104), we obtain

$$\iint_{4\pi} S_r(\theta, \phi) \, d\Omega = \frac{1}{2\eta R^2} \iint_{A_p} |E_a(x_a, y_a)|^2 \, dx_a \, dy_a. \tag{3.128}$$

Upon replacing the numerator and denominator of (3.126) with the results obtained in (3.127) and (3.128), we have

$$D_0 = \frac{4\pi \left| \iint_{A_p} E_a(x_a, y_a) \, dx_a \, dy_a \right|^2}{\lambda^2 \iint_{A_p} |E_a(x_a, y_a)|^2 \, dx_a \, dy_a}. \tag{3.129}$$

For the uniform-amplitude illumination case $(E_a(x_a, y_a)=E_0)$, the above expression reduces to

$$D_0 = \frac{4\pi A_p}{\lambda^2} \tag{3.130}$$

Otherwise, for a complex-valued function, Schwartz's inequality states that

$$\left| \iint_{A_p} E_a(x_a, y_a) \, dx_a \, dy_a \right|^2 \leq A_p \iint_{A_p} |E_a(x_a, y_a)|^2 \, dx_a \, dy_a. \tag{3.131}$$

Thus, in the general case,

$$D_0 \leq \frac{4\pi A_p}{\lambda^2} \tag{3.132}$$

provided the phase distribution is constant. The equality applies to the special case of a uniform amplitude distribution. To accommodate the general case, an effective antenna area A_{eff} can be defined such that

$$D_0 = \frac{4\pi A_{eff}}{\lambda^2} \tag{3.133}$$

along with an aperture efficiency η_a relating the directive performance of the subject antenna to an identical antenna with uniform illumination,

$$\eta_a = A_{eff}/A_p. \qquad (3.134)$$

3-13 NONUNIFORM ILLUMINATIONS—GENERAL CONSIDERATIONS

In the general case, the antenna aperture illumination may consist of an amplitude distribution function and a phase distribution function, which jointly determine the far-field antenna radiation pattern through the Fourier-transform relations established previously. These relations provide a convenient method for synthesizing the appropriate aperture illumination that will give rise to the desired far-field pattern. To describe the effects of the amplitude and phase distribution on the far-field pattern, use will be made of the rectangular aperture discussed earlier. With appropriate change of variables, the analysis techniques also are applicable to circular apertures with circularly symmetric amplitude illumination functions.

For most rectangular aperture distributions that are of interest in antenna design, $E_a(x_a, y_a)$ is separable into x_a and y_a functions,

$$E_a(x_a, y_a) = E_1(x_a)E_2(y_a), \qquad (3.135)$$

in which case the form factor defined by (3.85) may be written as

$$h(u, v) = \int_{-\infty}^{\infty} E_1(x_a)e^{j2\pi u x_a} dx_a \int_{-\infty}^{\infty} E_2(y_a)e^{j2\pi v y_a} dy_a$$

$$= h_1(u)h_2(v), \qquad (3.136)$$

where

$$h_1(u) = \mathscr{F}^{-1}\{E_1(x_a)\}, \qquad (3.137a)$$

$$h_2(v) = \mathscr{F}^{-1}\{E_2(y_a)\}, \qquad (3.137b)$$

and, as previously defined, $u = (\sin\theta\cos\phi)/\lambda$ and $v = (\sin\theta\sin\phi)/\lambda$. Thus, a separable illumination function produces a separable far-field pattern. In other words, the problem reduces to an evaluation of two one-dimensional Fourier transforms instead of one two-dimensional transform. Hence, in later discussions, consideration will be limited to one dimension. In general, $E_1(x_a)$ (and similarly $E_2(y_a)$) is a complex quantity consisting of an amplitude function $E_{10}(x_a)$ and a phase function $\psi_1(x_a)$:

$$E_1(x_a) = E_{10}(x_a)e^{j\psi_1(x_a)}. \qquad (3.138)$$

The above form will be used now in discussing the dependence of $h_1(u)$ on $E_{10}(x_a)$ and $\psi_1(x_a)$. The dependence on $\psi_1(x_a)$ will be discussed first for convenience of presentation.

3-14 NONUNIFORM-PHASE ILLUMINATION

The most commonly used phase distributions across the aperture are the linear and quadratic phase functions. As will be shown below, linear-phase illumination is used to move electronically (steer) the antenna radiation pattern in angle, which is the basic principle behind electronic scanning with antenna arrays (Section 3.20). Quadratic-phase illumination functions are used primarily to effect far-field conditions in the Fresnel region of the diffracted field. This may be shown by considering the Fresnel form factor defined by (3.76); if $E_a(x_a, y_a) = |E_a(x_a, y_a)| \exp[(jk/2f)(x_a^2 + y_a^2)]$, the integral equation reduces to the far-field representation (3.79) at $R = f$. Such a phase distribution can be introduced by using a double-convex lens with focal length f. For further discussion of the use of the quadratic phase function, the reader is referred to Goodman (1968, Chapter 5), Sherman (1970), and Steinberg (1976).

3-14.1 Scanned Planar Aperture

Consider a rectangular aperture in the $x_a y_a$-plane, excited by the complex field

$$E_a(x_a, y_a) = E_{10}(x_a) e^{j\psi_1(x_a)} E_{20}(y_a) e^{j\psi_2(y_a)}. \tag{3.139}$$

Let $\psi_1(x_a)$ be given by the linear distribution

$$\psi_1(x_a) = -\frac{2}{a}\psi_0 x_a, \qquad |x_a| \leq \frac{a}{2}, \tag{3.140}$$

where ψ_0, the slope of the linear phase function, is a constant. Without loss of generality, we shall take $\psi_2(y_a) = 0$. Let us define an angle θ_0, which later we shall call the *scan angle*, in terms of ψ_0 as follows:

$$\theta_0 = \sin^{-1}\left(\frac{\psi_0 \lambda}{\pi a}\right). \tag{3.141}$$

Rewriting (3.140), we have

$$\psi_1(x_a) = -\frac{2\pi}{\lambda} x_a \sin\theta_0, \qquad |x_a| \leq \frac{a}{2}. \tag{3.142}$$

Using (3.139) and (3.142), the far-field form factors are then given by

$$h_1(u) = \int_{-a/2}^{a/2} E_{10}(x_a) \exp\left[j2\pi\left(u - \frac{1}{\lambda}\sin\theta_0\right)x_a\right] dx_a \tag{3.143a}$$

and

$$h_2(v) = \int_{-b/2}^{b/2} E_{20}(y_a) \exp[j2\pi v y_a] \, dy_a, \tag{3.143b}$$

where u and v are as defined by (3.84). Introducing the new variable

$$u' = u - (1/\lambda) \sin \theta_0$$

$$= \frac{1}{\lambda} (\sin \theta \cos \phi - \sin \theta_0), \tag{3.144}$$

the form factors become

$$h_1(u') = \mathcal{F}^{-1}\{E_{10}(x_a)\} \tag{3.145a}$$

and

$$h_2(v) = \mathcal{F}^{-1}\{E_{20}(y_a)\}. \tag{3.145b}$$

Thus, the application of linear phase along the x_a-axis has no effect on $h_2(v)$, and, except for a translation from u to u', both form factors are given by the inverse Fourier transforms of the amplitude distribution. From (3.88) and (3.136), the power density is now given by

$$S_r(u', v) = \frac{1}{2\eta\lambda^2 R^2} \left(\frac{1 + \cos \theta}{2} \right)^2 |h_1(u') h_2(v)|^2. \tag{3.146}$$

To gain further insight into this problem, let us examine the effect of linear phase on the radiation pattern in the xz-plane. For $\theta = 0$, u' reduces to

$$u' = \frac{1}{\lambda} (\sin \theta - \sin \theta_0). \tag{3.147}$$

This result provides a convenient way to obtain the radiation pattern with linear-phase illumination for any amplitude illumination by simply shifting the pattern obtained for uniform-phase illumination by $\sin \theta_0$ along the $\sin \theta$ axis. Since the magnitude of θ_0 is governed by ψ_0 (the slope of the linear-phase term), the antenna beam can be steered in angle by controlling ψ_0. If the antenna configuration is such that ψ_0 can be controlled electronically, then the antenna beam can be electronically steered into the direction of interest. The angle θ_0 usually is referred to as the *scan-angle* or *steering angle*.

3-14.2 An Example: The Uniform-Amplitude Case

As an example, the far-field power density of a uniformly illuminated rectangular aperture (both amplitude and phase) is, from (3.98), given by

$$S_r(\theta) = S_0 \operatorname{sinc}^2 \left(\frac{a}{\lambda} \sin \theta \right). \tag{3.148}$$

The above equation is for the xz-plane ($\phi=0$). If the phase of the illumination is of the form defined by (3.142) rather than uniform,

$$S_r(\theta)=S_0\left(\frac{1+\cos\theta}{2}\right)^2 \operatorname{sinc}^2\left(\frac{a}{\lambda}(\sin\theta-\sin\theta_0)\right).\qquad(3.149)$$

The quantity $[(1+\cos\theta)/2]^2$ is the square of the obliquity factor, which we earlier set equal to unity because the angular region of interest was the region about the z-axis. With linear phase, however, the main lobe may be steered away from the direction $\theta=0$, in which case the approximation will no longer be valid.

For $a/\lambda\gg1$, the obliquity factor has a minor effect on the shape of the pattern in comparison with the sinc function of (3.149). Hence the direction of maximum radiation is $\theta=\theta_0$ and the corresponding maximum value of the power density is $S_r(\theta_0)=S_0(1+\cos\theta_0)^2/4$. The xz-plane normalized radiation pattern is then given by

$$F_n(\theta)=\frac{S_r(\theta)}{S_r(\theta_0)}=\left(\frac{1+\cos\theta}{1+\cos\theta_0}\right)^2 \operatorname{sinc}^2\left(\frac{a}{\lambda}(\sin\theta-\sin\theta_0)\right).\qquad(3.150)$$

Beamwidth

When $\theta_0=0$, maximum radiation is in the z-direction, which is "broadside" to the aperture axis as shown in Fig. 3.18(a). The rectangular aperture is shown as a line source because the normalized radiation pattern in the xz-plane is independent of the aperture width b. The half-power beamwidth $\beta_{1/2}$ was found earlier to be approximately (see (3.101))

$$\beta_{1/2}(\theta_0=0)\simeq\lambda/a,\qquad\text{broadside direction.}\qquad(3.151)$$

As the beam is steered towards $\theta_0=90°$ (known as the *end-fire direction*), the beam-shape remains approximately invariant with respect to the variable $\sin\theta$, but not with respect to the angle θ. Consequently, $\beta_{1/2}$ changes relative to its value at broadside. For $\theta_0=90°$, (3.150) becomes

$$F_n(\theta)=(1+\cos\theta)^2\left\{\frac{\sin[(\pi a/\lambda)(\sin\theta-1)]}{(\pi a/\lambda)(\sin\theta-1)}\right\}^2.\qquad(3.152)$$

The obliquity factor is approximately unity over a narrow range about $\theta=90°$. The sinc^2 function drops to one-half of its peak value at the half-power angles θ_1 and θ_2, as shown in Fig. 3.18(b). The angle θ_1 occurs for

$$(\pi a/\lambda)(\sin\theta_1-1)=-1.39.\qquad(3.153)$$

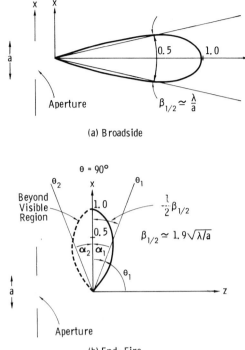

(a) Broadside

(b) End-Fire

Fig. 3.18 Comparison of (a) broadside (uniform phase) and (b) end-fire (linear phase with $\psi_0 = \pi a / \lambda$) patterns.

Replacing θ_1 with its complement α_1, we have

$$(\pi a / \lambda)(\cos \alpha_1 - 1) = -1.39, \tag{3.154}$$

from which α_1 is derived as

$$\alpha_1 = \cos^{-1}\left(1 - \frac{1.39\lambda}{\pi a}\right). \tag{3.155}$$

If the approximation

$$\cos \alpha_1 \simeq 1 - \frac{\alpha_1^2}{2}, \qquad \alpha_1 \leqslant 1 \text{ radian}, \tag{3.156}$$

is used, α_1 reduces to the simple expression

$$\alpha_1 \simeq \left(\frac{2.78\lambda}{\pi a}\right)^{1/2}. \tag{3.157}$$

Although α_1 and α_2 are not exactly equal (due to the beam asymmetry), they are approximately equal for $\lambda/a \ll 1$, which is the case under consideration. Hence, the half-power beamwidth at end fire is approximately

$$\beta_{1/2}(\theta_0 = 90°) \simeq 2\alpha_1 = 1.9\sqrt{\lambda/a}\,, \qquad \text{end-fire direction.} \qquad (3.158)$$

Thus, the end-fire half-power beamwidth varies as $\sqrt{\lambda/a}$, in contrast to the λ/a variation of the broadside beamwidth (see (3.151)). Figure 3.19 shows the variation of $\beta_{1/2}(\theta_0)$ normalized to its value at broadside ($\theta_0 = 0$), plotted as a function of the scan angle θ_0. Strictly speaking, the plots are only valid for the region between $\theta_0 = 0$ and $\theta_0 = 90° - \alpha_2$, since the definition of beamwidth is not valid for the region to the left of the aperture (Fig. 3.18(b)).

Also shown is a plot of

$$\beta_{1/2}(\theta_0) = \frac{\beta_{1/2}(0)}{\cos\theta_0}\,, \qquad (3.159)$$

which is a useful approximation for scan angles smaller than about 70°.

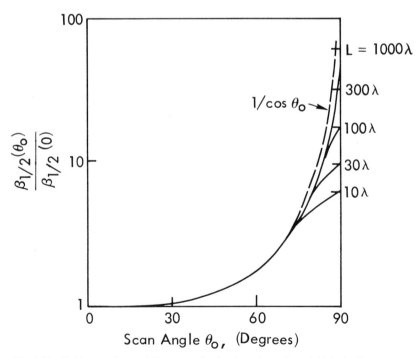

Fig. 3.19 Half-power beamwidth (normalized to its value at broadside) of a line source as a function of scan angle. The curves are valid only in the region that is visible through the aperture. (From Steinberg, 1976.)

Directivity

Associated with the increase of $\beta_{1/2}$ with θ_0 is a reduction in the antenna directivity D_0. As was noted earlier, the directivity at broadside is given by (3.107) as $D_0 = 4\pi A_p / \lambda^2$. To compute the directivity D_0 for a steering angle $\theta_0 \neq 0$, we need to apply (3.21):

$$D_0 = \frac{4\pi}{\int_{\phi=0}^{2\pi}\int_{\theta=0}^{\pi/2} F_n(\theta, \phi)\, d\Omega}, \tag{3.160}$$

with the limit on θ defined for the hemisphere in the $+z$ direction (since it is assumed that the aperture does not radiate in the $-z$ direction). For the uniform-amplitude illumination $E_{10}(x_a) = E_{20}(y_a) = E_0$ over the aperture, and a linear phase function in the x_a-direction as defined by (3.142), the power density obtained through the use of (3.145a), (3.145b), and (3.146) is given by

$$S_r(\theta, \phi) = S_0 \left(\frac{1 + \cos\theta}{2} \right)^2 \text{sinc}^2(au')\,\text{sinc}^2(bv), \tag{3.161}$$

where $S_0 = E_0^2 A_P^2 / (2\eta\lambda^2 R^2)$ and

$$u' = \frac{1}{\lambda}(\sin\theta\cos\phi - \sin\theta_0), \tag{3.162a}$$

$$v = \frac{1}{\lambda}(\sin\theta\sin\phi). \tag{3.162b}$$

For a given value of the scan angle θ_0, the normalized radiation pattern is

$$F_n(\theta, \phi) = \left(\frac{1 + \cos\theta}{1 + \cos\theta_0} \right)^2 \text{sinc}^2(au')\,\text{sinc}^2(bv). \tag{3.163}$$

In principle, D_0 now may be obtained by inserting (3.163) into (3.160) and integrating. However, the integration is complicated and does not yield a closed-form solution (Hansen, 1964). If the integration is limited to the main beam, however, the approximate solution

$$D_0 \simeq \frac{4\pi A_p}{\lambda^2} \cos\theta_0 \tag{3.164}$$

is obtained, where $A_p = ab$. This result, which is valid only over a limited range of θ_0 as shown in Fig. 3.20, indicates that the directivity decreases as $\cos\theta_0$; or equivalently, it is the broadside directivity of an effective aperture equal to $A_p \cos\theta_0$, which is the projection of the physical aperture A_p into the plane normal to the direction of maximum radiation, $\theta = \theta_0$ and $\phi = 0$. Figure 3.20 (from Hansen (1964)) provides curves for $D_0(\theta_0)$, normalized to its value at

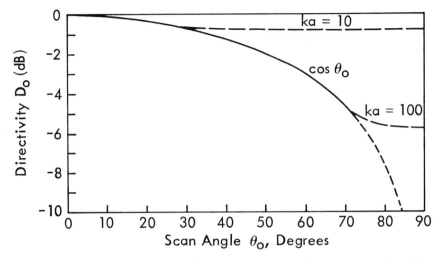

Fig. 3.20   Uniform square aperture directivity versus scan angle; a is aperture side and $k = 2\pi/\lambda$ (from Hansen, 1964).

broadside, plotted as a function of θ_0. The two cases shown (along with the $\cos\theta_0$ approximation) are for square apertures with sides of $ka = 10$ and $ka = 100$, where $k = 2\pi/\lambda$.

For a uniform-phase distribution, the far-field radiation pattern is governed by the amplitude illumination across the aperture. As was observed above, except for a rotation in angle, the same relations apply when the phase illumination varies linearly across the aperture. Quadratic phase functions are used for beam focusing of large apertures, as with the synthetic aperture radar. Higher-order-phase illuminations usually are associated with antenna construction errors, and will not be discussed here; instead, the reader is referred to Ruze (1966) and Schanda (1967). Next, we will consider the effects of amplitude illumination on the far-field radiation pattern, with the phase distribution assumed uniform over the aperture.

3-15 NONUNIFORM-AMPLITUDE ILLUMINATION

In antenna design, the Fourier-transform relations provide a convenient way to synthesize an amplitude illumination across the aperture that will give rise to a specific set of desired characteristics in the far field. By controlling the shape of the amplitude illumination, the antenna designer can optimize certain features of interest such as the antenna directivity, the side-lobe level, or the location of the nulls in the radiation pattern. Since these features usually are interrelated (for example, usually associated with side-lobe reduction is a reduction in directivity), the optimization process is determined by the intended application.

TABLE 3.1
Radiation Patterns Produced by Various Types of Amplitude Distribution over a Rectangular Aperture of Length a [a]

Amplitude distribution		Relative directivity [b]	First side-lobe level (dB) [c]	Half-power (-3-dB) beamwidth, (radians) [d]
Cosine:				
$E_{10}(x_1)=\cos^n(\pi x_1/2)$				
$n=0$ [e]		1.00	13.2	$0.88\lambda/a$
1		0.81	23	$1.20\lambda/a$
2		0.67	32	$1.45\lambda/a$
3		0.58	40	$1.66\lambda/a$
4		0.52	48	$1.94\lambda/a$
Parabolic:				
$E_{10}(x_1)=1-(1-\Delta)x_1^2$				
$\Delta=1.0$ [e]		1.00	13.2	$0.88\lambda/a$
0.8		0.99	15.8	$0.92\lambda/a$
0.5		0.97	17.1	$0.97\lambda/a$
0		0.83	20.6	$1.15\lambda/a$
Triangular:				
$E_{10}(x_1)=1-|x_1|$		0.75	26.4	$1.28\lambda/a$

[a] The variable $x_1=(2/a)x_a$, and $|x_1|\leqslant 1$.
[b] Relative to uniform distribution.
[c] Below maximum intensity.
[d] In xz-plane.
[e] Same as uniform-distribution case.

TABLE 3.2
Radiation Patterns Produced by the Amplitude Distribution Function $E(\rho_1)=(1-\rho_1^2)^n$ over a Circular Aperture of Diameter d [a]

n	Relative directivity [b]	First side-lobe level (dB) [c]	Half-power (-3-dB) beamwidth (radians)
0 (uniform)	1.00	17.6	$1.02\lambda/d$
1	0.75	24.6	$1.27\lambda/d$
2	0.55	30.6	$1.47\lambda/d$
3	0.45	36.1	$1.65\lambda/d$

[a] The variable $\rho_1=(2/d)\rho_a$.
[b] Relative to uniform distribution.
[c] Below maximum intensity.

To illustrate the influence of the amplitude illumination on the far-field pattern, we consider some commonly used distributions. For simplicity, we shall limit our discussion to the xz-plane ($\phi=0$), uniform-phase illumination, and unity-amplitude illumination in the y_a direction ($E_2(y_a)=1$). Introducing the new variables

$$x_1 = \frac{2}{a}x_a, \tag{3.165a}$$

$$u_1 = \frac{\pi a}{\lambda}\sin\theta, \tag{3.165b}$$

the form factors $h_1(u)$ and $h_2(v)$ defined by (3.136) become

$$h_1(u_1) = \frac{a}{2}\int_{-1}^{1} E_{10}(x_1)e^{ju_1 x_1}\,dx_1,$$

$$h_2(v) = h_2(0) = b. \tag{3.166}$$

Antenna radiation performance usually is described in terms of the normalized radiation pattern $F_n(\theta)$, which is proportional to $|h|^2 = |h_1 h_2|^2 = b^2|h_1|^2$. Table 3.1 provides a summary of three important characteristics of $|h(u_1)|^2$ for several classes of amplitude illumination $E_{10}(x_1)$. These characteristics are the maximum directivity D_0 relative to the uniform illumination case, the side-lobe level in dB below peak intensity, and the half-power beamwidth $\beta_{1/2}$. Complete expressions for $h_1(u_1)$ for these and other illuminations are available in the literature (Silver, 1949; Hansen, 1964).

For the first class of illuminations in Table 3.1, $E_{10}(x_1) = \cos^n(\pi x_1/2)$, the illumination decreases from 1.0 at the center of the aperture ($x_1=0$) to zero at the edges ($x_1 = \pm1$) for $n>1$. As n increases, faster illumination tapers are produced, resulting in lower side-lobe levels, at the expense, however, of lower directivities and wider beamwidths. This is true also for the second class of illuminations included in Table 3.1 as well as for the illuminations given in Table 3.2 for circular apertures.

3-16 VECTOR FORMULATION

Despite its non-Maxwellian nature, the scalar formulation introduced in Section 3-7 provides fairly accurate far-zone results provided the aperture dimensions are much larger than the wavelength λ. However, if this condition is not satisfied, as in the case of slot antennas, vector diffraction theory is needed.

The vector equivalent of Kirchhoff's scalar diffraction integral may be derived by direct integration of Maxwell's equations (Stratton, 1941) or through the angular-spectrum approach (Collin, 1969) which makes use of the Fourier-transform relations. For brevity, only the results for the far-zone field will be presented here. The interested reader is referred to an extensive review by Bouwkamp (1954).

Given an electric field aperture distribution $E_a(x_a, y_a)$, the far-zone electric field components are given by

$$E_\theta = \frac{j}{\lambda R} \left(\frac{1 + \cos \theta}{2} \right) e^{-jkR} [h_x \cos \phi + h_y \sin \phi], \qquad (3.167a)$$

$$E_\phi = \frac{j}{\lambda R} \left(\frac{1 + \cos \theta}{2} \right) e^{-jkR} [\cos \theta (h_y \cos \phi - h_x \sin \phi)], \qquad (3.167b)$$

where

$$\mathbf{h} = \hat{\mathbf{x}} h_x + \hat{\mathbf{y}} h_y$$

$$= \iint_{A_P} \mathbf{E}_a(x_a, y_a) \exp[jk \sin \theta (x_a \cos \phi + y_a \sin \phi)] \, dx_a \, dy_a \qquad (3.168)$$

and the integration is over the aperture A_p. The **H** field is related to the **E** field as in a spherical TEM wave:

$$\mathbf{H} = \frac{1}{\eta} (\hat{\mathbf{r}} \times \mathbf{E}).$$

Comparison of (3.167a) and (3.167b) with their scalar equivalents, (3.92a) and (3.92b), reveals a great deal of similarity. The quantity preceding the square brackets in the expressions for E_θ and E_ϕ is identical with that of the scalar case appearing in (3.92). The vector form factor **h** is now given by the vector Fourier transform of the vector aperture distribution, $\mathbf{E}_a$. On axis ($\theta = 0$, $\phi = 0$), the vector expressions are identical to the scalar expressions, but in directions far removed from the z-axis the scalar and vector results are different in both magnitude and polarization. For the power density we have

$$S_r(\theta, \phi) = \frac{1}{2\eta} \left(|E(\theta, \phi)|^2 \right)$$

$$= \frac{1}{2\eta} \left(|E_\theta|^2 + |E_\phi|^2 \right). \qquad (3.169)$$

It can be shown that substitution of (3.167) into the above expression leads to the expression provided by the scalar approach (see (3.93)) for small values of θ (such that the $\cos \theta$ factor inside the square bracket of (3.167b) may be set equal to unity).

3-17 ANTENNA ARRAYS

3-17.1 Background

An *array antenna* consists of several similar radiating elements, such as dipoles or slots. The radiative properties of the antenna are determined by the spacing between elements and the amplitude and phase distributions of the currents or fields of the individual radiators. Usually, identical elements are used in a linear one-dimensional array or a two-dimensional lattice, with all the elements excited by the same type of current or field distribution. The desired shape of the far-field radiation pattern of the array antenna can be synthesized by controlling the relative amplitudes of the array elements, in a manner similar to that discussed earlier in connection with antenna apertures. With the advent of electronically controlled solid-state phase shifters, the beam direction can be steered electronically by controlling the relative phases of the array elements. This flexibility of the array antenna has led to numerous applications including electronic scanning and multiple-beam generation.

The purpose of the next four sections is to introduce the reader to the basic principles of array theory and to the design techniques used in shaping the antenna pattern and steering the main lobe. The presentation will be confined to the one-dimensional linear array with equal spacing between elements. For more detailed discussions, the reader is referred to the books by Hansen (1964), Steinberg (1976), and Collin and Zucker (1969).

If the array antenna is composed of identical elements, its far-field pattern is governed by four factors: (1) the normalized radiation pattern of an individual element, (2) the spacing between elements, (3) the amplitude distribution among the elements, and (4) the phase distribution among the elements. Through a presentation of array theory, we shall show that the radiation pattern of an array antenna can be expressed as a product of the element-radiation pattern and an array factor, the latter being a function of parameters (2) to (4) only. This relation will prove useful in computing the far-field radiation pattern of a given array configuration, as well as in the inverse problem, namely, pattern synthesis.

3-17.2 Pattern Multiplication Principle

In this section, we shall consider the far-zone field due to N radiating elements, all with identical polarization configurations. In the far-field region of any radiating element, the electric-field intensity may be expressed as a product of two functions, one describing the dependence on the range r in the form of a spherical propagation factor e^{-jkr}/r and the other describing the dependence on direction (θ, ϕ). Thus, the element electric-field intensity can be written as

$$E_e(r, \theta, \phi) = \frac{e^{-jkr}}{r} f_e(\theta, \phi),$$

(3.170)

and the corresponding power density S_e is

$$S_e(r, \theta, \phi) = \frac{1}{2\eta r^2} |f_e(\theta, \phi)|^2 \triangleq \frac{1}{2\eta r^2} F_e(\theta, \phi).$$

(3.171)

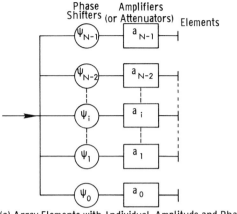

(a) Array Elements with Individual Amplitude and Phase Control

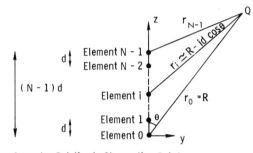

(b) Array Geometry Relative to Observation Point

Fig. 3.21   Linear-array configuration and geometry.

Now consider a linear array of N identical radiators arranged along the z-axis as shown in Fig. 3.21. The radiators are fed by an oscillator through a branching network. In each branch, an attenuator (or amplifier) and phase shifter are inserted in series to control the amplitude and phase of the signal feeding the radiator in that branch. The field due to the ith element may then be written in the form

$$E_i(r,\theta,\phi)=A_i\frac{e^{-jkr_i}}{r_i}f_e(\theta,\phi), \qquad (3.172)$$

where r_i is the distance between the ith element and the observation point, and A_i is a *feeding coefficient* (after Eaton et al., in Silver, 1949) representing the amplitude and phase of the excitation giving rise to E_i, relative to a reference excitation. In practice, one of the elements is used as reference. By Huygens's principle, the total field at the observation point is the sum of the fields due to the N elements:

$$E(r,\theta,\phi)=\left[\sum_{i=0}^{N-1}A_i\frac{e^{-jkr_i}}{r_i}\right]f_e(\theta,\phi).\tag{3.173}$$

Hence, the power density $S_r(r,\theta,\phi)$ of the array antenna is given by

$$S_r(r,\theta,\phi)=\left|\sum_{i=0}^{N-1}A_ie^{-jkr_i}\right|^2S_e(r,\theta,\phi),\tag{3.174}$$

where use has been made of (3.171) and where differences in distances to the individual elements have been ignored in comparison with their magnitudes. The above expression is the product of two factors. The second factor, $S_e(r,\theta,\phi)$, is the power directional pattern of an individual element, and the first, usually called the *array factor*, is a function of the positions of the individual elements and their feeding coefficients, but not a function of the specific type of radiators used. Except for a multiplication constant, *the array factor is equal to the far-field radiation pattern of the N elements had the elements been isotropic radiators* ($S_e(r,\theta,\phi)$=constant at a fixed distance r). Denoting the array factor by

$$F_a(\theta,\phi)=\left|\sum_{i=0}^{N-1}A_ie^{-jkr_i}\right|^2,\tag{3.175}$$

the array-antenna power density is then written as

$$S_r(r,\theta,\phi)=F_a(\theta,\phi)S_e(r,\theta,\phi).\tag{3.176}$$

The above equation is called the *pattern multiplication principle*. It allows us to find the far-field power density $S_r(r,\theta,\phi)$ of the array antenna by first computing the far-field power pattern with the array elements replaced by isotropic radiators, which yields the array factor $F_a(\theta,\phi)$, and then multiplying the result by $S_e(r,\theta,\phi)$. This principle is also very valuable in pattern synthesis applications.

It should be noted that the pattern multiplication principle as defined by (3.176) is not limited to linear arrays; it is applicable to any spatial distribution of the array elements, provided the far-field condition always is satisfied. Moreover, for any array, linear or otherwise, the effects of mutual coupling between elements should be considered if the elements are close to one another, and if the spatial positioning of the elements causes blockage in some directions, this too will affect the array-antenna pattern.

The feeding coefficient A_i is, in general, a complex quantity consisting of an amplitude factor a_i and a phase factor ψ_i:

$$A_i=a_ie^{j\psi_i}.\tag{3.177}$$

For a linear array with equal spacing d between adjacent elements (Fig. 3.21(b)), the approximation

$$r_i \simeq R - id\cos\theta \qquad (3.178)$$

may be used in the phase part of the propagation factor. Insertion of (3.177) and (3.178) into (3.175) leads to

$$F_a(\theta,\phi) = F_a(\theta) = \left| \sum_{i=0}^{N-1} a_i e^{j\psi_i} e^{jikd\cos\theta} \right|^2 . \qquad (3.179)$$

The above array factor is governed by two input functions: the array amplitude distribution given by the a_i's and the array phase distribution given by the ψ_i's. In practice, the amplitude distribution serves to control the shape of the radiation pattern, according to the same basic principles discussed earlier for the continuous aperture, while linear phase usually is used to steer the antenna beam into the desired direction. Below, we shall first consider the effects of the amplitude distribution on the radiation pattern for an array with uniform phase distribution, and then examine the technique of beam steering and its effects on the shape of the pattern (and hence directivity of the array antenna).

3-18 TWO-ELEMENT ARRAY

Before we proceed to the general case of N elements, it will be useful to consider first the simple case of the two-element array. The two isotropic radiators shown in Fig. 3.22(a) are spaced by a distance d and excited with unity amplitude and equal phase. From (3.179), the array factor is

$$F_a(\theta) = |1 + e^{jkd\cos\theta}|^2$$
$$= 4\cos^2\left(\frac{\pi d}{\lambda}\cos\theta \right), \qquad (3.180)$$

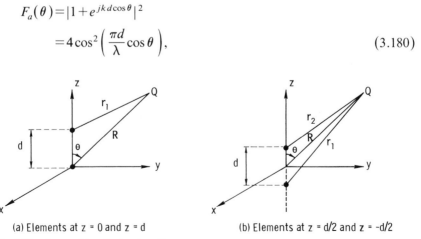

(a) Elements at z = 0 and z = d   (b) Elements at z = d/2 and z = -d/2

Fig. 3.22 Array of two isotropic radiators.

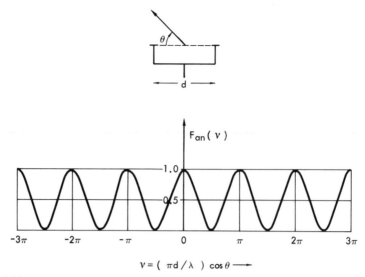

$$v = (\pi d / \lambda) \cos \theta \longrightarrow$$

Fig. 3.23 Radiation pattern of two isotropic in-phase radiators.

where k has been replaced with $2\pi/\lambda$. It can be shown easily that an identical expression would be obtained if the two elements were symmetrically arranged with respect to the xy-plane as shown in Fig. 3.22(b). Shown in Fig. 3.23 is a plot of $F_{an}(v)$ as a function of $v=(\pi d/\lambda)\cos\theta$. In addition to the main lobe centered at $\theta=\pi/2$ (broadside direction), the pattern includes other lobes, with the same amplitude, occurring periodically along the v-axis with centers at

$$\cos\theta = \pm\frac{n\lambda}{d}, \tag{3.181}$$

where n is an integer. These lobes, usually called *grating lobes*, can be eliminated by choosing $d<\lambda$. For $d=\lambda/2$, only the broadside lobe pointing in the direction $\theta=\pi/2$ remains. In Fig. 3.24, polar diagrams are shown for the array factor of a two-element array with unit amplitudes ($a_0=a_1=1$) for several values of d and three different values of δ, the phase difference between the two elements ($\delta=\psi_1-\psi_0$). Since $F_a(\theta)$ is independent of ϕ, the patterns always are symmetrical with respect to the z-axis.

To illustrate how the pattern multiplication principle can be applied, let us consider the example shown in Fig. 3.25, where two half-wave dipoles are placed $\lambda/2$ apart along the x'-axis. The power pattern of an individual dipole is from (3.64) given by

$$S_e(\theta') = \frac{15I_0^2}{\pi R^2}\left(\frac{\cos^2[\frac{1}{2}\pi\cos\theta']}{\sin^2\theta'}\right). \tag{3.182}$$

The array factor for two elements along the z'-axis is given by (3.180). By

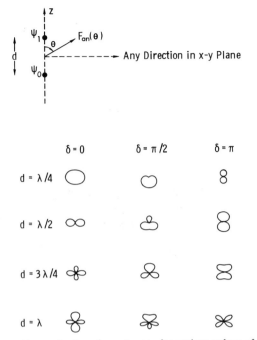

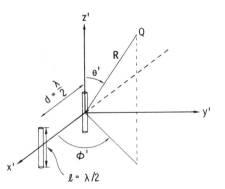

Fig. 3.24 Array patterns of a two-element array for various values of d and δ, where $\delta = \psi_1 - \psi_0$.

rotating the xz-plane of Fig. 3.22(a) about the y-axis so that the z-axis becomes coincident with the x'-axis of Fig. 3.25, the angle θ of Fig. 3.22(a) can be related to the angles θ' and ϕ' in Fig. 3.25. Specifically, it can be shown that $\cos \theta = \sin \theta' \cos \phi'$. Hence, in the primed coordinate system of Fig. 3.25, and with $d = \lambda/2$, the array factor is

$$F_a(\theta', \phi') = 4 \cos^2 \left(\tfrac{1}{2} \pi \sin \theta' \cos \phi' \right),$$ (3.183)

Fig. 3.25 Two $\lambda/2$ dipoles along the x'-axis.

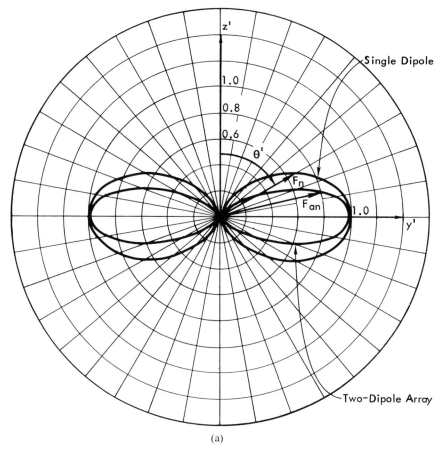

(a)

Fig. 3.26 Comparison of radiation pattern of a single half-wave dipole with the pattern of an array of two half-wave dipoles (see Fig. 3.25) in (a) the $y'z'$-plane and (b) the $x'y'$-plane.

and the power pattern of the two-element dipole array is

$$
S_r(\theta',\phi') = F_a(\theta',\phi')S_e(\theta')
$$

$$
= \frac{60 I_0^2}{\pi R^2}\left(\frac{\cos^2\left(\frac{1}{2}\pi\sin\theta'\cos\phi'\right)\cos^2\left(\frac{1}{2}\pi\cos\theta'\right)}{\sin^2\theta'} \right). \qquad (3.184)
$$

For $\phi'=\pi/2$ ($y'z'$-plane), the array power-pattern given by (3.184) reduces to the power pattern of the single dipole given by (3.182), except for a factor of 4 in magnitude which accounts for the fact that the input power needed to feed two dipoles each with a peak current I_0 is four times the amount of power needed to feed only one. In the azimuth plane ($x'y'$-plane) the array exhibits a directive pattern with maximum radiation along the y'-axis while the single dipole is nondirective (Fig. 3.26).

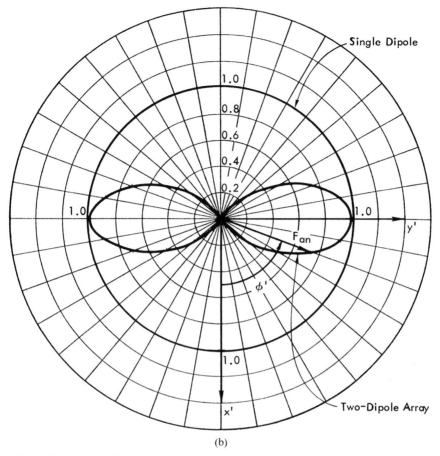

(b)

Fig. 3.26 (*continued*)

3-19 *N*-ELEMENT ARRAY WITH UNIFORM PHASE DISTRIBUTION

In this section we consider an array of N elements with equal spacing d and equal-phase excitations; that is, $\psi_i = \psi_0$ for $i = 1, 2, 3, \ldots, N-1$. Such an array of in-phase elements is sometimes referred to as a broadside array because the main beam of its radiation pattern is always in the direction broadside to the array axis. From (3.179) its array factor is given by

$$F_a(\gamma) = \left| e^{j\psi_0} \sum_{i=0}^{N-1} a_i e^{ji\gamma} \right|^2 = \left| e^{j\psi_0} \right|^2 \left| \sum_{i=0}^{N-1} a_i e^{ji\gamma} \right|^2$$

$$= \left| \sum_{i=0}^{N-1} a_i e^{ji\gamma} \right|^2, \tag{3.185}$$

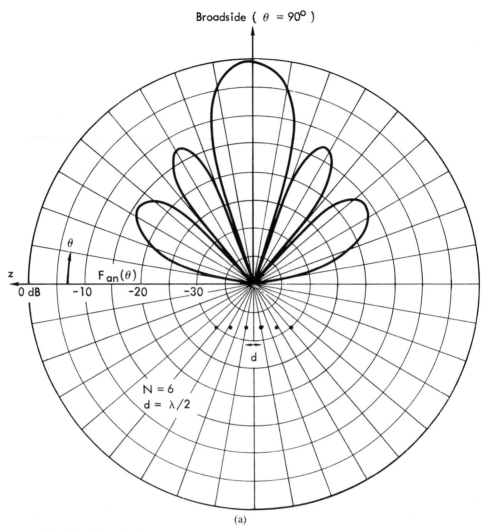

Fig. 3.27   Normalized array pattern of a six-element array with spacing between elements of (a) $\lambda/2$ and (b) $3\lambda/2$.

where
$$\gamma = kd\cos\theta = (2\pi d/\lambda)\cos\theta \tag{3.186}$$
is the phase difference of the fields from adjacent elements.

3-19.1 Uniform Amplitude Distribution

For $a_i = 1$, $i = 0, 1, 2, \ldots, N-1$, (3.185) assumes the form of a geometric series which can be converted to the form

$$F_a(\gamma) = \frac{\sin^2(N\gamma/2)}{\sin^2(\gamma/2)}. \tag{3.187}$$

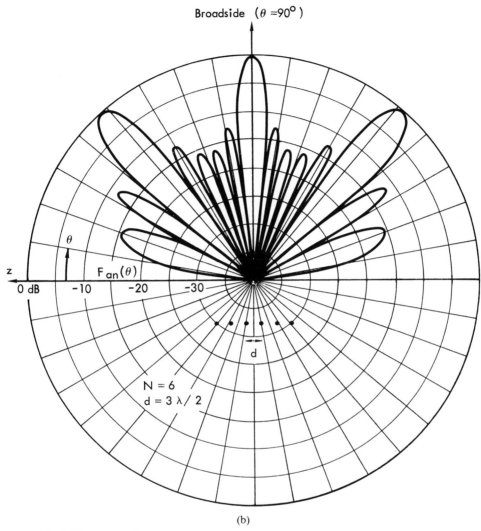

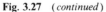

(b)

Fig. 3.27 (*continued*)

The maximum value of F_a can be shown to occur at $\gamma=0$ (or $\theta=\pi/2$) and is equal to N^2. The normalized array factor is therefore given by

$$F_{an}(\gamma)=\frac{F_a(\gamma)}{F_a(0)}=\frac{\sin^2(N\gamma/2)}{N^2\sin^2(\gamma/2)}.\tag{3.188}$$

Although the above function is defined for all values of γ, only the interval $0\leqslant\theta\leqslant\pi$ pertains to the real antenna problem. This interval is often referred to as the visible region of the antenna array. Polar plots of $F_{an}(\theta)$ with $N=6$ are shown in Fig. 3.27 for two different values of d/λ. It is observed that for the first case, $d=\lambda/2$, no grating lobes exist, but for the case $d=3\lambda/2$ there exist three similar main lobes. The grating lobes, which are introduced by the repetitive behavior of the sine function in the denominator of (3.188), are spaced 2π apart along the γ-axis. Hence, to avoid grating lobes

$$|\gamma|=|(2\pi d/\lambda)\cos\theta|\leqslant 2\pi. \tag{3.189}$$

Over the visible region, $0\leqslant\theta\leqslant\pi$, the above inequality is satisfied if $d\leqslant\lambda$. For $d=\lambda$ two grating lobes exist, one on each side of the main lobe, with their peaks (of the same amplitude as that of the main lobe) pointing along the two directions of the array axis. Since the radiation pattern of the array antenna is the product of the array factor and the radiation pattern of an individual element, grating lobes may be unimportant if the element pattern has small values (relative to its peak value) in those directions. When phase delay is introduced between adjacent array elements at their inputs in order to steer the antenna beam into a direction other than broadside, avoiding grating lobes requires that $d\leqslant\lambda/2$. This condition, which will be verified later in Section 3-20, is analogous to the Nyquist sampling theorem in communication theory.

Figure 3.28 presents plots of $F_{an}(\gamma)$ as a function of γ over the interval $0\leqslant\gamma\leqslant\pi$ for various values of N. For a given value of d/λ, increasing N corresponds to increasing the array length, which results in a narrower main lobe and higher directivity.

The width of the main lobe between first nulls β_{null} is equal to 2Δ where Δ is the angle between $\theta=\pi/2$ (peak value of $F_{an}(\theta)$) and the first null. From

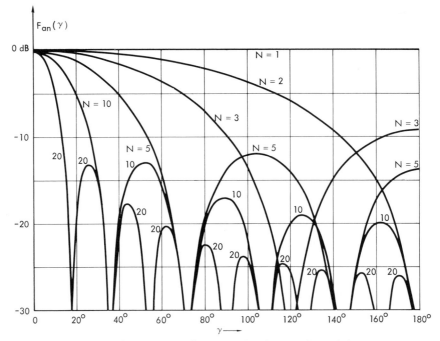

Fig. 3.28   Normalized array pattern for arrays of various numbers of elements N.

(3.188) the first zero of $F_{an}(\gamma)$ occurs when $N\gamma/2 = \pm\pi$. Thus,

$$\frac{N\gamma}{2} = \frac{N\pi d}{\lambda}\cos\left(\frac{\pi}{2} \pm \Delta\right) = \mp\pi, \tag{3.190}$$

from which β_{null} is derived as

$$\beta_{null} = 2\Delta = 2\sin^{-1}\left(\frac{\lambda}{Nd}\right) \simeq \frac{2\lambda}{l}, \tag{3.191}$$

where $l = Nd$. The above approximation, where the sine was set equal to its argument, is only valid for $Nd \gg \lambda$. The length of the array between the centers of the elements on the two ends of the array is $(N-1)d$, which for large N is approximately equal to l. It is worth noting that (3.191) is identical in form to (3.100), which defines β_{null} for the continuous rectangular aperture with uniform distribution.

For the continuous aperture distribution, it was stated in Section 3.12 that the uniform field distribution across the aperture yields the highest possible directivity. The same statement is valid for the array factor; for a given number of elements N and spacing d, it can be shown that the uniform array (all elements excited with equal amplitudes) has a higher directivity than any nonuniform array, provided all the elements are excited in phase with respect to one another. In the general case where the amplitudes and phases of the array elements can be individually chosen, directivities higher than that of the uniform array are possible. Such arrays are called *supergain arrays* (Elliott, 1966).

3-19.2 Binomial Distribution

In some applications, it may be preferable to have a slightly less directive array factor than that of the uniform array, but with lower side-lobe level. To reduce the side-lobe level, several nonuniform amplitude distributions have been proposed. Among these is the *binomial distribution*, so designated because the a_i's, the amplitudes of array elements, are proportional to the binomial coefficients:

$$a_i = \frac{(N-1)!}{i!(N-i-1)!} \tag{3.192}$$

with $i = 0, 1, \ldots, N-1$. To illustrate with an example, the relative amplitudes of a seven-element binomial array are $a_0 = a_6 = 1$, $a_1 = a_5 = 6$, $a_2 = a_4 = 15$, and $a_3 = 20$. With these coefficients, the array factor defined by (3.185) becomes

$$F_a(\gamma) = |1 + 6e^{j\gamma} + 15e^{j2\gamma} + 20e^{j3\gamma} + 15e^{j4\gamma} + 6e^{j5\gamma} + e^{j6\gamma}|^2. \tag{3.193}$$

Transferring the array phase reference from the edge to the center by factoring

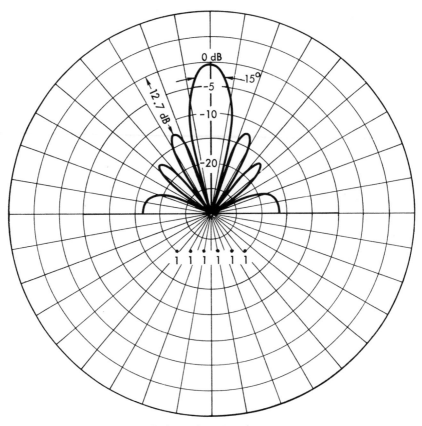

(a) Uniform Distribution

Fig. 3.29 Normalized array pattern for an array of 7 elements spaced $\lambda/2$ apart. All sources are in phase, but the relative amplitudes are distributed according to the following distributions: (a) uniform, (b) binomial, (c) edge, and (d) Dolph-Chebyshev.

out $e^{j3\gamma}$, the array factor can be expressed in terms of cosine functions of γ:

$$F_a(\gamma)=|e^{j3\gamma}(e^{-j3\gamma}+6e^{-j2\gamma}+15^{-j\gamma}+20+15e^{j\gamma}+6e^{j2\gamma}+e^{j3\gamma})|^2$$

$$=(20+30\cos\gamma+12\cos2\gamma+2\cos3\gamma)^2. \qquad (3.194)$$

The pattern maximum occurs at $\gamma=0$, and the corresponding peak value is $F_a(0)=(64)^2=4096$. The normalized array factor, $F_{an}(\gamma)=F_a(\gamma)/F_a(0)$, is shown in Fig. 3.29 for $d=\lambda/2$, along with plots of the array factor of the uniform array and other distributions to be discussed later. The binomial array exhibits no minor lobes, but its half-power beamwidth is substantially larger than that of the uniform array.

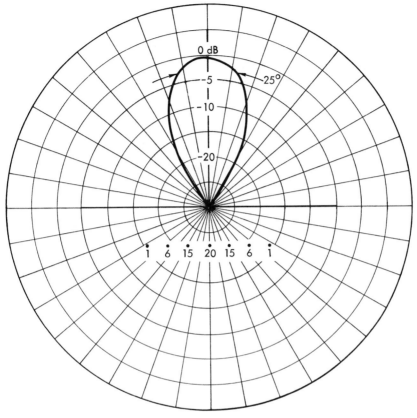

(b) Binomial Distribution

Fig. 3.29 (*continued*)

3-19.3 Edge Distribution

The *edge distribution* pattern shown in Fig. 3.29 is produced by an array in which only the end elements are excited, which is identical to the two-element array discussed earlier. Because the spacing between the two elements is now $7\lambda/2$, the pattern has grating lobes with peak values equal to that of the main lobe. However, the half-power beamwidth of the edge distribution pattern is considerably narrower than those of the uniform and binomial distributions.

3-19.4 Dolph-Chebyshev Distribution

From a design standpoint, it is desirable to have a procedure that can provide the amplitude distribution yielding the narrowest possible beamwidth for a specified side-lobe level, and conversely, the lowest possible side-lobe level for a given beamwidth. Such a procedure was developed by Dolph (1946) for

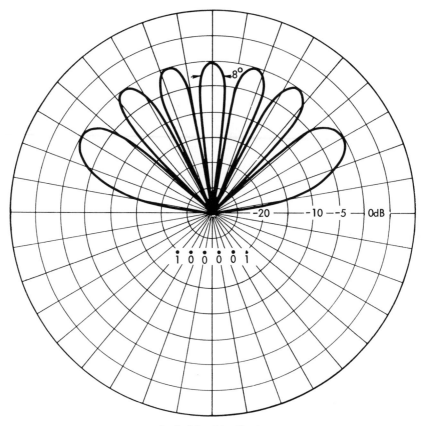

(c) Edge Distribution

Fig. 3.29 (*continued*)

broadside arrays. Because the feeding coefficients are determined through the use of the Chebyshev polynomial, the resultant array frequently is referred to as the *Dolph-Chebyshev array*. The procedure is fairly lengthy and available in most antenna books; hence it will not be discussed here. For comparison, however, the normalized pattern of a seven-element Dolph-Chebyshev array designed for a side-lobe level of -20 dB is shown in Fig. 3.29. The side-lobe level is 7.3 dB lower than that of the uniform distribution, but of course the reduction in side-lobe level is achieved at some sacrifice in gain (larger beamwidth).

3-20 PHASE SCANNING OF ARRAYS

The preceding discussion was concerned with uniform-phase arrays, where the phases of the feeding coefficients, ψ_0 to ψ_{N-1}, are all equal. In this section, the use of phase delay between adjacent elements is examined.

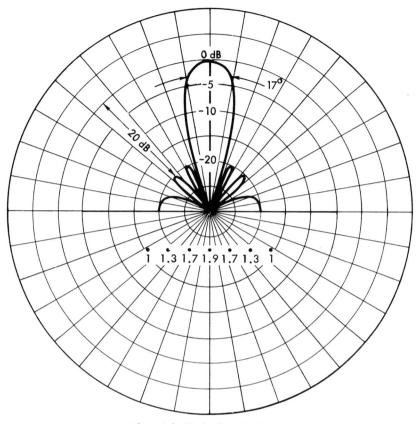

(d) Dolph-Chebyshev Distribution

Fig. 3.29 (*continued*)

When a linear phase distribution was applied to the continuous aperture of Section 3.14, it was observed that the radiation pattern shifted in direction from broadside to the angle θ_0, whose magnitude was governed by the slope of the linear phase function. The same principle applies to the array antenna. In the discrete case of an equally spaced linear array (sampled aperture), a linear phase distribution is achieved by applying linearly progressive phase delays from element to element across the array. Thus, relative to the phase of the zeroth element (Fig. 3.30), the phase of the ith element is

$$\psi_i = -i\delta \tag{3.195}$$

where δ is the incremental phase shift between adjacent elements. Insertion of (3.195) into (3.179) leads to

$$F_a(\gamma') = \left| \sum_{i=0}^{N-1} a_i e^{ji\gamma'} \right|^2, \tag{3.196}$$

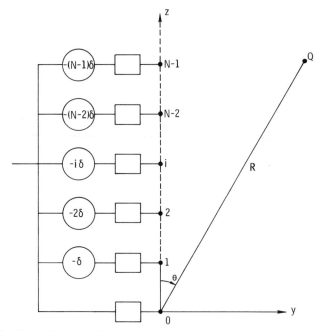

Fig. 3.30   The application of linear phase.

where

$$\gamma' = kd\cos\theta - \delta$$
$$= \gamma - \delta. \tag{3.197}$$

For convenience, γ' may be expressed in the form

$$\gamma' = kd(\cos\theta - \cos\theta_0), \tag{3.198}$$

where

$$\theta_0 = \cos^{-1}(\delta/kd). \tag{3.199}$$

The array factor given by (3.196) has the same functional form as the array factor developed earlier for the case of the uniform phase distribution (see (3.185)) except that γ is replaced with γ'. Hence, for any amplitude distribution across the array, the array factor with a linear phase distribution may be obtained from the expression developed for the uniform phase distribution, simply by replacing γ with γ'. For an amplitude distribution symmetrical with respect to the array center, the array factor $F_a(\gamma')$ is maximum when its argument $\gamma' = 0$. When the phase is uniform ($\delta = 0$), this condition corresponds to the direction $\theta = 90°$. As was mentioned earlier, the uniform-phase case is called a broadside array. According to (3.198), in the more general case of a linearly phased array, $\gamma'=0$ for $\theta=\theta_0$. Thus, by applying linear phase across the array, the array pattern is shifted along the $\cos\theta$ axis by an amount $\cos\theta_0$, and the direction of maximum radiation is steered from the broadside direction ($\theta=90°$) to the direction $\theta=\theta_0$. To steer the beam all the way to the end-fire direction ($\theta=0$), the incremental phase-shift δ should be equal to kd radians.

3-20.1 An Example: Equal-Amplitude Excitation

The normalized array factor $F_{an}(\gamma')$ of a linearly phased array excited by a uniform-amplitude distribution may be obtained from (3.188) by replacing γ with γ':

$$F_{an}(\gamma')=\frac{\sin^2(N\gamma'/2)}{N^2\sin^2(\gamma'/2)}. \qquad (3.200)$$

Through analogy with the uniform-amplitude-distribution case discussed earlier, the condition for avoidance of grating lobes may be obtained from (3.189). The result is

$$|\gamma'|=|(2\pi d/\lambda)(\cos\theta-\cos\theta_0)|\leqslant 2\pi, \qquad (3.201)$$

which is satisfied for all values of θ and θ_0 over the visible region of the antenna if $d\leqslant\lambda/2$.

For $N=10$ and $d=\lambda/2$, plots of the main lobe of $F_{an}(\theta)$ are shown in Fig. 3.31 for $\theta_0=0$, $45°$, and $90°$. We note that the half-power beamwidth increases as the array beam is steered from broadside to end-fire. This variation is consistent with our previous observations in connection with the beamwidth dependence on scan angle for a continuous aperture (Fig. 3.19).

In Section 3-19.1, it was shown that the beamwidth between first nulls, β_{null}, of the broadside array ($\theta_0=\pi/2$) is given by

$$\beta_{null}=\frac{2\lambda}{Nd}, \qquad \text{broadside array.} \qquad (3.202)$$

For a long array with narrow main lobe pointing in the direction θ_0, β_{null} can be shown to be given by the approximate expression

$$\beta_{null}\simeq 2\Delta, \qquad (3.203)$$

where Δ is the solution of the equation (Bach and Hansen, 1969)

$$\Delta^2\cos\theta_0+2\Delta\sin\theta_0-\frac{2\lambda}{Nd}=0. \qquad (3.204)$$

When $\theta_0=\pi/2$, the solution of the above equation gives us (3.202), and when

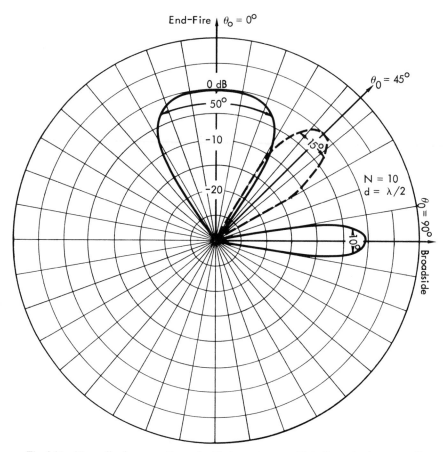

Fig. 3.31 Normalized array pattern of a 10-element array with $\lambda/2$ spacing between adjacent elements. All elements are excited with equal amplitude. Through the application of linear phase across the array, the main beam can be steered from the broadside direction ($\theta_0 = 90°$) to any scan angle θ_0. Equiphase excitation corresponds to $\theta_0 = 90°$.

$\theta_0 = 0$ (end-fire) it gives us

$$\beta_{null} \simeq \sqrt{\frac{8\lambda}{Nd}}, \qquad \text{end-fire array.} \tag{3.205}$$

Another property of interest is the level of the first side lobe of the normalized array factor. The first secondary maximum of (3.200) occurs at approximately $\gamma' = 3\pi/N$, and the side-lobe level is therefore given by

$$F_{an}(3\pi/N) = \frac{1}{N^2 \sin^2(3\pi/2N)}$$

$$\simeq \frac{1}{N^2(3\pi/2N)^2} = \frac{4}{9\pi^2}. \tag{3.206}$$

The above approximation, where the sine is set equal to its argument, is valid only for large N. According to (3.206), for arrays with many elements the side-lobe level is -13.5 dB and is independent of the number of elements N and of the scanning angle θ_0.

3-20.2 Array Feeding

According to the foregoing discussion, to steer the antenna beam to an angle θ_0, two conditions must be satisfied: (1) the phase distribution must be linear across the array, and (2) the magnitude of the incremental phase shift δ must satisfy (3.199). The combination of these two conditions provides the necessary translation of the phase front from $\theta = \pi/2$ (broadside) to $\theta = \theta_0$. Figure 3.32(a) shows a configuration where the phase of the excitation (field or current) of each radiating element is individually controlled through the use of electronically controlled phase shifters. Equivalently, the incremental phase delay may be provided by delay lines with variable time delay, as illustrated in Fig. 3.23(b). Both techniques require individual control of all the excitations of the

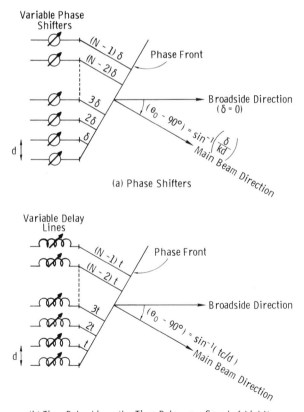

Fig. 3.32 Array-feeding techniques used for steering the main beam.

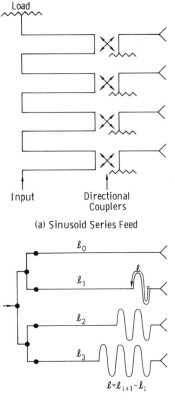

(a) Sinusoid Series Feed

(b) Parallel Feed

Fig. 3.33   Feeding arrangements for frequency-scanned arrays.

array elements. In contrast, a technique known as *frequency scanning* can provide simultaneous control of the phases of all elements. Figure 3.33 shows two different feeding arrangements employed in frequency-scanning arrays. The principle of operation is the same for both arrangements; hence the discussion will be limited to only the parallel feed distribution network. Relative to the zeroth element, the path between the common feed point and a radiating element is longer by l for the first element, by $2l$ for the second and by $3l$ for the third. If l is chosen such that at a given frequency f_0 the phase delay due to propagation through the delay line is 2π radians,

$$\delta_1(f_0) = \frac{2\pi}{v} f_0 l = 2\pi, \tag{3.207}$$

then all the radiating elements will be in phase ($\delta_2(f_0) = 4\pi$ and $\delta_3(f_0) = 6\pi$). Thus, at f_0 the array radiates in the broadside direction. The quantity v is the velocity of propagation of the transmission line. If f is changed to $f_0 + \Delta f$, the new phase shift of the first element relative to the zeroth element is

$$\delta_1 = \frac{2\pi}{v}(f_0 + \Delta f)l = \frac{2\pi f_0 l}{v} + \left(\frac{2\pi l}{v}\right)\Delta f$$

$$= 2\pi + \left(\frac{2\pi l}{v}\right)\Delta f, \tag{3.208}$$

and correspondingly, $\delta_2 = 2\delta_1$ and $\delta_3 = 3\delta_1$. Ignoring the factor 2π and its multiples since they exercise no influence on the relative phases of the radiated fields, we see that the incremental phase shifts are directly proportional to the frequency deviation Δf. Thus, for an array with N elements, controlling Δf provides a direct control of δ_1 (and hence $\delta_2, \delta_3, \ldots, \delta_N$), which in turn controls the scan angle θ_0 according to (3.199).

3-21 ANTENNA TYPES

Antennas are constructed in a wide variety of geometrical configurations and feeding arrangements. The properties for which specific antenna type usually is chosen are the antenna radiation pattern, gain, polarization, impedance, and bandwidth. In some applications, geometry also may be important. For example, the antenna used for a side-looking airborne radar (SLAR) needs to be long in the direction of flight (so as to produce a narrow beam in the along-track direction) and narrow in height (so as to illuminate a wide swathwidth on the ground). Although the waveguide slot array antenna and the cylindrical reflector antenna fed by a dipole array can both provide the desired illumination pattern, the waveguide slot array is more suitable aerodynamically.

A thorough treatment of the various types of antennas used in microwave remote sensing would constitute a sizable volume in itself. Therefore, we have chosen to consider below two basic types of antennas—the electromagnetic horn and the slot antennas—as examples to illustrate how the techniques discussed in previous sections may be applied to determine the radiation properties. The section on slot antennas demonstrates also the technique of frequency-scanning using a waveguide slot array. More detailed treatments of these and other types of antennas, including reflector, log-periodic, and lens antennas, are contained in the books and handbooks referenced in this chapter.

3-22 HORN ANTENNAS

Electromagnetic horns are used widely in microwave communication and remote sensing systems. Small horns with modest gain are used commonly as primary antennas to illuminate ("feed") large apertures such as reflector-type antennas, while large horns with high gain are employed on their own in some applications.

The horn antenna provides a gradual transition between a waveguide and free space. If the waveguide dimensions are such that it can support only the dominant propagation mode, then by gradually flaring the terminal section of the waveguide, the excitation of higher-order modes may be avoided. Thus, a horn can provide simultaneously single-mode propagation (which is difficult to achieve with an oversize open-ended waveguide) as well as a large radiating aperture (compared to the single-mode waveguide). Furthermore, horns are broader-band antennas than dipole and slot antennas.

Horns are constructed in a variety of shapes, some of the more frequently used types are illustrated in Fig. 3.34. The combination of size and shape of a horn dictates its directivity, impedance, shape of radiation pattern, and polarization properties. The horn shown in Fig. 3.34(a) is known as a *pyramidal horn*. It is often called a "standard-gain horn" because it is commonly used in antenna measurements as a reference antenna of known gain. A pyramidal horn flared in only one plane is known as a *sectoral horn*. If the waveguide is flared to increase the aperture dimension in the direction of the electric field (Fig. 3.34(b)), it is referred to as an *E-plane sectoral horn*, and if the flaring is in the direction of the magnetic field, it is an *H-plane sectoral horn* (Fig. 3.34(c)). In the nonflared direction, the sectoral horn usually has the same dimension as the waveguide connected to its throat. Another horn configuration is the *conical horn* (Fig. 3.34(d)), which, by virtue of its axial symmetry, produces a symmetrical radiation pattern. Horn antennas also have been

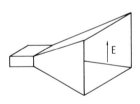

(a) Pyramidal

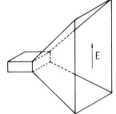

(b) E-Plane Sectoral

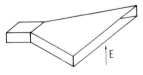

(c) H-Plane Sectoral

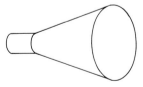

(d) Conical

Fig. 3.34   Commonly used horn types.

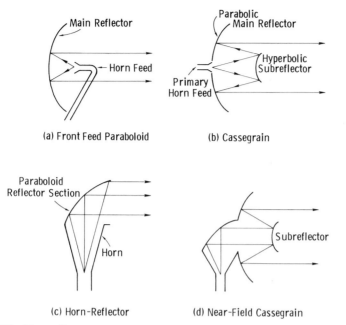

(a) Front Feed Paraboloid   (b) Cassegrain

(c) Horn-Reflector   (d) Near-Field Cassegrain

Fig. 3.35   Horn-reflector antennas.

combined with reflector antennas in a variety of different configurations, some of which are illustrated in Fig. 3.35.

3-22.1 Rectangular Horns

Expressions for the radiation from open-ended waveguides and horns of rectangular aperture were derived by Barrow and Chu (1939) and Chu (1940), and are given by Risser (in Silver, 1949). They used Maxwell's equations in spherical coordinates to solve for the field at the aperture and then applied the theory of vector diffraction (Section 3-16) to compute the far-zone field. An equivalent approach using cylindrical coordinates is available in Compton and Collin (1969a). The resultant expressions are fairly involved; hence they will not be reproduced in this presentation. Instead, we devote the remainder of this section to discussions of directivity as a function of horn dimensions.

The geometry of the E-plane sectoral horn is shown in Fig. 3.36. The angle θ_e is called the *flare angle*, and l_e is the *slant length*. A similar geometry applies to the H-plane sectoral horn, as shown in Fig. 3.37.

The maximum directivity D_0 of rectangular horns, which include the pyramidal horn and the E-plane and H-plane sectoral horns, was computed by Schelkunoff (1943) for the TE_{10} mode on the basis of simplified theoretical calculations using the scalar formulation approach discussed earlier (Section 3-7). Despite its theoretical simplicity, Schelkunoff's derivations provide results that have been found to be quite accurate in practice (Jakes, 1951).

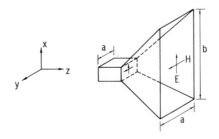

(a) Geometry

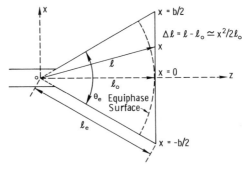

(b) x-z Plane Cross-Section

Fig. 3.36 *E*-plane sectoral horn geometry and coordinates.

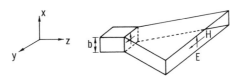

(a) Geometry

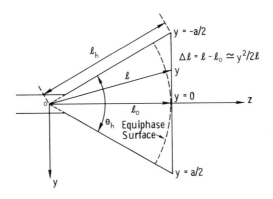

(b) y-z Plane Cross-Section

Fig. 3.37 *H*-plane sectoral horn geometry and coordinates.

E-plane Sectoral Horn

Schelkunoff's expression for the directivity of an *E*-plane horn is given by

$$D_{0e} = \frac{64al_e}{\pi \lambda b} \left[C^2 \left(\frac{b}{\sqrt{2\lambda l_e}} \right) + S^2 \left(\frac{b}{\sqrt{2\lambda l_e}} \right) \right], \qquad (3.209)$$

where *a*, *b*, and l_e are as defined in Fig. 3.36, and *C* and *S* are the *Fresnel integrals*

$$C(x) = \int_0^x \cos \left(\frac{\pi x^2}{2} \right) dx, \qquad (3.210a)$$

$$S(x) = \int_0^x \sin \left(\frac{\pi x^2}{2} \right) dx. \qquad (3.210b)$$

Plots of D_{0e} as a function of b/λ are shown in Fig. 3.38 for several values of the slant length l_e. It is observed that for a given slant length, the directivity increases with the aperture height *b* until it reaches a maximum value, and then beyond this optimum aperture height the directivity decreases. This behavior is due to the nonuniform phase distribution across the aperture. From consideration of the field inside the horn (Fig. 3.36(b)), it can be shown that the phase of

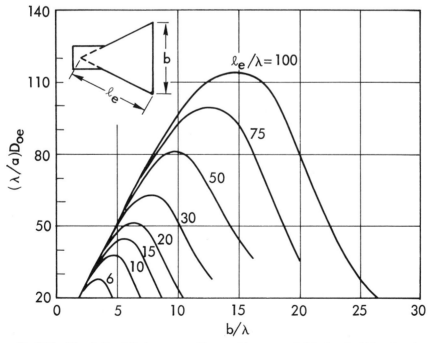

Fig. 3.38 Directivity of *E*-plane sectoral horns with aperture height *b* and width *a* (based on Fig. 16.4 of Schelkunoff and Friis, 1952).

the field at a point x lags the phase at $x=0$ by approximately $kx^2/2l_0$. Thus, the field E_{ax} in the aperture is given approximately by

$$E_{ax}(y)=E_0\cos\left(\frac{\pi y}{a}\right)e^{-jkx^2/2l_0}, \tag{3.211}$$

where the cosine function describes its amplitude variation for the TE_{10} mode. The maximum phase deviation introduced by the quadratic phase factor is $\psi_{max}=kb^2/8l_0$ and occurs at the edges ($x=\pm b/2$). The ratio b/l_0 is governed by the flare angle θ_e. For small flare angles, ψ_{max} is small and therefore the phase distribution is approximately uniform across the aperture. Consequently, for a fixed value of l_0 the directivity increases (and the beamwidth decreases) as θ_e is increased. But beyond a certain value of θ_e, some of the Huygens sources at the aperture get out of phase with others. This condition leads to destructive interference in the far field, which results in wider beamwidth and lower directivity.

For a given value of l_e, the horn is said to be optimum if b is chosen so that the directivity D_{0e} is maximum. This occurs when $l_e-l_0=\lambda/4$, or equivalently, $\psi_{max}=k\lambda/4=\pi/2$ (Jakes, 1961). Under this condition, b and l_e are related by

$$b\simeq\sqrt{2l_e\lambda} \tag{3.212}$$

In the E-plane (xz-plane in Fig. 3.36), $\beta_{1/2}\simeq\lambda/b$ radians and $\beta_{null}\simeq2\lambda/b$ for the optimum E-plane sectoral horn.

H-Plane Sectoral Horns

The directivity D_{0h} of the H-plane horn as given by Schelkunoff (1943) is

$$D_{0h}=\frac{4\pi bl_h}{\lambda a}\left\{\left[C(u)-C(v)\right]^2+\left[S(u)-S(v)\right]^2\right\}, \tag{3.213}$$

where

$$u=\frac{1}{\sqrt{2}}\left(\frac{\sqrt{\lambda l_h}}{a}+\frac{a}{\sqrt{\lambda l_h}}\right), \tag{3.214a}$$

$$v=\frac{1}{\sqrt{2}}\left(\frac{\sqrt{\lambda l_h}}{a}-\frac{a}{\sqrt{\lambda l_h}}\right). \tag{3.214b}$$

Plots of D_{0h} as a function of a/λ are shown in Fig. 3.39 for several values of the slant length l_h. The curves are similar to those of Fig. 3.38 for the E-plane horn. The H-plane sectoral horn of Fig. 3.37 is optimum when $l_h-l_0=3\lambda/8$, which corresponds to a maximum phase deviation $\psi_{max}=3\pi/4$ and leads to

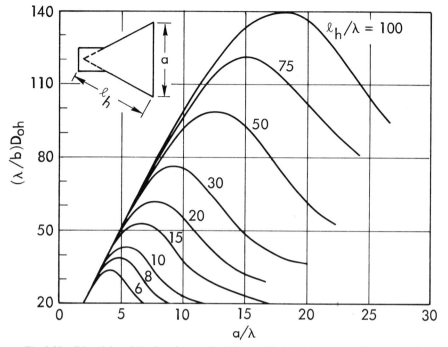

Fig. 3.39 Directivity of *H*-plane horns of width *a* and height *b* (based on Figure 16.3 of Schelkunoff and Friis, 1952).

the approximate relation (Jakes, 1961)

$$a \simeq \sqrt{3l_h\lambda} \ . \tag{3.215}$$

Pyramidal Horn

The *E*-plane and *H*-plane sectoral horns have a narrow beam in the flared direction and a wide beam in the unflared direction. Such a beam is sometimes called a fan beam. If the application calls for narrow beams in both directions, the horn can be flared along both axes, in which case we have a pyramidal horn. Thus, a pyramidal horn may be regarded as a superposition of an *E*-plane and an *H*-plane sectoral horn.

The directivity of the pyramidal horn, D_{0p} (Schelkunoff, 1943), may be expressed in terms of the directivities D_{0e} and D_{0h} as follows:

$$D_{0p} = \frac{\pi\lambda^2}{32\,ab}D_{0e}D_{0h}, \tag{3.216}$$

where D_{0e} and D_{0h} are given by (3.209) and (3.213), respectively. That is, D_{0p} may be obtained by multiplying the product of the directivities D_{0e} and D_{0h} obtained from Figs. 3.38 and 3.39 by the factor appearing in (3.216).

3-22.2 Conical Horns

A conical horn (Fig. 3.34(d)) usually is connected to a circular waveguide excited with a TE_{11} mode. Its performance is similar to that of the pyramidal horn in that, for a fixed length, its directivity increases as a function of the aperture diameter d up to a certain optimum value. This is demonstrated in Fig. 3.40, which contains theoretical curves that were derived by Gray and

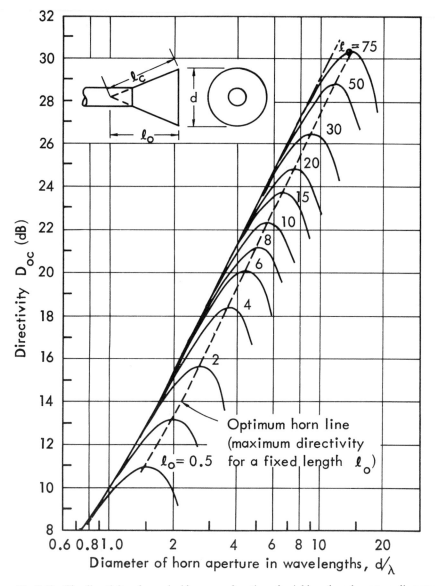

Fig. 3.40 The directivity of a conical horn as a function of axial length and aperture diameter d in wavelengths (from King, 1950).

Schelkunoff and reported by King (1950). Note that the family of curves is for different values of the *axial length* l_0, unlike the plots in Figs. 3.38 and 3.39, where the parameter was the slant length. Experimental measurements made over a wide range of values of l_0 and d were found to be in excellent agreement with the calculated values. The dashed line of Fig. 3.40 describes the dimensions of the optimum horn. The conical horn is optimum (maximum directivity for a fixed slant length l_c) when its diameter is (Jakes, 1961)

$$d \simeq \sqrt{3l_c\lambda}, \tag{3.217}$$

which is the same criterion as for the *H*-plane sectoral horn. Under this condition, the directivity in dB is given by

$$D_{0c} = 20\log\left(\frac{\pi d}{\lambda}\right) - 2.82 \text{ dB}, \tag{3.218}$$

and its effective area is equal to 52 percent of its physical aperture area; $A_{eff} = 0.52 A_p$, where $A_p = \pi d^2/4$.

3-22.3 Lens-Corrected Horns

According to (3.217) and (3.218), an optimum horn with a 26-dB directivity should have a slant length $l_c \simeq 26\lambda$ and a diameter $d \simeq 8.8\lambda$. If $\lambda = 3$ cm ($f = 10$ GHz), for example, these dimensions translate into a 78-cm-long horn with an aperture diameter of 26.4 cm. For many applications, such long lengths are undesirable. If l_c were to be limited to a certain value, so would d and the directivity D_{0c}. Because of the quadratic phase error in the aperture, increasing the aperture diameter (by increasing the flare angle) beyond its optimum value results in a loss, rather than gain, in directivity. This limitation on the maximum flare angle for a given horn length has led to the development of the lens-corrected horn.

By mounting a lens in the horn aperture (Fig. 3.41) to correct the phase distribution across the aperture, the limitation on the maximum flare angle can be removed, thereby allowing the use of large apertures to increase the directivity. This technique has been implemented successfully in both rectangular and conical horns. Without the lens, the phase shift between the vortex o and the point $x = x_1$ on the aperture (Fig. 3.41) is larger than it is to the point $x = 0$ (cone axis) because of the longer travel time. Through proper design of the lens shape and its index of refraction, the total phase shift between o and x_1 can be made equal to the phase-shift between o and the point $x = 0$ for any value of x_1 on the aperture. Effectively, the wave propagating along the cone axis has to traverse a longer thickness of the lens (in which the velocity of propagation is lower than that in air) than the wave traveling to x_1, thereby arriving in phase at the aperture.

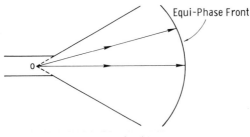

(a) Empty Sectoral Horn

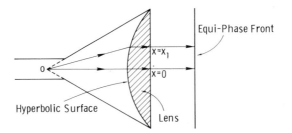

(b) Lens-Corrected Sectoral Horn

Fig. 3.41   A hyperbolic lens of the appropriate index of refraction can transform the phase front to a uniform distribution across the aperture.

Since the index of refraction of the lens is different from that of air, only part of the energy incident upon it is transmitted into the lens, and the remainder is reflected. Multiple reflections from the surface of the lens and the surface of the cone can result in amplitude and phase variations across the aperture. To reduce these reflections, several techniques have been developed to match the lens surface to air through the use of quarter-wave transformers (Compton and Collin, 1969a). The wave impedance of the lens can be matched to that of free space by covering the lens surface with a dielectric layer of appropriate thickness and index of refraction, or by cutting slots of appropriate thickness and depth in the surface of the lens (Collin, 1959).

3-23 SLOT ANTENNAS

In this section we consider the far-field radiation properties of a rectangular slot antenna, followed by a brief discussion of waveguide slot arrays.

Examples of slots cut into the walls of a rectangular waveguide are shown in Fig. 3.42. When a slot interrupts the flow of transverse surface currents, it couples energy from the waveguide to free space. Figure 3.43 shows the distribution of currents flowing along the inner walls of a rectangular waveguide propagating a TE_{10} mode. Among the slots shown in Fig. 3.42, the only

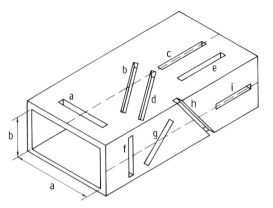

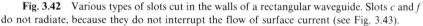

Fig. 3.42 Various types of slots cut in the walls of a rectangular waveguide. Slots *c* and *f* do not radiate, because they do not interrupt the flow of surface current (see Fig. 3.43).

nonradiating slots are those labeled c and f (their axes are parallel to the direction of current-flow). The magnitude of the energy coupled by a slot is a function of the waveguide dimensions; the slot dimensions, orientation, and position; and the density of the current interrupted by the slot.

To demonstrate the approach used for computing the far-zone fields of a slot antenna, we shall consider the simple case of a half-wave rectangular slot excited by an aperture electric field that is orthogonal to the slot axis, as shown in Fig. 3.44. More complicated configurations are beyond the scope of this presentation and will not be discussed here; the interested reader is referred to Compton and Collin (1969b).

3-23.1 Half-Wave Slot

In reference to the coordinate system shown in Fig. 3.44(b), the tangential electric field in the aperture plane is everywhere zero except in the region of the

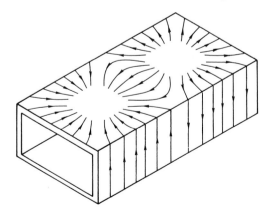

Fig. 3.43 The flow of surface currents in the walls of a rectangular waveguide excited with a TE_{10} mode.

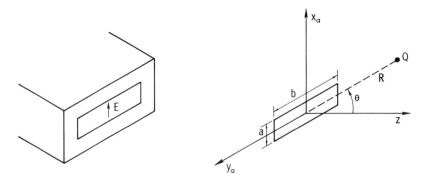

(a) Slot in Waveguide   (b) Coordinate System

Fig. 3.44   Rectangular slot with a tangential electric field in the $\hat{x}$ direction.

slot, where it is assumed to be given by

$$\mathbf{E}_a(x_a, y_a) = \hat{x} E_0 \cos\left(\frac{\pi y_a}{b}\right), \qquad |x_a| \leqslant \frac{a}{2}, \quad |y_a| \leqslant \frac{b}{2}. \qquad (3.219)$$

Here a is the height of the slot and b is its width. The far-zone electric-field components can be computed using the vector diffraction formulation of Section 3-16. Specifically, by applying (3.167) and (3.168) to this aperture distribution and performing the integration, the far-zone electric field components can be shown to be

$$E_\theta = j \frac{aE_0}{\pi} \frac{e^{-jkR}}{R} \left(\frac{1+\cos\theta}{2}\right) \cos\phi \, h_x(\theta, \phi), \qquad (3.220a)$$

$$E_\phi = -j \frac{aE_0}{\pi} \frac{e^{-jkR}}{R} \left(\frac{1+\cos\theta}{2}\right) \sin\phi \cos\theta \, h_x(\theta, \phi), \qquad (3.220b)$$

where

$$h_x(\theta, \phi) = \frac{\cos\left(\frac{1}{2}\pi \sin\phi \sin\theta\right)}{1 - \sin^2\phi \sin^2\theta}. \qquad (3.221)$$

The above expressions are for $b = \lambda/2$ and $a \ll \lambda$. To determine the far-field power density, we apply (3.169). The result is

$$S_r(\theta, \phi) = S_0 \left(\frac{1+\cos\theta}{2}\right)^2 (\cos^2\phi + \sin^2\phi \cos^2\theta) h_x^2(\theta, \phi), \qquad (3.222)$$

where $S_0 = S_r(0,0) = a^2 E_0^2 / (2\eta\pi^2 R^2)$.

In the xz-plane ($\phi=0$), E_ϕ is zero, h_x is unity, and E_θ is approximately omnidirectional (governed by the slowly varying obliquity factor, $(1+\cos\theta)/2$). In this plane, S_r is given by

$$S_r(\theta,0)=S_0\left(\frac{1+\cos\theta}{2}\right)^2. \tag{3.223}$$

In the yz-plane ($\phi=\pi/2$), E_θ is zero and E_ϕ exhibits a directional pattern as a function of θ. Figure 3.45 shows a polar plot of the normalized radiation pattern $F_n(\theta,\pi/2)$, which is given by

$$F_n\left(\theta,\tfrac{1}{2}\pi\right)=\frac{S_r\left(\theta,\tfrac{1}{2}\pi\right)}{S_0}$$

$$=\left[\left(\frac{1+\cos\theta}{2}\right)\frac{\cos\left(\tfrac{1}{2}\pi\sin\theta\right)}{\cos\theta}\right]^2. \tag{3.224}$$

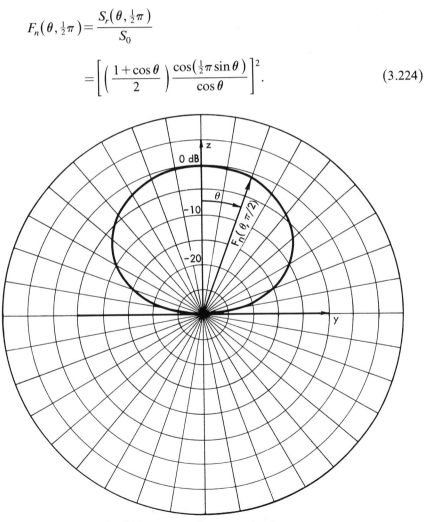

Fig. 3.45 Normalized radiation pattern of a rectangular slot.

3-23.2 Waveguide Slot Array

The theory of linear arrays and the techniques used to provide shaped beams and electronic scanning were discussed in Sections 3-17 and 3-20. We consider now how these techniques are applied to an array of slot radiators cut in one of the walls of a rectangular waveguide.

The choice of the geometrical configuration of the slotted waveguide array is dictated in part by the desire to minimize mutual coupling between the individual slots. Mutual coupling can influence the radiation properties of the slots as well as change their input impedance, thereby causing reflections toward the feed structure, which will in turn modify the amplitude and phase distributions among the array elements. The array consisting of longitudinal slots cut in the broad side of the waveguide (Fig. 3.46) has been found to exhibit negligible mutual coupling between adjacent slots (Eurlich and Short, 1954). For the purpose of this introductory presentation, the discussion to follow will be limited to this type of configuration, and the rectangular waveguide will be assumed to be excited in the dominant TE_{10} mode.

Longitudinal slot arrays are commonly divided into two types, the *resonant array* and the *nonresonant array*. A brief description of each follows.

Resonant Array

The *resonant array* (Fig. 3.46(a)) is an in-phase array configured for broadside operation at a single frequency. For the slots to be excited in phase, they must be spaced one guide wavelength λ_g apart. From previous considerations of linear-array theory, it was noted that in order to avoid grating lobes in the visible region of the array, the spacing between elements must be less than one free-space wavelength λ. Since in air-filled waveguides $\lambda_g > \lambda$, the λ_g spacing required for in-phase excitation results in grating lobes. The solution of this problem is to arrange the slots $\lambda_g/2$ apart with adjacent elements on opposite sides of the longitudinal axis of the waveguide, as shown in Fig. 3.46(a). The $\lambda_g/2$ spacing provides a phase difference of π between adjacent elements, and because the x-component of the surface current flows in opposite directions on the two sides of the longitudinal axis, an additional phase difference of π is introduced in the excitation between adjacent slots. Thus, the slots are excited in phase, and if the guide dimensions are such that $\lambda_g/2 < \lambda$, grating lobes will not occur.

The transmission-line equivalent of the slot array is shown in Fig. 3.46(b). Associated with the ith slot is a shunt conductance g_i whose magnitude is given by (Compton and Collin, 1969b)

$$g_i = K \sin^2\left(\frac{\pi x_i}{a}\right), \tag{3.225}$$

where K is a constant and x_i is the displacement of the slot from the longitudinal axis as shown in Fig. 3.46(a). The constant K is related to the

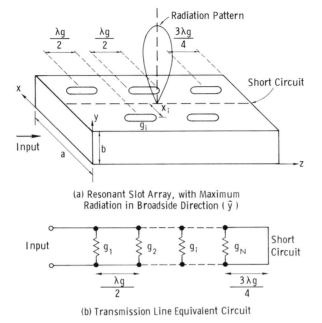

(a) Resonant Slot Array, with Maximum
Radiation in Broadside Direction ($\hat{y}$)

(b) Transmission Line Equivalent Circuit

Fig. 3.46   The resonant slot array.

waveguide dimensions a and b and to the wavelengths λ and λ_g. For a given voltage across the transmission line, the power radiated by a given slot is proportional to its conductance g_i, and hence to the displacement x_i. Thus, a desired amplitude distribution of the element feeding coefficients can be achieved by specifying the displacements x_i of the array slots. Since the amplitude distribution is usually defined in terms of the excitation field (or current) rather than power, the slot displacements should be chosen so that the desired relative amplitudes are proportional to $\sqrt{g_i}$, or $\sin(\pi x_i/a)$. Finally, by terminating the waveguide in a short circuit at a distance of $3\lambda_g/4$ from the last slot, such a termination translates to an open circuit at the last slot, thereby exerting no effect on its conductance. To satisfy this condition and to maintain the excitations of the slots in phase with one another, the array design is configured for operation at a single frequency, which has led to the name "resonant array." Consequently, a resonant slot array has a small bandwidth, typically of the order of $\pm 50\%/N$, where N is the number of slots.

Nonresonant Array

Unlike the fixed-frequency broadside resonant array, the *nonresonant array* usually is designed for operation over a large bandwidth so that the direction of the main lobe of the antenna array can be steered electronically by changing the frequency of the input signal. The array shown in Fig. 3.47 is terminated in a matched load to avoid reflections. Since part of the input power now is absorbed in the matched load, the nonresonant array is less efficient than the

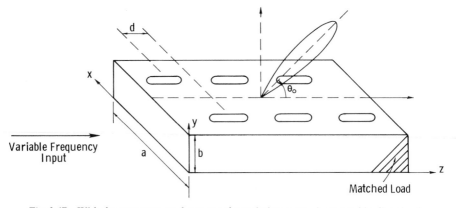

Fig. 3.47 With the nonresonant slot array, the main beam may be steered in direction by varying the frequency of the input signal.

resonant array, but on the other hand, the use of the matched load allows operation over a much wider frequency range than is possible with the resonant array.

A constant spacing d between adjacent slots results in progressive (linear) phase shift along the array. If the wavelength of the input signal is such that d corresponds to $\lambda_g/2$, then the elements are excited in phase and the resultant beam is in the broadside direction ($\theta_0 = \pi/2$ in Fig. 3.47). In the general case, however, the beam angle θ_0 is governed by the relationship

$$\cos \theta_0 = \frac{\lambda}{\lambda_g} - \frac{\lambda}{2d},$$

and for the TE_{10} mode in an unloaded waveguide

$$\frac{\lambda}{\lambda_g} = \sqrt{1 - \left(\frac{\lambda}{2a}\right)^2}$$

Thus, the nonresonant slot array is amenable to frequency scanning (Section 3-20.2) where the main lobe of the array is made to scan in the yz-plane by changing the frequency of the input signal. For more details regarding the design of slot arrays, the reader is referred to Compton and Collin (1969b).

PROBLEMS

3.1. The far-zone electric field of an antenna is given by

$$E_\theta = \begin{cases} \dfrac{e^{-jkr}}{r} \cos^2 \theta, & 0 \leqslant \theta \leqslant \pi/2, \\ 0 & \text{elsewhere,} \end{cases}$$

$$E_\phi = 0.$$

Calculate:

(a) The pattern solid angle Ω_p.
(b) The main-beam solid angle Ω_M.
(c) The half-power beamwidths in the xz- and yz-planes.
(d) The maximum directivity D_0.
(e) The maximum directivity D_0, calculated through the approximation given by (3.23). Compare with the result from (d).
(f) The effective antenna aperture, A_{eff} (the wavelength is 30 cm).

3.2. The input power to an antenna with a radiation efficiency of 0.85 is 20 W. If the measured radiation intensity has a maximum value of 1000 $W\,sr^{-1}$, what is the maximum directivity of the antenna?

3.3. A ground-to-satellite communication link operating at 6 GHz consists of a 10-m-diameter ground antenna and a 1-m-diameter satellite antenna. The satellite is in geosynchronous orbit at a height of 35,860 km above the ground station. Assuming unit aperture and radiation efficiencies for both antennas, find the maximum received power if the transmitted power is 1 kW.

3.4. A 3.2-cm-wavelength (X-band) side-looking airborne radar (SLAR) antenna is 3 m long and 6 cm high. The antenna is mounted along the belly of the aircraft with the long side parallel to the direction of flight.

(a) Calculate the approximate half-power azimuthal (in direction of flight) and elevation (perpendicular to the direction of flight) beamwidths.
(b) If the aircraft is flying at a height of 3 km above the terrain, and if the direction of maximum radiation in the elevation plane is at an angle of 50° from nadir, calculate the ground "swathwidth" illuminated by the antenna beam (between the half-power points) in the elevation plane.

3.5. Derive an expression for the far-zone normalized radiation pattern of a rectangular aperture with dimensions a and b, illuminated by

(a) $E_a(x_a, y_a) = \begin{cases} E_0 \cos\left(\dfrac{\pi x_a}{a}\right) & \text{for } |x_a| \leqslant \dfrac{a}{2} \text{ and } |y_a| \leqslant \dfrac{b}{2}, \\ 0 & \text{otherwise}, \end{cases}$

(b) $E_a(x_a, y_a) = \begin{cases} \dfrac{E_0}{2}\left[1 + \cos\left(\dfrac{\pi x_a}{a}\right)\right] & \text{for } |x_a| \leqslant \dfrac{a}{2} \text{ and } |y_a| \leqslant \dfrac{b}{2}, \\ 0 & \text{otherwise}. \end{cases}$

(c) Plot the xz-plane radiation patterns of the uniformly illuminated aperture and the above two apertures. Compare half-power beamwidths and side-lobe levels.

3.6. Find the far-field radiation pattern of a Gaussianly illuminated rectangular aperture,

$$E_a(x_a, y_a) = \begin{cases} \dfrac{1}{\sqrt{2\pi\sigma^2}} \exp\left(\dfrac{-x_1^2}{2\sigma^2}\right) & \text{for } |x_1| \leqslant 1 \text{ and } |y_1| \leqslant 1, \\ 0 & \text{otherwise,} \end{cases}$$

where $x_1 = 2x_a/a$ and $y_1 = 2y_a/b$.

3.7. Use (3.129) to calculate the maximum directivity for the two illumination functions of Problem 3.5.

3.8. Given a uniformly illuminated square aperture with sides equal to 100λ each:

   (a) Find the far-zone distance R.
   (b) Use the far-zone expressions to compute the power density S_r at R in the broadside direction. Call it $S_r(R)$. Assume unit illumination across the aperture.
   (c) Use the expression for the Fresnel region to compute the power density $S_r(r)$ in the broadside direction for r between $0.1R$ and R in steps of $0.1R$. Plot $S_r(r)/S_r(R)$ vs. r and compare with Fig. 3.16.

3.9. A rectangular aperture is illuminated by the function

$$E_a(x_a, y_a) = \begin{cases} E_0 f(x_1) & \text{for } |x_1| \leqslant 1, \ |y_1| \leqslant 1, \\ 0 & \text{otherwise,} \end{cases}$$

where $f(x_1)$ is shown below, and x_1 and y_1 are as defined in Problem 6.

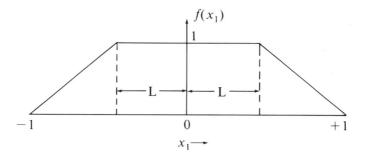

   (a) Express $f(x_1)$ as a convolution of two rectangular functions: $f(x_1) = f_1(x_1) * f_2(x_1)$.
   (b) Use the convolution property of the Fourier transform to obtain the normalized radiation pattern of the aperture.

3.10. Linear phase is used to steer the main beam of a 100λ-long aperture to a direction $60°$ from its normal. What is the phase shift between the center of the aperture and its edges?

3.11. Fill in the missing steps between (3.185) and (3.188).

3.12. Find and plot the normalized array factor for a five-element binomial array whose interelement spacing is

(a) $d=\lambda/2$,
(b) $d=3\lambda/2$.

3.13. Find the normalized array pattern of the four-element array shown below. All elements are fed with equal amplitude and with the phases indicated in the figure. $d=\lambda/2$. Plot the xz pattern.

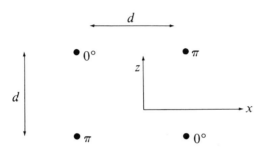

3.14. Design a 3-cm-wavelength optimum pyramidal horn, given the constraint that the axial length l_0 cannot exceed 30 cm. Find its maximum directivity, D_{0p}.

3.15. Fill in the missing steps between (3.219) and (3.222).

References

Bach, H., and J. E. Hansen (1969), Uniformly Spaced Arrays, in *Antenna Theory*, R. E. Collin and F. J. Zucker, eds., McGraw-Hill, New York, Part I, Chapter 5.

Barrow, W. L., and L. J. Chu (1939), Theory of the Electromagnetic Horn, *Proc. IRE*, 27, pp. 51–64.

Born, M., and E. Wolf (1965), *Principles of Optics*, Pergamon Press, Oxford, Chapter 8.

Bouwkamp, C. J. (1954), Diffraction Theory, *Rept. Prog. Phys.*, 17, pp. 35–100.

Chu, L. J. (1940), Calculation of the Radiation Properties of Hollow Pipes and Horns, *J. Appl. Phys.*, 11, pp. 603–610.

Collin, R. E. (1959), Properties of Slotted Dielectric Interfaces, *IRE Trans.*, AP-7, pp. 62–73.

Collin, R. E. (1969), Radiation from Apertures, in *Antenna Theory*, R. E. Collin and F. J. Zucker, eds., McGraw-Hill, New York, Part I, Chapter 3.

Collin, R. E., and F. J. Zucker, eds. (1969), *Antenna Theory*, McGraw-Hill, New York.

Compton, R. T., Jr., and R. E. Collin (1969a), Open Waveguides and Small Horns, in *Antenna Theory*, R. E. Collin and F. J. Zucker, eds., McGraw-Hill, New York, Part I, Chapter 15.

Compton, R. T., Jr., and R. E. Collin (1969b), Slot Antennas, in *Antenna Theory*, R. E. Collin and F. J. Zucker, eds., McGraw-Hill, New York, Part I, Chapter 14.

Dolph, C. L. (1946), A Current Distribution for Broadside Arrays which Optimizes the Relationship between Beamwidth and Side-Lobe Level, *Proc. IRE*, 34, pp. 335–348.

Eaton, J. E., L. J. Eyges, and G. G. Macfarlane (1949), Linear-Array Antennas and Feeds, in *Microwave Antenna Theory and Design*, S. Silver, ed., McGraw-Hill, New York, Chapter 9.

Elliott, R. S. (1966), The Theory of Antenna Arrays, in *Microwave Scanning Antennas*, R. C. Hansen, ed., Academic Press, New York, II, Chapter 1.

Eurlich, J. J., and J. Short (1954), Mutual Coupling Considerations in Linear Slot Array Design, *Proc. IRE*, 42, pp. 956–961.

Goodman, J. W. (1968), *Introduction to Fourier Optics*, McGraw-Hill, New York.

Hansen, R. C. (1964), Aperture Theory, in *Microwave Scanning Antennas*, R. C. Hansen, ed., Academic Press, New York, I, Chapter 1.

Hickman, T. G., J. S. Hollis, and L. Clayton (1970), Polarization Measurements, in *Microwave Antenna Measurements*, J. S. Hollis, T. J. Lyon, and L. Clayton, eds., Scientific Atlanta, Inc., Atlanta, Chapter 10.

IEEE (1979), *Standard Test Procedures for Antennas*, IEEE, Chapter 11.

Jakes, W. C., Jr. (1951), Gain of Electromagnetic Horns, *Proc. IRE*, 39, pp. 160–162.

Jakes, W. C., Jr. (1961), Horn Antennas, in *Antenna Engineering Handbook*, H. Jasik, ed., McGraw-Hill, New York, Chapter 10.

King, A. P. (1950), The Radiation Characteristics of Conical Horn Antennas, *Proc. IRE*, 38, pp. 249–251.

Kraus, J. D. (1950), *Antennas*, McGraw-Hill, New York.

Mathis, H. F. (1951), A Short Proof that an Isotropic Antenna is Impossible, *Proc. IRE*, 39, p. 970.

Ramo, S., J. R. Whinnery, and T. Van Duzer (1965), *Fields and Waves in Communication Electronics*, John Wiley and Sons, New York, p. 265.

Risser, J. R. (1949), Waveguide and Horn Feeds, in *Microwave Antenna Theory and Design*, S. Silver, ed., McGraw-Hill, New York, Chapter 10.

Ruze, J. (1966), Antenna Tolerance Theory—A Review, *Proc. IEEE*, 54, pp. 633–640.

Schanda, E. (1967), The Effects of Random Amplitude and Phase Errors of Continuous Apertures, *IEEE Trans.*, AP-15, pp. 471–473.

Schelkunoff, S. A. (1939), A General Radiation Formula, *Proc. IRE*, 27, pp. 660–666.

Schelkunoff, S. A. (1943), *Electromagnetic Waves*, D. Van Nostrand Co., New York, Section 9.23.

Schelkunoff, S. A. and H. T. Friis (1952), *Antennas, Theory and Practice*, John Wiley and Sons, Inc., New York, pp. 528–529.

Sherman, J. W., III (1970), Aperture Antenna Analysis, in *Radar Handbook*, M. I. Skolnik, ed., McGraw-Hill, New York, Chapter 9.

Silver, S. (1949), *Microwave Antenna Theory and Design*, McGraw-Hill, New York, Chapter 6.

Sissala, J. E., ed. (1975), *Nimbus 6 User's Guide* Section 4, National Aeronautics and Space Administration (NASA), Goddard Space Flight Center (GSFC), Greenbelt, Maryland.

Skolnik, M. I., ed. (1970), *Radar Handbook*, McGraw-Hill, New York, Chapter 9.

Steinberg, B. D. (1976), *Principles of Aperture and Array System Design*, John Wiley and Sons, New York, Chapter 2.

Stratton, J. A. (1941), *Electromagnetic Theory*, McGraw-Hill, New York, Section 8.14.

Chapter 4

Radiometry

4-1 INTRODUCTION

The bulk of the energy received by the planet earth is in the form of solar electromagnetic radiation. Part of the incident solar energy is scattered and absorbed by the earth's atmosphere, and the remainder is transmitted to the earth's surface. Of the latter, a part is scattered outward and the remainder is absorbed. According to thermodynamic principles, absorption of electromagnetic energy by a material medium is a transformation into thermal energy, which is accompanied by a rise in the thermometric temperature of the material. The reverse process, that of "thermal" emission, serves to create a balance between absorbed solar radiation and radiation emitted by the earth's surface and its atmosphere. These transformation processes are treated by the *theory of radiative transfer.*

Radiometry is a field of science and engineering related to the measurement of electromagnetic radiation. This chapter begins by introducing radiometric quantities of interest, and then proceeds to treat the radiometric measurement problem, with special emphasis on the microwave region of the electromagnetic spectrum. In the process, several topics are discussed, including blackbody radiation, radiative transfer, and terrestrial emission and scattering.

4-2 RADIOMETRIC QUANTITIES

The term "radiometry" means the measurement of incoherent radiant electromagnetic energy. As will be discussed in future sections, all material media (gases, liquids, solids, and plasma) radiate (emit) electromagnetic energy. In this section, we shall define the radiometric quantities of interest and develop the relation between the directional distribution of power incident upon an antenna and the power measured at its output terminals. The nomenclature, symbolism, and units used to express radiometric quantities, which often are different from those used in optical and infrared radiometry, are chosen from

Fawwaz T. Ulaby, Richard K. Moore, and Adrian K. Fung,
Microwave Remote Sensing: *Active and Passive*,
Vol. I: *Microwave Remote Sensing Fundamentals and Radiometry*   ISBN 0-201-10759-7

the standpoint of microwave engineering. Table 4.1 provides a list of these quantities along with their optical counterparts.

4-2.1 Brightness

Consider the situation illustrated in Fig. 4.1, where a transmitting antenna of (effective) area A_t is at a distance R from a lossless receiving antenna of area A_r. The two antennas are oriented in the direction of maximum directivity, each relative to the other, and the distance R is assumed to be large enough so that the power density S_t due to the transmitting antenna may be considered constant over the solid angle Ω_r (Fig. 4.1). The power intercepted by the receiving antenna is then given by

$$P = S_t A_r. \tag{4.1}$$

Alternatively, (4.1) may be expressed in terms of the radiation intensity F_t of the transmitting antenna, which is related to S_t by $F_t = S_t R^2$ (see (3.7)). Thus,

$$P = \frac{F_t A_r}{R^2}. \tag{4.2}$$

The reader may recall that F_t, whose units are $W\,sr^{-1}$, is governed by the power input to the transmitting antenna and by its effective area A_t (among

TABLE 4.1
Standard Units, Symbols, and Defining Equations for Fundamental Radiometric Quantities

Quantity					
Microwave terminology	*Optical terminology*	*Symbol*	*Defining equation*	*Unit*	*Abbr.*
Energy	Radiant energy	$\mathcal{E}$		joule	J
Energy density	Radiant density	$\mathcal{E}_v$	$\mathcal{E}_v = \partial \mathcal{E}/\partial v$	joule per cubic meter	$J\,m^{-3}$
Power	Radiant flux	P	$P = \partial \mathcal{E}/\partial t$	watt	W
Power (or flux) Density	Radiant flux	S	$S = \partial P/\partial A$	watt per square meter	$W\,m^{-2}$
Radiation intensity (or radiation pattern)	Radiant intensity	F	$F = \partial P/\partial \Omega$	watt per steradian	$W\,sr^{-1}$
Brightness	Radiance	B	$B = \partial^2 P/\partial \Omega\, \partial A$	watt per steradian per sq. m.	$W\,sr^{-1}m^{-2}$
Emissivity	Emissivity	e	$e = B/B_{blackbody}$		
Reflectivity	Reflectance	Γ	$\Gamma = P_r/P_i^a$		
Absorptivity	Absorptance	a	$a = P_a/P_i$	(unitless)	
Transmissivity	Transmittance	Υ	$\Upsilon = P_t/P_i$		

[a]Subscripts: i=incident, r=reflected, a=absorbed, and t=transmitted.

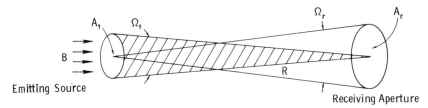

Fig. 4.1   Geometry for power received from an emitting source.

other factors). Thus, although the transmitting antenna has a finite aperture A_t, it is treated as a point source with a directional distribution function $F_t(\theta, \phi)$. In radiometry, both point and extended sources are of interest. To provide an appropriate definition for an extended source of incoherent radiation (such as the sky or terrain), we may define a quantity representing the radiated power per unit solid angle per unit area as

$$B = \frac{F_t}{A_t}. \tag{4.3}$$

The quantity B is known as the *brightness*, and its units are $W\,sr^{-1}\,m^{-2}$. The received power is given now by

$$P = BA_r \frac{A_t}{R^2}. \tag{4.4}$$

The above expression may be written in a more convenient form by noting that the solid angle Ω_t subtended by the transmitting antenna area (Fig. 4.1) is, by definition, given by

$$\Omega_t = \frac{A_t}{R^2}. \tag{4.5}$$

When this is used in (4.4), the latter reduces to

$$P = BA_r\Omega_t. \tag{4.6}$$

Replacing the solid angle Ω_t by a differential solid angle $d\Omega$, the corresponding differential power received by the antenna through the solid angle $d\Omega$ from an extended source with brightness $B(\theta, \phi)$ along the direction (θ, ϕ) relative to the antenna coordinates (Fig. 4.2) is

$$dP = A_r B(\theta, \phi) F_n(\theta, \phi)\, d\Omega, \tag{4.7}$$

where $F_n(\theta, \phi)$, the normalized radiation pattern of the receiving antenna, now is inserted in the above expression to account for the antenna directionality (thereby removing the restriction that the emitting source is being observed by the receiving antenna in the direction of maximum directivity).

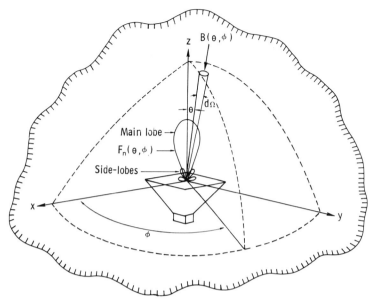

Fig. 4.2 Geometry of radiation incident on an antenna with effective aperture A_r and normalized radiation pattern $F_n(\theta, \phi)$.

So far, no reference has been made to the spectral behavior of the emission from the surface of the "chamber" surrounding the antenna. To this end, the *spectral brightness* $B_f(\theta, \phi)$ is defined as the brightness per unit bandwidth df; its units are $W\,m^{-2}\,sr^{-1}\,Hz^{-1}$. The total power received by an antenna over a bandwidth Δf, extending from a frequency f to a frequency $f + \Delta f$, is then given by

$$P = A_r \int_f^{f+\Delta f} \iint_{4\pi} B_f(\theta, \phi) F_n(\theta, \phi)\, d\Omega\, df, \tag{4.8}$$

where the solid-angle integration is carried out over all 4π steradians. The above relation allows us to compute the received power in terms of the directional distribution of the spectral brightness $B_f(\theta, \phi)$. If $B_f(\theta, \phi)$ is unpolarized (which is the case for atmospheric emission), then since an antenna is polarized, the antenna will detect only half of the total power incident upon its surface. Hence, a factor of $\frac{1}{2}$ should be introduced in (4.8):

$$P = \tfrac{1}{2} A_r \int_f^{f+\Delta f} \iint_{4\pi} B_f(\theta, \phi) F_n(\theta, \phi)\, d\Omega\, df. \tag{4.9}$$

For partially polarized sources, such as terrestrial surfaces, the polarization of $B_f(\theta, \phi)$ is accounted for through the polarized emissivity, which will be introduced in a later section.

4-2.2 Brightness-Related Quantities

The spectral brightness B_f is a fundamental radiometric quantity. Other quantities, defined in terms of B_f, are:

Spectral Power, P_f

The power received by the antenna in a bandwidth of 1 Hz is called the *spectral power*, and its units are $W\,Hz^{-1}$. That is, (4.9) may be written as

$$P = \int_f^{f+\Delta f} P_f\,df, \tag{4.10}$$

where

$$P_f = \tfrac{1}{2} A_r \iint_{4\pi} B_f(\theta,\phi) F_n(\theta,\phi)\,d\Omega. \tag{4.11}$$

Spectral Flux Density, S_f

The integral in (4.11) often is referred to as the *spectral flux density S_f* of the radiating source:

$$S_f = \iint_{4\pi} B_f(\theta,\phi) F_n(\theta,\phi)\,d\Omega; \tag{4.12}$$

its units are $W\,m^{-2}\,Hz^{-1}$.

 If the antenna is observing radiation from a discrete source, such as a star, and if the source subtends a solid angle Ω_s that is much smaller than the antenna main-beam solid angle, so that $F_n(\theta,\phi) \cong 1$ over Ω_s (Fig. 4.3), then (4.12) reduces to

$$S_f = B_{fs}\Omega_s, \tag{4.13}$$

where B_{fs} is the spectral brightness of the source, assumed constant over Ω_s.

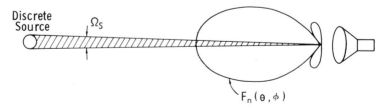

Fig. 4.3 Emission by a discrete source subtending a small solid angle.

4-3 THERMAL RADIATION

4-3.1 Quantum Theory of Radiation

All substances at a finite absolute temperature radiate electromagnetic energy. Atomic gases radiate electromagnetic waves at discrete frequencies, or wavelengths; that is, they have *line spectra*. According to quantum theory, each spectral line in the radiation spectrum of an atomic gas corresponds to a specific transition by an electron from one atomic energy level to another (lower) energy level. When the transition is between quantum level $\mathcal{E}_1$ and $\mathcal{E}_2$, the frequency f of the emitted radiation (photon) is given by Bohr's equation

$$f = (\mathcal{E}_1 - \mathcal{E}_2)/h \tag{4.14}$$

where h is Planck's constant. Quantum theory defines the quantum energy levels of an atom and the allowed transitions between them, thereby defining the line spectrum of an atomic gas.

Energy incident upon an atom can be absorbed by the atom to provide the necessary energy to move an electron to a higher energy level, provided the frequency of the incident wave satisfies the Bohr condition. Thus, the absorption spectrum of a gas is identical to its emission spectrum. As will be discussed later, this principle applies also to more complicated structures including molecular gases, liquids, and solids.

Emission of radiation by an atom is caused by collision with another atom or particle. The probability that a collision (and hence emission) will take place is governed by the density of atoms and the kinetic energy of their random motion. And since the kinetic (or heat) energy of a substance is defined in terms of its absolute temperature, it follows that the intensity of energy radiated by a substance increases with its temperature.

Associated with a molecule consisting of two or more atoms is a set of vibrational and rotational modes describing the motion of the atoms relative to one another. These modes define a corresponding set of allowable energy levels. With contributions from vibrational, rotational, and electronic transitions, the spectra of molecules again consist of discrete lines, but the number of lines is much larger than for atoms. In the visible region of the spectrum, the spectral lines of some molecular gases are so close together that it is difficult to resolve individual lines, especially for molecules consisting of a large number of atoms.

As we go from gases to liquids and solids, the interaction between particles increases and the radiation (or absorption) spectrum becomes more complicated. A liquid or solid may be regarded as an enormous molecule with a correspondingly increased number of degrees of freedom, which leads to such a large number of closely spaced spectral lines that the radiation spectrum becomes effectively continuous, all frequencies being radiated.

The radiation mechanisms described above for atoms and molecules are based on Planck's quantum theory, which he introduced in 1901 in his derivation of the *blackbody radiation law*. Prior to Planck's work, attempts by nineteenth-century physicists to derive an expression for the radiation spectrum of solids were unsuccessful because of their reliance on classical mechanics. The key to Planck's solution was his assumption that the emitted radiation occurs only in discrete energy quanta. It is this assumption that marks the origin of the quantum theory.

The remainder of this section is devoted to further discussion of radiation from solids (and liquids). Microwave spectra of atmospheric gases are discussed in Chapter 5.

4-3.2 Planck's Blackbody Radiation Law

The concept of a blackbody radiator is of fundamental importance to an understanding of the thermal emission of real materials because its emission-spectrum represents a reference, relative to which the radiant emittance of a material can be expressed. In general, of the radiation incident upon the surface of a solid (or liquid) substance, a certain fraction is absorbed and the remainder is reflected. *A blackbody is defined as an idealized, perfectly opaque material that absorbs all the incident radiation at all frequencies, reflecting none.* The quantum-mechanical model of a blackbody may be described as consisting of such a large number of quantized energy levels with a correspondingly large number of allowable transitions, that any photon, whatever its energy or frequency, is absorbed when incident upon the blackbody. In addition to being a perfect absorber, *a blackbody is also a perfect emitter*, since energy absorbed by a material would increase its temperature if no energy were emitted.

In practice, a good approximation to a blackbody is a hollow body with a small opening. Any radiation entering the container through the opening is absorbed or undergoes many reflections on the inside surfaces, so that all the original energy effectively is absorbed before it can be reflected back out through the opening. If the container is maintained at some fixed temperature T, its inner surfaces will emit and absorb photons at the same rate, and therefore the energy leaking out through the opening resembles radiation by a blackbody in thermodynamic equilibrium. At microwave frequencies, good approximations to ideal blackbodies are the highly absorbing materials used in the construction of anechoic chambers.

According to Planck's radiation law, a blackbody radiates uniformly in all directions with a spectral brightness B_f given by

$$B_f = \frac{2hf^3}{c^2}\left(\frac{1}{e^{hf/kT}-1}\right),\tag{4.15}$$

where B_f = Blackbody spectral brightness, $W\,m^{-2}\,sr^{-1}\,Hz^{-1}$
        h = Planck's constant = 6.63×10^{-34} joules,

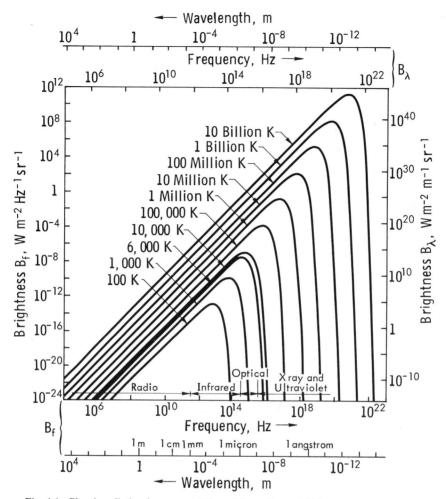

Fig. 4.4 Planck radiation-law curves (adapted from Kraus, 1966).

f = frequency, Hz,
k = Boltzmann's constant = 1.38×10^{-23} joule K^{-1}
T = absolute temperature, K,*
c = velocity of light = 3×10^8 m s^{-1}.

The only two variables in (4.15) are f and T. A family of curves of B_f as a function of frequency is shown in Fig. 4.4 (with T as parameter). Logarithmic scales are used on both axes so that a wide range of values can be accommodated. The curves exhibit two interesting features: (1) as the temperature T is

---

*Until recently, the unit of thermodynamic temperature was the degree Kelvin with the symbol °K. However, in 1967 the General Conference on Weights and Measures redefined it as the kelvin with the abbreviation K.

increased, the overall level of the spectral brightness curve increases, and (2) the frequency at which B_f is maximum increases with T.

Over a narrow frequency interval df centered at f, the brightness is given by

$$dB = B_f \, df. \tag{4.16}$$

It is sometimes of interest to express the spectral brightness in terms of B_λ rather than B_f, where B_λ is the power per unit area per unit solid angle per unit wavelength. Over a wavelength interval $d\lambda$ corresponding to the frequency interval df above, the area under the curve contains the same brightness dB. Thus,

$$dB = B_\lambda \, d\lambda. \tag{4.17}$$

Equating (4.16) and (4.17) and noting that

$$df = -\frac{c}{\lambda^2} d\lambda, \tag{4.18}$$

the following expression for B_λ is obtained:

$$B_\lambda = \frac{2hc^2}{\lambda^5} \left(\frac{1}{e^{hc/\lambda kT} - 1} \right). \tag{4.19}$$

The negative sign in (4.18) has been ignored because it merely reflects the fact that f and λ increase in opposite directions and it has no bearing on the magnitudes of $d\lambda$ and df. The curves shown in Fig. 4.4 are also plots of B_λ, with the right-hand ordinate scale expressing B_λ and the corresponding frequency and wavelength scales given as abscissa along the top of the chart (adapted from Kraus (1966)).

4-3.3 Properties of Planck's Law

Stefan-Boltzmann Law

The total brightness B for a blackbody at a temperature T is the integral of B_f (or B_λ) over all frequencies (or all wavelengths). Thus,

$$\begin{aligned} B &= \int_0^\infty B_f \, df \\ &= \frac{2h}{c^2} \int_0^\infty \left(\frac{f^3}{e^{hf/kT} - 1} \right) df \end{aligned} \tag{4.20}$$

Introducing the substitution

$$x = \frac{hf}{kT}, \tag{4.21}$$

we obtain the expression

$$B = \frac{2}{c^2 h^3} (kT)^4 \int_0^\infty \frac{x^3}{e^x - 1} dx. \tag{4.22}$$

The definite integral of (4.22) is a constant. Its value may be evaluated by expanding the denominator of the integral into a series,

$$\frac{1}{e^x - 1} = \frac{e^{-x}}{1 - e^{-x}} = e^{-x}(1 + e^{-x} + e^{-2x} + \dots)$$

$$= \sum_{n=1}^\infty e^{-nx}. \tag{4.23}$$

The integral becomes

$$\int_0^\infty \frac{x^3}{e^x - 1} dx = \sum_{n=1}^\infty \int_0^\infty x^3 e^{-nx} dx. \tag{4.24}$$

The new definite integral in (4.24) is available in standard tables of integrals, where it is given as

$$\int_0^\infty x^3 e^{-nx} dx = \frac{6}{n^4}. \tag{4.25}$$

Combining (4.22), (4.24), and (4.25), we obtain

$$B = \frac{12}{c^2 h^3} (kT)^4 \sum_{n=1}^\infty \frac{1}{n^4}. \tag{4.26}$$

The sum can be evaluated easily and has the value $\pi^4/90 = 1.08$. Combining this value with the values of the other constants in (4.26), we obtain the relation

$$B = \frac{\sigma T^4}{\pi}, \qquad \mathrm{W\,m^{-2}\,sr^{-1}}, \tag{4.27}$$

which is known as the Stefan-Boltzmann law. Here σ is called the Stefan-Boltzmann constant. Its value is

$$\sigma = 5.673 \times 10^{-8}\ \mathrm{W\,m^{-2}\,K^{-4}\,sr^{-1}}.$$

According to (4.27) the total brightness B of a blackbody increases as the fourth power of its temperature T. This temperature dependence is not valid for B_f or B_λ.

Wien Displacement Law

It was noted before that the frequency f_m at which the maximum radiation occurs increases as the temperature increases (Fig. 4.4). This frequency can be obtained from (4.15) by noting that the derivative of B_f with respect to f is equal to zero for $f=f_m$. Thus for a given value of T,

$$\frac{dB_f}{df}=0=\frac{2h}{c^2}\left[\frac{3f_m^2}{e^{hf_m/kT}-1}-\frac{f_m^3 h}{kT}\frac{e^{hf_m/kT}}{\left(e^{hf_m/kT}-1\right)^2}\right]. \qquad (4.28)$$

Setting $x_m=hf_m/kT$, the above equation reduces to

$$\left(1-\frac{x_m}{3}\right)e^{x_m}=1 \qquad (4.29)$$

The solution of the above transcendental equation can be shown to be

$$x_m=\frac{hf_m}{kT}=2.82, \qquad (4.30)$$

or

$$f_m=5.87\times10^{10}T \quad \text{Hz} \qquad (T \text{ in K}). \qquad (4.31)$$

Substitution of (4.31) into (4.15) gives the maximum spectral brightness $B_f(f_m)$ with respect to f,

$$B_f(f_m)=c_1T^3 \qquad (4.32)$$

where $c_1=1.37\times10^{-19}\,\mathrm{W\,m^{-2}\,sr^{-1}\,Hz^{-1}\,K^{-3}}$.

The relations given by (4.31) and (4.32) are characteristic of the spectral brightness per unit frequency bandwidth, B_f. They are not, however, characteristic of the spectral brightness per unit wavelength, B_λ. From $c=f\lambda$, the wavelength at which B_f is maximum can be obtained from (4.31), but this wavelength is different from the wavelength at which B_λ is maximum. The latter can be obtained by differentiating (4.19) with respect to λ and setting the result equal to zero, which can be shown to reduce to the transcendental equation

$$\left(1-\frac{Y_m}{5}\right)e^{Y_m}=1, \qquad (4.33)$$

where

$$Y_m=\frac{hc}{\lambda_m kT} \qquad (4.34)$$

and λ_m is the wavelength at which B_λ is maximum. The solution of (4.33) is

$$Y_m = 4.965,$$

which gives the relation known as *Wien's displacement law*,

$$\lambda_m T = 2.879 \times 10^{-3} \text{ m K}. \qquad (4.35)$$

At $\lambda = \lambda_m$, B_λ takes the form

$$B_\lambda(\lambda_m) = c_2 T^5, \qquad (4.36)$$

where c_2 is a constant. Whereas $B_f(f_m)$ was observed to vary as T^3 (Equation (4.32)), $B_\lambda(\lambda_m)$ varies as T^5, and the total brightness B varies as T^4 (Equation (4.27)).

If we designate the frequency at which B_λ is maximum by f_m', then from (4.35)

$$f_m' = \frac{c}{\lambda_m} = 10.35 \times 10^{10} T \text{ Hz} \qquad (T \text{ in K}), \qquad (4.37)$$

which is about twice the value of the frequency f_m at which B_f is maximum, as given by (4.31).

Wien Radiation Law

A well-known approximation to Planck's law for short wavelengths (high frequencies) is the Wien radiation law. For $hf/kT \gg 1$,

$$\frac{1}{e^{hf/kT} - 1} \simeq \frac{1}{e^{hf/kT}} = e^{-hf/kT},$$

and (4.15) reduces to

$$B_f = \frac{2h}{c^2} f^3 e^{-hf/kT}. \qquad (4.38)$$

Rayleigh-Jeans Law

The low-frequency counterpart to the Wien radiation law is known as the *Rayleigh-Jeans law*. If $hf/kT \ll 1$, the approximation

$$e^x - 1 = \left(1 + x + \frac{x^2}{2} + \cdots\right) - 1$$

$$\simeq x \qquad \text{for} \quad x \ll 1$$

can be used to simplify (4.15) to

$$B_f = \frac{2f^2 kT}{c^2} = \frac{2kT}{\lambda^2}.$$ (4.39)

The above Rayleigh-Jeans approximation is very useful in the microwave region; it is mathematically simpler than Planck's law and yet its fractional deviation from Planck's expression (4.15) is less than 1 percent if

$$\lambda T > 0.77 \text{ m K},$$ (4.40a)

or equivalently

$$f/T < 3.9 \times 10^8 \text{ Hz K}.$$ (4.40b)

For a blackbody at a room temperature of 300 K, the above inequalities will hold if $\lambda > 2.57$ mm, or $f < 117$ GHz, which covers the entire radio region and most of the usable part of the microwave spectrum. At 300 GHz, the fractional deviation is about 3 percent.

A comparison of Planck's law with its high-frequency (Wien) and low-frequency (Rayleigh-Jeans) approximations is provided in Fig. 4.5. The spec-

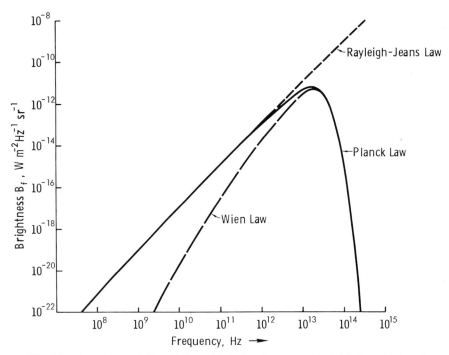

Fig. 4.5 Comparison of Planck's law with its low-frequency (Rayleigh-Jeans law) and high-frequency (Wien's law) approximations at 300 K.

tral variation of the Rayleigh-Jeans law appears as a straight line on a log-log graph because B_f varies as f^2. In the low-frequency region defined for $f \leqslant 10^{-2} f_m$, where f_m is the frequency at which B_f of Planck's law is a maximum, the Rayleigh-Jeans line in Fig. 4.5 is practically coincident with the curve describing Planck's law. As the frequency is increased beyond this region, the deviation grows without limit. Although it is a low-frequency approximation to Planck's law, the Rayleigh-Jeans law was derived by Jeans on the basis of classical mechanics before Planck introduced his quantum theory in 1901.

4-4 POWER-TEMPERATURE CORRESPONDENCE

Consider a lossless microwave antenna placed inside a blackbody chamber maintained at a constant temperature T as illustrated in Fig. 4.6 (the effects of antenna ohmic losses will be considered in Section 4-6.2). The power received by the antenna due to emission by the chamber is given by (4.9) in the form of an integral involving the spectral brightness directional distribution $B_f(\theta, \phi)$. Upon inserting (4.39) into (4.9), we obtain

$$P_{bb} = \tfrac{1}{2} A_r \int_f^{f+\Delta f} \iint_{4\pi} \frac{2kT}{\lambda^2} F_n(\theta, \phi) \, d\Omega \, df, \tag{4.41}$$

where the subscript bb denotes a blackbody enclosure. If the detected power is limited to a narrow bandwidth Δf such that B_f is approximately constant over Δf (i.e., $\Delta f \ll f^2$), then (4.41) reduces to

$$P_{bb} = kT\Delta f \frac{A_r}{\lambda^2} \iint_{4\pi} F_n(\theta, \phi) \, d\Omega. \tag{4.42}$$

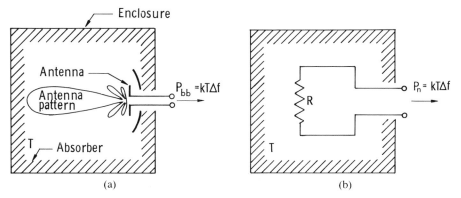

Fig. 4.6 The power delivered by (a) an antenna placed inside a blackbody enclosure of temperature T is equal to the power delivered by (b) a resistor maintained at the same temperature T (assuming each is connected to a matched receiver of bandwidth Δf).

The integral is recognized as the pattern solid angle Ω_p of the antenna, defined by (3.9) as

$$\iint\limits_{4\pi} F_n(\theta, \phi)\, d\Omega = \Omega_p, \tag{3.9}$$

and Ω_p is related to the effective aperture A_r, through (3.24), by

$$\Omega_p = \frac{\lambda^2}{A_r}. \tag{4.43}$$

Hence, (4.42) becomes

$$P_{bb} = kT\Delta f. \tag{4.44}$$

The above result is of fundamental significance in microwave remote sensing; the direct linear relationship between power and temperature has led to the interchangeable use of the two terms.

   A result that is analogous to (4.44) was derived by Nyquist in 1928 for a resistor at a temperature T (Fig. 4.6(b)). He showed that the noise power P_n available at the resistor terminals is

$$P_n = kT\Delta f. \tag{4.45}$$

From the standpoint of an ideal receiver of bandwidth Δf, the antenna connected to its input terminals is equivalent to a resistance R_r, called the *antenna radiation resistance* (see Section 3-4.3). Although in both cases the receiver is connected to a "resistor," in the case of the real resistor of Fig. 4.6(b) the noise power available at its output terminals is determined by the physical temperature of the resistor, while in the case of the antenna the power at its output terminals is determined by the temperature of the blackbody enclosure, whose walls may be at any distance from the antenna. Moreover, the physical temperature of the antenna structure has no bearing on its output power (as long as it is lossless).

4-5 NONBLACKBODY RADIATION

4-5.1 Brightness Temperature

A blackbody is an idealized body which, when in thermodynamic equilibrium at a temperature T, radiates at least as much energy as any other body at the same temperature T. Also, a blackbody is a perfect absorber. Real materials, usually referred to as *grey bodies*, emit less than a blackbody does and do not necessarily absorb all the energy incident upon them. In the microwave region,

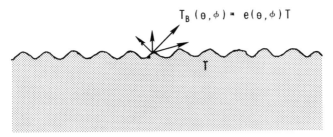

Fig. 4.7 Brightness temperature of a semiinfinite isothermal medium.

the brightness B_{bb} of a blackbody at a temperature T is, from (4.39),

$$B_{bb} = B_f \Delta f = \frac{2kT}{\lambda^2} \Delta f \tag{4.46}$$

for a narrow bandwidth Δf. Consider the semiinfinite material shown in Fig. 4.7. If its brightness, which may be direction-dependent, is $B(\theta, \phi)$ and its physical temperature is T, a blackbody equivalent radiometric* temperature may be defined so that $B(\theta, \phi)$ can assume a form similar to (4.46). Such a temperature usually is called the *brightness temperature*, $T_B(\theta, \phi)$, and accordingly $B(\theta, \phi)$ is defined as

$$B(\theta, \phi) = \frac{2k}{\lambda^2} T_B(\theta, \phi) \Delta f. \tag{4.47}$$

The brightness $B(\theta, \phi)$ of the material relative to that of a blackbody at the same temperature is defined as the *emissivity* $e(\theta, \phi)$:

$$e(\theta, \phi) = \frac{B(\theta, \phi)}{B_{bb}} = \frac{T_B(\theta, \phi)}{T}. \tag{4.48}$$

Since $B(\theta, \phi) \leqslant B_{bb}$, $0 \leqslant e(\theta, \phi) \leqslant 1$. Thus, the brightness temperature $T_B(\theta, \phi)$ of a material always is smaller than or equal to its physical temperature T. When $e < 1$, the material is said to have a "cooler" brightness temperature than its physical temperature.

Implied in the above definition of emissivity is the assumption that the material is homogeneous and of uniform temperature. Departures from this case are considered in later sections.

4-5.2 Apparent Temperature

Consider the antenna shown in Fig. 4.8(a). The radiation incident upon the antenna from any specific direction may contain components originating from

---

*To avoid confusion between physical and radiometric temperatures, the latter always carries uppercase subscripts, while the former carries either no subscript or lowercase subscripts.

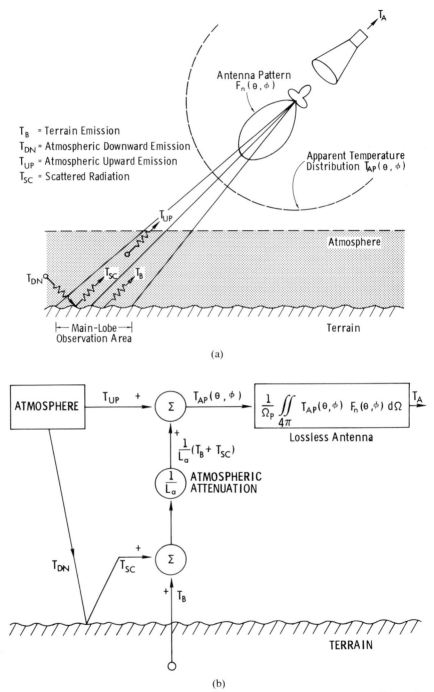

T_B = Terrain Emission
T_{DN} = Atmospheric Downward Emission
T_{UP} = Atmospheric Upward Emission
T_{SC} = Scattered Radiation

(a)

Fig. 4.8 Relationships between antenna temperature T_A, apparent temperature T_{AP}, and brightness temperature T_B: (a) schematic representation (the apparent temperature distribution represents the energy incident upon the antenna); (b) block-diagram representation.

several different sources. Specifically, we have self-emitted radiation from the terrain, self-emitted upward radiation from the atmosphere, and downward-emitted atmospheric radiation that is reflected by the terrain in the direction of the antenna. Moreover, the terrain-reflected and self-emitted components are attenuated as they propagate through the intervening atmosphere between the terrain and the antenna.

To relate the power at the output terminals of the antenna to the radiation from the "scene" observed by the antenna, we shall divide the problem into two steps. First, we relate the antenna output power to an *apparent radiometric temperature distribution* $T_{AP}(\theta, \phi)$, and next (in the following section) we relate $T_{AP}(\theta, \phi)$ to the source of radiation. $T_{AP}(\theta, \phi)$ is a blackbody-equivalent temperature distribution representing the brightness distribution $B_i(\theta, \phi)$ of the energy incident upon the antenna; it is defined in the same manner used earlier to define the brightness temperature $T_B(\theta, \phi)$ of a material:

$$ B_i(\theta, \phi) = \frac{2k}{\lambda^2} T_{AP}(\theta, \phi) \Delta f. \tag{4.49} $$

Because the brightness temperature $T_B(\theta, \phi)$ and the apparent temperature $T_{AP}(\theta, \phi)$ are both blackbody-equivalent radiometric temperatures, the two phrases often have been used in the literature to denote the same quantity, which in some cases has led to confusion. *In this treatment, we adopt the use of the term "brightness temperature" in connection with the self-emitted radiation from a surface or volume, and the term "apparent temperature" in connection with the energy incident upon the antenna.* In the case of Fig. 4.8(a), T_{AP} consists of several terms, each of which is related to the brightness temperature of the source represented by that term. If the atmosphere is lossless, for example, the only contribution to T_{AP} is emission from the terrain (ignoring extraterrestrial emission), in which case $T_{AP} = T_B$. As will be discussed in the next chapter, the condition of a lossless atmosphere can be realized approximately by operating in the 1–10-GHz frequency region under clear-sky conditions. In the general case, however, $T_{AP} \neq T_B$.

4-5.3 Antenna Temperature

In Section 4-4, an expression was obtained for the power at the output terminals of a lossless antenna placed inside a blackbody enclosure. For a nonblackbody brightness distribution defined in terms of an apparent temperature $T_{AP}(\theta, \phi)$ as in (4.49), the received power is

$$ P = \frac{1}{2} A_r \iint_{4\pi} \frac{2k}{\lambda^2} T_{AP}(\theta, \phi) \Delta f F_n(\theta, \phi) \, d\Omega. \tag{4.50} $$

The receiver transfer function of a microwave radiometer usually is established by measuring the output voltage as a function of the physical temperature of a

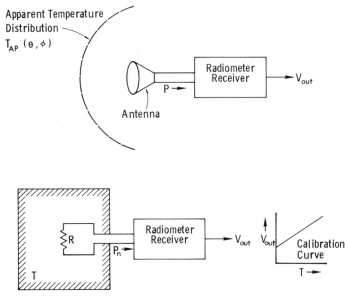

Fig. 4.9 The power received by an antenna is equivalent to the noise power delivered by a matched resistor.

matched resistor placed at the receiver input (in place of the antenna), as shown in Fig. 4.9. This procedure follows from the fact that the noise power P_n delivered by a resistor is proportional to its physical temperature (see (4.45)). Corresponding to the power P provided by the antenna to the receiver, a resistor-equivalent temperature T_A can be defined such that the noise power delivered by a resistor at that temperature is equal to P. Thus,

$$P_n = k T_A \Delta f = P. \tag{4.51}$$

Introducing the expression for P from (4.50) leads to

$$T_A = \frac{A_r}{\lambda^2} \iint_{4\pi} T_{AP}(\theta, \phi) F_n(\theta, \phi) \, d\Omega. \tag{4.52}$$

T_A is called the *antenna radiometric temperature*. Using (3.9) and (4.43), T_A assumes the form

$$T_A = \frac{\displaystyle\iint_{4\pi} T_{AP}(\theta, \phi) F_n(\theta, \phi) \, d\Omega}{\displaystyle\iint_{4\pi} F_n(\theta, \phi) \, d\Omega}. \tag{4.53}$$

According to (4.53), T_A is equal to the apparent temperature distribution $T_{AP}(\theta, \phi)$ integrated over 4π solid angle according to the antenna weighting function $F_n(\theta, \phi)$ and normalized by the integral of the weighting function (which is the pattern solid angle Ω_p). For a blackbody enclosure at temperature T, $T_{AP}(\theta, \phi) = T$, in which case (4.53) reduces to $T_A = T$.

For a discrete source such as the sun, observed by an antenna oriented in the direction of the sun and whose main-beam solid angle is much larger than the solid angle subtended by the sun (Fig. 4.3), the antenna temperature is

$$T_A = \frac{\Omega_s}{\Omega_p} T_S, \tag{4.54}$$

where Ω_s is the solid angle subtended by the sun, T_S is the apparent temperature of the sun, and Ω_p is the antenna-pattern solid angle. The above expression is based on the assumptions that the atmosphere is lossless and that the contributions by sources other than the sun are negligible.

4-5.4 Summary of Relations between Radiometric Temperatures

Figure 4.8(b) is a block-diagram equivalent of Fig. 4.8(a). For a lossless antenna (antenna losses are considered in the next section), its output power, represented by T_A, is equal to the integrated apparent temperature distribution $T_{AP}(\theta, \phi)$, weighted by the antenna directional pattern. For each direction (θ, ϕ), $T_{AP}(\theta, \phi)$ consists of two sources of radiation, both incident upon the antenna from the direction (θ, ϕ). The first source is *atmospheric self-emission*, denoted by T_{UP}. The second source starts at the terrain surface and consists of two components: T_B, representing self-emission by the terrain, and T_{SC}, which is the radiometric temperature of energy scattered by the terrain in the direction (θ, ϕ). The primary source of T_{SC} is the downward-emitted atmospheric radiation (represented by T_{DN}), although it also may have a component due to extraterrestrial radiation incident upon the terrain. This component has a radiometric temperature of about 3 K above 1 GHz and usually is ignored above 10 GHz in comparison with the downward-emitted atmospheric temperature.

The combination, $T_B + T_{SC}$, is attenuated by the *atmospheric loss factor* L_a as the energy travels between the terrain surface and the antenna.

4-6 ANTENNA EFFICIENCY CONSIDERATIONS

4-6.1 Beam Efficiency

Several techniques are available to the radar designer to attain the desired spatial and/or angular resolution (Chapter 7). A microwave radiometer, on the other hand, is a passive device, and therefore the designer has to rely on the shape of the antenna radiation pattern $F_n(\theta, \phi)$ to attain resolution. Ideally, one would design an antenna having a narrow pencil beam and no sidelobes.

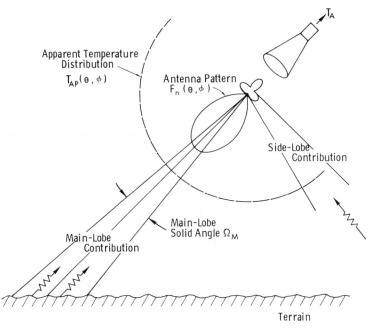

Fig. 4.10 Main-lobe and side-lobe contributions to the antenna temperature T_A.

In reality, however, in addition to the thermal emission received through the antenna main beam, the antenna receives other contributions through the remainder of the antenna pattern (Fig. 4.10). To evaluate the significance of these undesirable contributions, let us divide the integral in the numerator of (4.53) into two parts, one representing the main-lobe contributions and the other representing contributions received from directions outside the main lobe:

$$T_A = \frac{\displaystyle\iint_{main\ lobe} T_{AP}(\theta,\phi)F_n(\theta,\phi)\,d\Omega}{\displaystyle\iint_{4\pi} F_n(\theta,\phi)\,d\Omega} + \frac{\displaystyle\iint_{4\pi\text{-}main\ lobe} T_{AP}(\theta,\phi)F_n(\theta,\phi)\,d\Omega}{\displaystyle\iint_{4\pi} F_n(\theta,\phi)\,d\Omega}.$$

$$(4.55)$$

For ease in terminology, we shall refer to the second term in (4.55) as the side-lobe contribution. We now define the quantity $\overline{T}_{ML}$ as the *effective apparent temperature of the main-lobe contribution*,

$$\overline{T}_{ML} = \frac{\displaystyle\iint_{main\ lobe} T_{AP}(\theta,\phi)F_n(\theta,\phi)\,d\Omega}{\displaystyle\iint_{main\ lobe} F_n(\theta,\phi)\,d\Omega},$$

$$(4.56)$$

where the integration in both the numerator and the denominator is carried over the solid angle subtended by the main lobe of the antenna radiation pattern $F_n(\theta, \phi)$. The main-beam efficiency η_M was defined in Chapter 3 as

$$\eta_M = \frac{\displaystyle\iint_{main\ lobe} F_n(\theta, \phi)\, d\Omega}{\displaystyle\int_{4\pi} F_n(\theta, \phi)\, d\Omega}. \tag{4.57}$$

Note that the expression for the product $\eta_M \overline{T}_{ML}$ is identical to the first term in (4.55). Similarly, the second term in (4.55) is equal to the product $\eta_m \overline{T}_{SL}$, where η_m is the antenna stray factor,

$$\eta_m = \frac{\displaystyle\iint_{4\pi-main\ lobe} F_n(\theta, \phi)\, d\Omega}{\displaystyle\iint_{4\pi} F_n(\theta, \phi)\, d\Omega} = 1 - \eta_M, \tag{4.58}$$

and $\overline{T}_{SL}$ is defined as the *effective apparent temperature of the side-lobe contributions*. Its expression is identical to (4.56) except that the integration is carried over the solid angle of 4π excluding the main-lobe solid angle,

$$\overline{T}_{SL} = \frac{\displaystyle\iint_{4\pi-main\ lobe} T_{AP}(\theta, \phi) F_n(\theta, \phi)\, d\Omega}{\displaystyle\iint_{4\pi-main\ lobe} F_n(\theta, \phi)\, d\Omega}. \tag{4.59}$$

In terms of these new definitions, (4.55) becomes

$$T_A = \eta_M \overline{T}_{ML} + (1 - \eta_M) \overline{T}_{SL}. \tag{4.60}$$

4-6.2 Radiation Efficiency

The antenna temperature T_A of the previous section represents the power at the output terminals of a lossless receiving antenna. In practice, however, antennas are not lossless devices. As was discussed previously in Section 3-2.5, part of the energy received (or transmitted) by an antenna is absorbed by the antenna material in the form of heat loss. The ratio of received power (at the antenna terminals) to incident power is defined as the antenna radiation efficiency η_l. To account for the effects of antenna ohmic losses on the received power, we define T_A' as the *antenna temperature of a lossy antenna*, as "seen" from the receiver. Based on the power-temperature correspondence principle, T_A' is the product of T_A and η_l. But a lossy device is also a radiator; as will be shown later in Section 6-4, the noise power emitted by a passive device is characterized by a noise temperature T_N given by

$$T_N = (1 - \eta_l)T_0 \triangleq \left(1 - \frac{1}{L}\right)T_0,$$

where L is the loss factor (reciprocal of the power transmission coefficient) of the device and T_0 is its physical temperature. For an antenna with a radiation efficiency (power transmission coefficient) η_l, its noise temperature is given by the above equation with $L = 1/\eta_l$ and T_0 being the physical temperature of the antenna. Hence, (received radiation) = (radiation transmitted through antenna) + (self-emitted antenna radiation), or

$$T_A' = \eta_l T_A + (1 - \eta_l)T_0. \tag{4.61}$$

Introducing (4.60) into (4.61) gives

$$T_A' = \eta_l \eta_M \overline{T}_{ML} + \eta_l(1 - \eta_M)\overline{T}_{SL} + (1 - \eta_l)T_0. \tag{4.62}$$

For an ideal antenna with a radiation efficiency $n_l = 1$ and a main-beam efficiency $\eta_M = 1$, (4.62) reduces to

$$T_A' = \overline{T}_{ML}. \tag{4.63}$$

4-6.3 Radar Signal Detection

From considerations of signal-to-noise ratio at the output of a radar receiver, the primary influence of the antenna radiation efficiency η_l is on the signal. Since the antenna is used for both transmission and reception, the signal level is modified by η_l^2.

Of the total noise appearing at the receiver output, part is generated by the receiver itself, and the remainder, represented by T_A', is contributed by the antenna. For system-design purposes, T_A' usually is taken to be around 300 K. This value is actually an upper limit, since the maximum value T_A can achieve is the physical temperature of the terrain and atmosphere (if assumed to be perfect blackbody radiators), which is around 300 K. If the physical temperature T_0 of the antenna is also around 300 K, (4.61) gives $T_A' = 300$ K. The *receiver noise temperature* T_{REC} (defined in Section 7.5) of commonly used radar receivers typically is several times larger than T_A', although recent advances in microwave technology have made it possible to achieve receiver noise temperature values lower than 300 K. With T_A' assumed to be 300 K, the radar designer can compute the total noise level of the antenna-receiver combination, and on that basis the transmitter power level and other parameters of interest can be chosen so that the received signal is several times higher than the noise level. This topic is treated in greater depth in Chapters 7 and 8.

4-6.4 Radiometer Signal Detection

To the radar receiver, T_A' represents a noise contribution. To a radiometer, on the other hand, T_A' is the signal containing the information about the emission characteristics of the scene under observation. Specifically, the objective in radiometric remote sensing is to relate the radiometer receiver output voltage V_{out} to $\overline{T}_{ML}$, the apparent temperature of the resolution cell delineated by the main beam of the antenna. Since the noise power generated by a matched load is linearly related to its physical temperature according to (4.45), the voltage V_{out} can be calibrated to "read" temperature. Thus, T_A' may be regarded as the measured quantity and $\overline{T}_{ML}$ as the quantity to be estimated from the measurement. Solving (4.62) for $\overline{T}_{ML}$, we obtain

$$\overline{T}_{ML} = \left(\frac{1}{\eta_l \eta_M} \right) T_A' - \left(\frac{1 - \eta_M}{\eta_M} \right) \overline{T}_{SL} - \left(\frac{1 - \eta_l}{\eta_l \eta_M} \right) T_0. \qquad (4.64)$$

The above equation takes the form of a linear equation in which $1/\eta_l \eta_M$ represents a scaling factor and the last two terms represent a bias. If η_l, η_M, $\overline{T}_{SL}$, and T_0 are known quantities, then $\overline{T}_{ML}$ can be recovered easily from T_A'. Techniques used for measuring η_l and η_M are covered in Chapter 6, and T_0, the physical temperature of the antenna structure, can be monitored easily with a thermistor. These three parameters determine the coefficients of the first two terms in (4.64) and the entire magnitude of the last term. Because the reciprocal of the product $(\eta_l \eta_M)$ is the coefficient of T_A', errors in the measurement of this product will produce an error not only in the absolute value of $\overline{T}_{ML}$ (due to the last term), but also in its relative value, since the error in the first term is multiplicative. Thus, it is imperative that the product $\eta_l \eta_M$ be measured with a high degree of accuracy in order to realize a good estimate of $\overline{T}_{ML}$.

The middle term in (4.64) is governed by the main-beam efficiency η_M and the side-lobe apparent temperature $\overline{T}_{SL}$. The latter, being a function of the shape of the antenna pattern outside the main lobe and the emission characteristics of the scene, can vary over a wide range of values. For an earth-pointing airborne or spaceborne system, where the scene is changing constantly (except perhaps over the ocean), the contribution of this second term of (4.64) obviously is not independent of time. Figure 4.11 shows plots of the magnitude of the second term as a function of $\overline{T}_{SL}$ for several values of the main-beam efficiency η_M. To restrict the magnitude of this term (and its fluctuation as a function of variations in side-lobe emission) to small values, the antenna should be designed for the highest possible value of η_M.

In conclusion, we state that the accuracy and precision of radiometric measurements are governed strongly by the magnitudes of the radiation and main-beam efficiencies, η_l and η_M, and by the accuracy with which they are known. Techniques for measuring these quantities are discussed in Section 6-16.3.

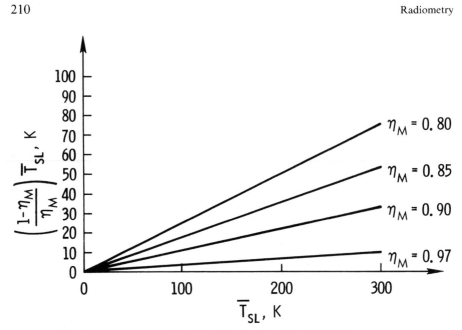

Fig. 4.11 Side-lobe factor as a function of the incident side-lobe brightness temperature $\bar{T}_{SL}$, for each of several values of the main-beam efficiency η_M.

4-7 THEORY OF RADIATIVE TRANSFER

Consider the scenes illustrated in Fig. 4.12. The next several sections are devoted to the methods of analysis used to derive expressions for the apparent temperature T_{AP} of these and similar scenes of interest in radiometric remote sensing. To this end, we first will derive the *equation of transfer*, and then consider its solution for some specific cases.

The interaction between radiation and matter is described by two processes: *extinction* and *emission*. If radiation traversing a medium is reduced in intensity, we have extinction, and if the medium adds energy of its own, we have emission. Usually the interaction consists of both processes occurring simultaneously.

4-7.1 Extinction

Let us consider a small cylindrical volume (Fig. 4.13) of cross-section dA and thickness dr of a material with density ρ. A brightness $B(r)$ is incident normally upon the lower face of the cylinder, as shown in the figure. Recall that brightness is energy per unit area dA, radiated in directions confined to a solid angle $d\Omega$, during a time interval of one second, in a specified frequency interval $(f, f+\Delta f)$. The loss in brightness by extinction due to propagation over the thickness dr is given by

$$dB(\text{extinction}) = \kappa_e B\, dr, \tag{4.65}$$

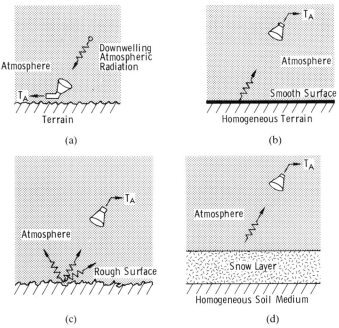

Fig. 4.12 Examples of configurations of interest in radiometric remote sensing: (a) upward-looking radiometer, (b) smooth-surface boundary, (c) rough-surface boundary, (d) two-layer terrain.

where $B =$ brightness, $\mathrm{W\,m^{-2}\,sr^{-1}}$,

$\kappa_e = $ *extinction coefficient* of the medium, $\mathrm{nepers\,m^{-1}}$.

κ_e also is known as the *power attenuation coefficient*. The energy lost from the incident radiation may have been absorbed by the material, scattered, or both. By absorption loss, we mean that the energy is transformed into other forms of energy, such as heat; and by scattering loss, we mean that the energy is caused

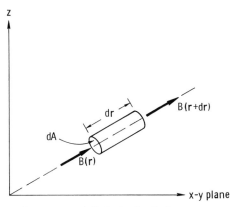

Fig. 4.13   Radiation transfer across an infinitesimal cylinder.

to travel in directions other than the direction of the incident radiation. Absorption and scattering are linear processes. Hence, the extinction coefficient may be expressed as the sum of an *absorption coefficient* κ_a and a *scattering coefficient* κ_s,

$$\kappa_e = \kappa_a + \kappa_s. \tag{4.66}$$

Sometimes it is convenient to express the extinction coefficient κ_e (and similarly κ_a and κ_s) in terms of a physical property of the medium such as the density ρ. In this case,

$$\kappa_e = \rho\kappa_{em} = \rho(\kappa_{am} + \kappa_{sm}) \tag{4.67}$$

where ρ = density of the material, $\mathrm{kg\,m}^{-3}$
κ_{em} = mass extinction coefficient, $\mathrm{Np\,kg}^{-1}\mathrm{m}^2$,
κ_{am} = mass absorption coefficient, $\mathrm{Np\,kg}^{-1}\mathrm{m}^2$,
κ_{sm} = mass scattering coefficient, $\mathrm{Np\,kg}^{-1}\mathrm{m}^2$.

4-7.2 Emission

The amount of brightness (representing energy) emitted by the cylindrical volume of Fig. 4.13 in the direction normal to the upper face at $r + dr$ is given by

$$dB(\text{emission}) = (\kappa_a J_a + \kappa_s J_s)\, dr \tag{4.68}$$

where J_a and J_s are *source functions* that account for thermal emission and scattering, respectively, into the direction $\hat{r}$. J_a is called the *absorption source function*, because under conditions of local thermodynamic equilibrium, thermal emission has to be equal to absorption. Expressions for J_a and the *scattering source function* J_s are deferred to the next section; the purpose of this section is to derive and solve the *equation of transfer* in general form. To this end, we introduce the *single-scattering albedo a*,

$$a = \frac{\kappa_s}{\kappa_e}, \tag{4.69}$$

and from (4.66) we have

$$1 - a = \frac{\kappa_a}{\kappa_e}. \tag{4.70}$$

Using (4.69) and (4.70), (4.68) can be written in the form

$$dB(\text{emission}) = \kappa_e \left(\frac{\kappa_a}{\kappa_e} J_a + \frac{\kappa_s}{\kappa_e} J_s \right) dr$$

$$= \kappa_e \left[(1-a) J_a + a J_s \right] dr. \tag{4.71}$$

For the remainder of this section, we shall call the quantity inside the brackets of (4.71) the *effective total source function J*:

$$J \triangleq (1-a)J_a + aJ_s. \tag{4.72}$$

In terms of J, (4.71) becomes

$$dB(\text{emission}) = \kappa_e J\, dr. \tag{4.73}$$

4-7.3 Differential Equation

The difference between the brightness $B(r+dr)$ leaving the cylinder in the direction normal to its upper face and the brightness $B(r)$ incident normally upon the lower face of the cylinder is equal to the excess of emission over extinction:

$$dB = B(r+dr) - B(r)$$

$$= dB(\text{emission}) - dB(\text{extinction}). \tag{4.74}$$

Inserting (4.65) and (4.73) into (4.74) yields

$$dB = \kappa_e\, dr\, (J-B). \tag{4.75}$$

The dimensionless product $\kappa_e\, dr$ is often abbreviated by

$$d\tau = \kappa_e\, dr, \tag{4.76}$$

where $d\tau$ is called an increment of *optical depth*. Upon inserting (4.76) into (4.75) and rearranging, we obtain the differential equation

$$\frac{dB}{d\tau} + B = J, \tag{4.77}$$

which is known as the *equation of transfer*. B and J are defined at a point $Q(r, \theta, \phi)$ and for propagation in the direction $\hat{r}$ (Fig. 4.14).

4-7.4 Formal Solution

Consider the general case of a semiinfinite medium ($+z$ region in Fig. 4.14) characterized by an extinction coefficient κ_e and a source function J. The brightness in the direction $\hat{r}$ at the boundary $z=0$ is given as $B(0)$. Of interest is $B(r)$ at a point r inside the medium in the direction $\hat{r}$.

The solution of (4.77) is facilitated by introducing the *optical thickness* $\tau(r_1, r_2)$ along a range from r_1 to r_2,

$$\tau(r_1, r_2) = \int_{r_1}^{r_2} \kappa_e\, dr, \tag{4.78}$$

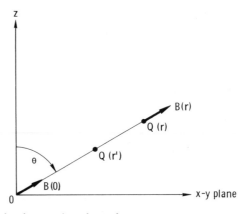

Fig. 4.14 Geometry for the equation of transfer.

which is obtained by integrating the increment of optical depth defined by
(4.76) between the points r_1 and r_2. Now we shall consider the equation of
transfer at an arbitrary point r' along the path shown in Fig. 4.14. Multiplying
both sides of (4.77) by $e^{\tau(0,r')}$, we obtain

$$\frac{dB(r')}{d\tau}e^{\tau(0,r')}+B(r')e^{\tau(0,r')}=J(r')e^{\tau(0,r')}, \tag{4.79}$$

where $\tau(0,r')$ is the optical thickness of the material between the boundary at
$r=0$ and the point at distance r'. The left-hand side of (4.79) is recognized as

$$\frac{dB(r')}{d\tau}e^{\tau(0,r')}+B(r')e^{\tau(0,r')}=\frac{d}{d\tau}\big[B(r')e^{\tau(0,r')}\big], \tag{4.80}$$

which leads to

$$\frac{d}{d\tau}\big[B(r')e^{\tau(0,r')}\big]=J(r')e^{\tau(0,r')}. \tag{4.81}$$

Integrating from 0 to r, we have

$$\int_0^{\tau(0,r)}\frac{d}{d\tau}\big[B(r')e^{\tau(0,r')}\big]\,d\tau=\int_0^{\tau(0,r)}J(r')e^{\tau(0,r')}\,d\tau, \tag{4.82}$$

which leads to

$$B(r')e^{\tau(0,r')}\big|_0^{\tau(0,r)}=\int_0^{\tau(0,r)}J(r')e^{\tau(0,r')}\,d\tau,$$

$$B(r)e^{\tau(0,r)}-B(0)=\int_0^{\tau(0,r)}J(r')e^{\tau(0,r')}\,d\tau. \tag{4.83}$$

Replacing $d\tau$ by $\kappa_e dr'$ in the integral on the right hand side of (4.83), and dividing both sides by $e^{\tau(0,\,r)}$ and rearranging, we have

$$B(r)=B(0)e^{-\tau(0,\,r)}+e^{-\tau(0,\,r)}\int_0^r \kappa_e(r')J(r')e^{\tau(0,\,r')}\,dr'. \qquad (4.84)$$

The above expression may be simplified further by noting that

$$e^{-\tau(0,\,r)}e^{\tau(0,\,r')}=e^{-\tau(r',\,r)},$$

which leads to the formal solution of the equation of transfer,

$$B(r)=B(0)e^{-\tau(0,\,r)}+\int_0^r \kappa_e(r')J(r')e^{-\tau(r',\,r)}\,dr'. \qquad (4.85)$$

The above solution states that the brightness $B(r)$ at any point r propagating in the direction $\hat{r}$ is given by two terms. The first term is the brightness $B(0)$ at the boundary (propagating in the direction $\hat{r}$), reduced in magnitude by the factor $e^{-\tau(0,\,r)}$ due to extinction by the material between 0 and r. The second term represents the emission and scattering by the material along the propagation path. The integral is the sum of contributions from infinitesimal thicknesses, each dr' in length; the contribution from a layer at point r' is given by the differential emitted brightness, $\kappa_e(r')J(r')\,dr'$ according to (4.73), reduced in magnitude by the factor $e^{-\tau(r',\,r)}$ due to extinction by the material between the layer at point r' and the observation point at r.

4-8 APPARENT TEMPERATURE OF AN ABSORBING AND SCATTERING MEDIUM

The general solution given by (4.85) is in terms of the brightness B. In the microwave region, the Rayleigh-Jeans form of Planck's law can be used to define $B(r)$ in terms of an apparent temperature T_{AP} according to (4.49):

$$B(r)=\frac{2k}{\lambda^2}T_{AP}(r)\Delta f. \qquad (4.86)$$

4-8.1 Source Functions

A similar approach may be used to define expressions for source functions. *Kirchhoff's law* states that under conditions of local thermodynamic equilibrium, thermal emission has to be equal to absorption, which leads to the conclusion that the absorption source function J_a is isotropic and that it is given by Planck's radiation law. Again assuming the Rayleigh-Jeans approximation to be applicable, we have

$$J_a(r)=\frac{2k}{\lambda^2}T(r)\Delta f, \qquad (4.87)$$

where $T(r)$ is the kinetic (physical) temperature of the medium at r. Although Kirchhoff's law is defined for conditions of strict thermodynamic equilibrium, it has been found to hold with good accuracy provided the spatial gradient of the temperature within the medium is not very large.

The scattering source function $J_s(\mathbf{r})$ accounts for radiation scattered in the direction $\hat{\mathbf{r}}$ in terms of radiation incident from all directions. If we designate the direction of incident radiation by the unit vector $\hat{\mathbf{r}}_i$, then $J_s(\mathbf{r})$ can be expressed as

$$J_s(\mathbf{r}) = \frac{1}{4\pi} \iint_{4\pi} \psi(\mathbf{r}; \mathbf{r}_i) B(\mathbf{r}_i) \, d\Omega_i, \tag{4.88}$$

where $B(\mathbf{r}_i)$ is the brightness of radiation incident from direction $\hat{\mathbf{r}}_i$ and $\psi(\mathbf{r}; \mathbf{r}_i)$, known as the *phase function*, accounts for the portion of energy scattered from direction $\hat{\mathbf{r}}_i$ into direction $\hat{\mathbf{r}}$. Analogous to the absorption source function, the scattering source function $J_s(\mathbf{r})$ can be defined in terms of a *scattered radiometric temperature* T_{SC} as follows:

$$J_s(\mathbf{r}) = \frac{2k}{\lambda^2} T_{SC}(\mathbf{r}) \Delta f. \tag{4.89}$$

Upon introducing (4.86) into (4.88) and equating the latter to (4.89), we have

$$T_{SC}(\mathbf{r}) = \frac{1}{4\pi} \iint_{4\pi} \psi(\mathbf{r}, \mathbf{r}_i) T_{AP}(\mathbf{r}_i) \, d\Omega_i. \tag{4.90}$$

By inserting (4.87) and (4.89) into (4.72), the total source function is obtained:

$$J(\mathbf{r}) = (1-a)J_a(r) + aJ_s(\mathbf{r})$$

$$= \left[(1-a)T(r) + aT_{SC}(\mathbf{r}) \right] \frac{2k}{\lambda^2} \Delta f. \tag{4.91}$$

4-8.2 General Solution

Finally, replacing $J(\mathbf{r})$ in (4.85) by the above expression and $B(r)$ by (4.86) and simplifying yields

$$T_{AP}(r) = T_{AP}(0)e^{-\tau(0, r)}$$

$$+ \int_0^r \kappa_e(r') \left[(1-a)T(r') + aT_{SC}(r') \right] e^{-\tau(r', r)} \, dr', \tag{4.92}$$

where $T_{AP}(0)$ is the apparent temperature at the boundary. Although not explicitly indicated, it is understood that all terms in (4.92) pertain to propagation in the direction $\hat{\mathbf{r}}$.

In the general case, the extinction coefficient κ_e consists of an absorption component κ_a and a scattering component κ_s. In the absence of absorption, the process is referred to as one of *perfect scattering*, and if absorption is the only extinction process, we have *perfect absorption*. Chandrasekhar (1960), in his book *Radiative Transfer*, provides an extensive treatment of the equation of transfer for the atmosphere under a variety of conditions, with special emphasis on problems involving a perfectly scattering medium. Microwave interactions with terrain and atmospheric media, however, rarely encounter situations characterized by perfect scattering. When both scattering and absorption are present, the general solution for $T_{AP}(\mathbf{r})$ as given by (4.92) requires the evaluation of an integral involving the scattered radiometric temperature $T_{SC}(\mathbf{r})$, which itself is determined by an integral involving $T_{AP}(\mathbf{r}_i)$ for all directions $\hat{\mathbf{r}}_i$ over 4π solid angle, as in (4.90). Thus, the solution at every point in the medium depends on the interactions at every other point, which leads to highly complicated formulations. If the single scattering albedo $a \ll 1$, the complexity of the problem is reduced immensely, as discussed below.

4-8.3 Radiative Transfer in a Scatter-Free Medium

In a scatter-free medium, $\kappa_s = 0$, (4.92) reduces to

$$T_{AP}(r) = T_{AP}(0)e^{-\tau(0,r)} + \int_0^r \kappa_a(r')T(r')e^{-\tau(r',r)}\,dr', \tag{4.93}$$

where now

$$\tau(r',r) = \int_{r'}^r \kappa_a\,dr. \tag{4.94}$$

For a terrain-looking radiometer at a range r from the terrain, the first term in (4.93) represents the apparent temperature of the terrain, $T_{AP}(0)$ reduced by $e^{-\tau(0,r)}$, which accounts for atmospheric absorption between the terrain and the radiometer, and the second term represents upwelling atmospheric self-emission in the direction of the radiometer.

4-8.4 Applicability of the Scatter-Free Assumption

Under clear sky conditions, the earth's atmosphere is free from scattering in the microwave region. When a cloud and/or rain is present, scattering by the water droplets may or may not be negligible depending upon the density and drop-size distribution of the water droplets relative to the wavelength. Generally, scattering effects may be ignored for most atmospheric weather conditions if the frequency is below 10 GHz. For further discussion of atmospheric absorption and scattering, the reader is referred to Chapter 5.

Scattering by particles contained inside a medium often is referred to as *volume scattering*, in contrast to scattering by an interface between two dissimilar media, such as the boundary between a soil medium and the atmosphere. The latter is referred to as *surface scattering*. Returning to the example given above in connection with (4.93), $T_{AP}(0)$ is, in part, the emission from the terrain upward into the atmosphere. This emission is related to the upward emission at a point just beneath the interface through the transmission coefficient of the boundary, which is governed by the dielectric properties of the terrain medium (relative to air) and by its surface geometry. Since transmission across and scattering from a boundary are related to one another, this has led to the use of the term *surface scattering* to describe the transfer of energy across the boundary between two dissimilar media. Chapter 12 is devoted to surface-scattering problems as they relate to radar backscatter and radiometric emission.

So far, we have examined briefly the transfer of radiation between the terrain and the downward-looking radiometer through the atmosphere. To compute the terrain self-emitted radiation, (4.92) needs to be solved for the terrain medium itself to determine the upward-emitted radiation at a point just beneath the surface. If the single-scattering albedo of the medium is very small, (4.93) can be used; otherwise, volume scattering has to be accounted for.

Absorption within a material medium is governed by the average conductivity of the medium, as discussed earlier in Chapter 2, while scattering is governed by the degree of spatial inhomogeneity and/or anisotropy of the dielectric properties of the medium, measured in wavelength units. To explain the mechanics of scattering, let us consider the example of dry snow. A snow volume with a density of 0.37 g cm^{-3} consists of 60 percent air and 40 percent ice (the density of ice is 0.916 g cm^{-3}). The relative permittivity of air is unity, and the microwave permittivity of ice is 3.15. Hence, the average permittivity of the medium is $= 0.6 \times 1 + 0.4 \times 3.15 = 1.86$. The diameters of the ice particles in the snow typically are of the order of 0.1–5 mm in size. If the wavelength of the propagating wave is much larger than the dimensions of the ice particles (and the average distance between particles), the medium appears electromagnetically homogeneous and no appreciable scattering takes place. But if the wavelength is of the same order of magnitude as the dimensions of the ice particles, the spatial inhomogeneity (due to the 3.15-to-1.0 ratio of the permittivity of the ice particles to that of the background) leads to volume scattering. Thus, at 1 GHz ($\lambda = 30$ cm in air and $30/\sqrt{1.86} \simeq 22$ cm in snow), snow may be considered purely absorptive, while at 30 GHz ($\lambda = 7.3$ mm in snow) both absorption and scattering have to be considered.

Another terrain cover that is characterized by dielectric inhomogeneities is vegetation, and in the case of row crops, the dielectric also is anisotropic.

In the next few sections, we shall examine the solution of the radiative transfer equation for scatter-free media with plane boundaries. Surface scattering from irregular boundaries and volume scattering in inhomogeneous media are considered respectively in Chapters 11-13.

4-9 APPARENT TEMPERATURE OF ATMOSPHERE AND TERRAIN

4-9.1 Upwelling Atmospheric Radiation

Consider the stratified atmosphere shown in Fig. 4.15(a), in which the temperature and absorption coefficients are functions of height (vertical coordinate z) only. The apparent temperature of the atmosphere (excluding contributions from the ground), observed at a point $Q(r, \theta)$ at a height H above the ground, is given by the second term of (4.93), with appropriate specifications. This apparent temperature, which will be denoted $T_{UP}(\theta; H)$, represents the net upward-emitted radiation by the entire atmospheric path between the ground and the observation point in the direction θ relative to the surface normal. Using the relations

$$r' = z' \sec \theta,$$

$$dr' = dz' \sec \theta,$$

$T_{UP}(\theta; H)$ is given by

$$T_{UP}(\theta; H) = \sec \theta \int_0^H \kappa_a(z') T(z') e^{-\tau(z', H)\sec \theta} \, dz', \qquad (4.95)$$

where

$$\tau(z', H) = \int_{z'}^H \kappa_a(z) \, dz. \qquad (4.96)$$

If H is sufficiently higher than the physical extent of the earth's atmosphere, it may be replaced by ∞, since $\kappa_a(z) = 0$ for free space.

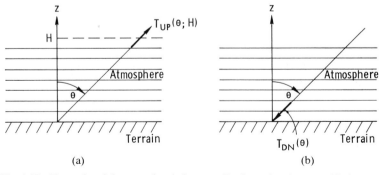

Fig. 4.15 Upward and downward emission contributions of a plane-stratified atmosphere: (a) upward atmospheric apparent temperature (excluding terrain emission); (b) downward atmospheric apparent temperature.

4-9.2 Downwelling Atmospheric Radiation

Now, let us consider the apparent temperature of the atmosphere, $T_{DN}(\theta)$, observed at the surface of the ground, as shown in Figure 4.15(b). By analogy to the previous case,

$$T_{DN}(\theta)=\sec\theta\int_0^\infty \kappa_a(z')T(z')e^{-\tau(0,\,z')\sec\theta}\,dz', \qquad (4.97)$$

where the atmosphere is considered semiinfinite in extent.

The physical meaning of the above equation is quite simple; the energy emitted by a stratum at height z' and of vertical thickness dz' (slant thickness $\sec\theta\,dz'$) is proportional to $\sec\theta\,\kappa_a(z')\,T(z')\,dz'$, which, after propagation down to the surface, is reduced by the factor $\exp[-\tau(0,z')\sec\theta]$ due to absorption by the intervening layers. Thus, of two adjacent layers with comparable temperature and absorption coefficients, the layer closer to the ground will provide the larger contribution to $T_{DN}(\theta)$.

According to (4.95) and (4.97), $T_{UP}(\theta;H)$ and $T_{DN}(\theta)$ of a stratified atmosphere are governed by the vertical profiles of $T(z)$ and $\kappa_a(z)$. For $\kappa_a(z)=0$ (lossless atmosphere), $T_{UP}=T_{DN}=0$, as would be expected from Kirchhoff's law. At the other extreme, how large can T_{UP} and T_{DN} be? As the medium becomes more absorptive, it approaches a perfect blackbody, in which case its apparent temperature becomes equal to its physical temperature. For a medium with a nonuniform temperature profile, the exact value of the apparent temperature will depend on the shape of the vertical profiles of the temperature and absorption coefficient, but will never exceed the maximum physical temperature in the profile.

For the special case of a plane homogeneous atmosphere (or cloud) with $T(z)=T_0$ and $\kappa_a(z)=\kappa_{a0}$ over the range $z=0$ to $z=H$, where T_0 and κ_{a0} are constants, the expression for $T_{DN}(\theta;H)$ becomes

$$T_{DN}(\theta;H)=\sec\theta\int_0^H \kappa_{a0}T_0 e^{-\kappa_{a0}z'\sec\theta}\,dz'$$

$$=T_0[1-e^{-\tau(0,\,H)\sec\theta}]. \qquad (4.98)$$

It can be shown easily that $T_{UP}(\theta;H)$ is given by the same expression. If the optical thickness of the cloud, $\tau(0,H)\sec\theta$, is very large, so that the second term inside the bracket of (4.98) is negligible compared to unity, the expression reduces to

$$T_{DN}=T_0. \qquad (4.99)$$

The variation of κ_a with frequency in the microwave region is discussed in Chapter 5 for atmospheric gases, clouds, and rain. Also, calculated and measured values of κ_a, T_{DN}, and other related parameters are presented.

4-9.3 Upwelling Radiation from Terrain and Atmosphere

The case of prime interest in radiometric remote sensing is that of an earth-looking radiometer, as illustrated in Fig. 4.16. The apparent temperature now includes both terms of (4.93). For a stratified atmosphere, $T_{AP}(\theta; H)$ is given by

$$T_{AP}(\theta, H) = T_{AP}(\theta; 0) e^{-\tau(0, H) \sec \theta} + T_{UP}(\theta; H),\qquad(4.100)$$

where $T_{UP}(\theta; H)$ is given by (4.95). The inverse of the exponential factor in the first term of (4.100) is known commonly as the *atmospheric loss factor* $L_a(\theta; H)$:

$$L_a(\theta; H) = e^{\tau(0, H) \sec \theta}.\qquad(4.101)$$

For a lossless atmosphere, $\tau = 0$, therefore, $L_a = 1$. In decibels the loss factor is given by

$$\begin{aligned} L_a(\mathrm{dB}) &= 10 \log L_a \\ &= 4.34 \tau(0, H) \sec \theta. \end{aligned}\qquad(4.102)$$

$T_{AP}(\theta; 0)$ is the apparent temperature of the terrain in the direction θ at the atmosphere-terrain boundary. That is, $T_{AP}(\theta; 0)$ is the apparent temperature that a downward-looking radiometer would observe if placed directly above the terrain surface (such as on a tower or a truck-mounted platform). If the terrain is not being irradiated by the upper hemisphere (lossless atmosphere),

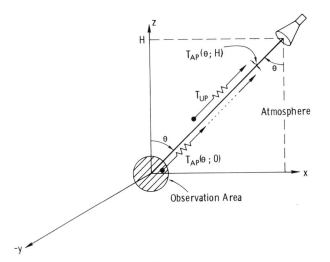

Fig. 4.16   The apparent temperature $T_{AP}(\theta; H)$ at a height H above the terrain consists of the apparent temperature of the terrain $T_{AP}(\theta; 0)$ at a point just above the terrain ($z = 0^+$) attenuated by the intervening atmosphere, and of an upward self-contributed atmospheric component, T_{UP}.

$T_{AP}(\theta;0)$ is equal to the brightness temperature $T_B(\theta)$ of the terrain (see Section 4-5). In the general case, however, $T_{AP}(\theta;0)$ includes another component, $T_{SC}(\theta)$, which represents that portion of the radiation impinging on the terrain surface from the upper hemisphere that gets scattered by the surface in the direction θ. Thus,

$$T_{AP}(\theta;0) = T_B(\theta) + T_{SC}(\theta). \qquad (4.103)$$

The radiation incident upon the surface may include downwelling atmospheric radiation (represented by T_{DN}) and cosmic and galactic radiation originating outside the earth's atmosphere. For most of the microwave region, the cosmic and galactic contributions are small compared to T_{DN} (Section 5-6.2) and hence may be ignored.

In the foregoing discussions, we ignored the dependence on the azimuth angle ϕ in accordance with the assumption that the atmosphere is stratified horizontally. Although this usually is a valid assumption for the atmosphere, it does not apply necessarily to the radiation emitted and scattered by the terrain. Furthermore, no consideration has been given yet to the polarization dependence of $T_{AP}(\theta, H)$. The radiation emitted by the atmosphere is randomly polarized (unpolarized); a radiometer with a linearly polarized antenna would measure the same amount of atmospheric emission regardless of the direction of the antenna polarization vector. Emission and scattering by a surface, on the other hand, usually are polarization-dependent. Generalizing our symbolism to account for the dependence on ϕ and on polarization, we define

$$T_{AP} = T_{AP}(\theta, \phi; z; p), \qquad (4.104)$$

where (θ, ϕ) denotes the direction to the observation point, z denotes the height of the observation point above the ground, and p denotes the linear polarization configuration of T_{AP}:

$$p = h \text{ or } v,$$

where h stands for horizontal polarization and v stands for vertical polarization, defined relative to the surface of the ground. A plane wave is horizontally polarized if its electric field vector is parallel to the surface, and it is vertically polarized if its magnetic field vector is parallel to the surface (see Section 2-6).

Rewriting (4.100) in terms of the above notation, the polarized apparent temperature of terrain observed from a height H above the terrain can be expressed as

$$T_{AP}(\theta, \phi; H; p) = \frac{1}{L_a(\theta, H)} \left[T_B(\theta, \phi; p) + T_{SC}(\theta, \phi; p) \right]$$

$$+ T_{UP}(\theta; H), \qquad (4.105)$$

where $L_a(\theta, H)$ is given by (4.101) and $T_{UP}(\theta; H)$ is given by (4.95). The atmospheric quantities $L_a(\theta; H)$ and $T_{UP}(\theta; H)$ are functions of the vertical profiles of the absorption coefficient $\kappa_a(z)$ and the physical temperature $T(z)$ of the atmosphere over the vertical range between $z=0$ and $z=H$. As will be shown in Chapter 5, $\kappa_a(z)$ exhibits a strong dependence on frequency in the microwave region. If the microwave frequency (and atmospheric conditions) are such that $\kappa_a(z)$ is very small (lossless atmosphere), (4.101) and (4.95) lead to $L_a \simeq 1$ and $T_{UP} \simeq 0$, respectively. Additionally, $T_{DN} \simeq 0$ (ignoring extraterrestrial radiation) which leads to $T_{SC} \simeq 0$. Therefore,

$$T_{AP}(\theta, \phi; H; p) \simeq T_B(\theta, \phi; p), \qquad \text{lossless atmosphere.} \qquad (4.106)$$

On the other hand, if the atmosphere is very lossy (L_a very large),

$$T_{AP}(\theta, \phi; H; p) \simeq T_{UP}(\theta; H), \qquad \text{very lossy atmosphere.} \qquad (4.107)$$

4-10 COORDINATE TRANSFORMATIONS

In the previous section, we related the polarized apparent temperature $T_{AP}(\theta, \phi; H; p)$ of terrain, observed from the direction (θ, ϕ) at a height H above the terrain, to the terrain emission and scattering properties and the absorption and emission properties of the atmosphere. This is the antenna temperature that would be measured by an ideal lossless antenna with a very narrow beam pointed along the direction (θ, ϕ). In the general case, however, the apparent temperature of the scene observed by the antenna main lobe may consist of several different targets with different emission characteristics. To treat this case, let us recall the expression for the main-lobe apparent temperature $\overline{T}_{ML}$,

$$\overline{T}_{ML} = \frac{\displaystyle\iint_{\text{main lobe}} T_{AP}(\theta, \phi) F_n(\theta, \phi) \, d\Omega_a}{\displaystyle\iint_{\text{main lobe}} F_n(\theta, \phi) \, d\Omega_a}, \qquad (4.56)$$

where θ_a and ϕ_a are the coordinate angles of the antenna pattern and $T_{AP}(\theta_a, \phi_a)$ is the apparent temperature distribution incident upon the antenna. Terrain-looking radiometers usually use pencil-beam antennas that have symmetrical patterns in ϕ_a; i.e., $F_n(\theta_a, \phi_a) = F_n(\theta_a)$. Figure 4.17 shows an elliptical terrain "cell" observed by the antenna main beam. The center of the main beam makes an angle θ with the normal to the surface. Without loss of generality, the antenna is placed in the xz-plane at a height H above the terrain surface. An infinitesimal terrain area $dx \, dy$ subtends a solid angle

$$d\Omega_a = \frac{\cos \theta_1}{r^2} dx \, dy, \qquad (4.108)$$

where θ_1 is the local angle of incidence (angle between the surface normal and

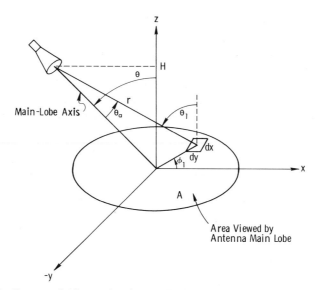

Fig. 4.17   Geometry for integrating the contributions from a nonhomogeneous observation area.

the vector $\hat{\mathbf{r}}$) and r is the distance between the antenna and the area $dx\,dy$. $\bar{T}_{ML}$ now can be written as an integral over the area A,

$$\bar{T}_{ML}(\theta, \pi; H; p) = \frac{1}{\Omega_M} \int_A T_{AP}(x, y; \theta_1, \phi_1; H; p) F_n(\theta_a) \frac{\cos\theta_1}{r^2} dx\,dy,$$

(4.109)

where p is the polarization state (v or h), Ω_M is the main-lobe solid angle (denominator of (4.56)), and T_{AP} is the apparent temperature of the terrain-atmosphere combination, as given by (4.105). If the terrain cell is homogeneous and if the antenna beam is sufficiently narrow so that T_{AP} can be assumed to be approximately constant over the range of angles subtended by the main beam, the above expression reduces to

$$\bar{T}_{ML}(\theta, \pi; H; p) = T_{AP}(\theta; H; p).$$

(4.110)

4-11 EMISSION AND SCATTERING BY TERRAIN

4-11.1 Preface

In the sections to follow, we shall focus our attention on the interaction of radiation with material media characterized by an abrupt discontinuity at the boundary. Specifically, we are interested in relating the terrain brightness temperature $T_B(\theta, \phi; p)$ and the scattered temperature $T_{SC}(\theta, \phi; p)$ to the characteristics of the terrain medium and its surface structure. Following detailed consideration of the flat-surface case, the more general case of a rough-surface boundary will be introduced briefly, as detailed treatment of the latter is given in Chapters 11-12.

4-11.2 Properties of the Specular Surface

Electromagnetically, a surface is considered smooth if its height variations are much smaller than the wavelength of the radiation. Such a surface usually is called a *specular surface*. Reflection from and transmission through a specular surface boundary are governed by Snell's law, which is covered in Chapter 2. For convenience, however, we shall provide a summary of the relevant quantities and expressions to facilitate the treatment that follows. Also, the symbols are somewhat different from those used in Chapter 2.

Consider two homogeneous media separated by a plane boundary, as shown in Fig. 4.18(a). Each medium is characterized by a complex permittivity (also known as complex dielectric constant) ε_c and magnetic permeability μ. It is common practice to express ε_c and μ in terms of the free-space permittivity ε_0 and permeability μ_0 by defining the dimensionless quantities ε_r and μ_r as follows:

$$\varepsilon_r = \varepsilon_c/\varepsilon_0, \tag{4.111a}$$

$$\mu_r = \mu/\mu_0, \tag{4.111b}$$

where ε_r and μ_r are referred to as the relative complex dielectric constant and relative permeability, respectively. In the microwave region $\mu_r \simeq 1$ for most earth materials including water, but it will be retained for completeness in the expressions that follow. The relative dielectric constant ε_r is, in general, a complex function composed of a real part, ε_r', and an imaginary part, ε_r'':

$$\varepsilon_r = \varepsilon_r' - j\varepsilon_r'', \tag{4.112}$$

where $j = \sqrt{-1}$. Expressions for ε_r' and ε_r'' are available in Appendix E of Volume III for several types of material media (water, soil, vegetation, snow, ice, etc.).

The field attenuation coefficient α is given by (2.26),

$$\alpha = \frac{2\pi}{\lambda_0}\left\{\frac{\mu_r \varepsilon_r'}{2}\left[\left(1 + \left(\frac{\varepsilon_r''}{\varepsilon_r'}\right)^2\right)^{1/2} - 1\right]\right\}^{1/2}, \tag{4.113}$$

where λ_0 is the free-space wavelength. The power absorption coefficient κ_a is twice α:

$$\kappa_a = 2\alpha. \tag{4.114}$$

If λ_0 is expressed in meters, the units of κ_a and α are $Np\,m^{-1}$.

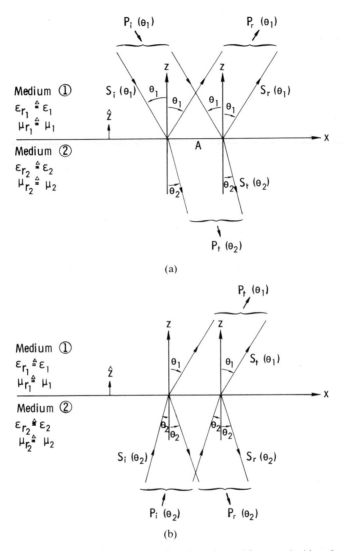

Fig. 4.18 Reflection and refraction at a plane boundary with power incident from (a) medium 1, (b) medium 2.

The intrinsic impedance of the medium is given by

$$\eta = \sqrt{\frac{\mu}{\varepsilon_c}}, \qquad \text{ohms,}$$

and the normalized (or relative) intrinsic impedance may be defined as

$$\eta_r = \eta/\eta_0 = \sqrt{\frac{\mu}{\varepsilon_c}} \bigg/ \sqrt{\frac{\mu_0}{\varepsilon_0}} = \sqrt{\frac{\mu_r}{\varepsilon_r}}, \qquad (4.115)$$

where η_0 is the intrinsic impedance of free space. In the material that follows, we adopt the abbreviated notation:

$$\varepsilon_i \overset{\triangle}{=} \varepsilon_{ri},$$

$$\mu_i \overset{\triangle}{=} \mu_{ri},$$

$$\eta_i \overset{\triangle}{=} \eta_{ri}$$

to denote the relative complex dielectric constant, relative permeability, and relative intrinsic impedance of the ith medium.

Consider electromagnetic energy propagating in medium 1 toward medium 2 as shown in Fig. 4.18(a). The incident, reflected, and transmitted time-average Poynting vectors are $\mathbf{S}_{ai}$, $\mathbf{S}_{ar}$, and $\mathbf{S}_{at}$, respectively, and their magnitudes (power densities) are denoted by

$$|\mathbf{S}_{ai}| = S_i(\theta_1; p),$$

$$|\mathbf{S}_{ar}| = S_r(\theta_1; p),$$

$$|\mathbf{S}_{at}| = S_t(\theta_2; p),$$

where θ_1 is the angle of incidence in medium 1, θ_2 is the angle of refraction in medium 2, and p denotes the polarization configuration of the wave (h or v). From (2.55) and (2.56), the reflectivity $\Gamma_{1,2}(\theta_1; p)$ and transmissivity $\Upsilon_{1,2}(\theta_2; p)$ are given by

$$\Gamma_{1,2}(\theta_1; p) = \frac{\hat{\mathbf{z}} \cdot \mathbf{S}_{ar}}{-\hat{\mathbf{z}} \cdot \mathbf{S}_{ai}} = \frac{S_r(\theta_1; p)\cos\theta_1}{S_i(\theta_1; p)\cos\theta_1} = \frac{S_r(\theta_1; p)}{S_i(\theta_1; p)}, \tag{4.116a}$$

$$\Upsilon_{1,2}(\theta_2; p) = \frac{\hat{\mathbf{z}} \cdot \mathbf{S}_{at}}{\hat{\mathbf{z}} \cdot \mathbf{S}_{ai}} = \frac{S_t(\theta_2; p)\cos\theta_2}{S_i(\theta_1; p)\cos\theta_1}. \tag{4.116b}$$

The subscript 1,2 denotes that the energy is incident from medium 1 towards medium 2. For the interface area A shown in Fig. 4.18(a), the power $P_i(\theta_1; p)$ incident upon it, the power $P_r(\theta_1; p)$ reflected by it, and the power $P_t(\theta_2; p)$ transmitted through it are related to the power densities by

$$P_i(\theta_1; p) = S_i(\theta_1; p)A\cos\theta_1, \tag{4.117a}$$

$$P_r(\theta_1; p) = S_r(\theta_1; p)A\cos\theta_1, \tag{4.117b}$$

$$P_t(\theta_2; p) = S_t(\theta_2; p)A\cos\theta_2. \tag{4.117c}$$

Using the above expressions in (4.116), we obtain

$$\Gamma_{1,2}(\theta_1; p) = \frac{P_r(\theta_1; p)}{P_i(\theta_1; p)}, \tag{4.118a}$$

$$\Upsilon_{1,2}(\theta_2; p) = \frac{P_t(\theta_2; p)}{P_i(\theta_1; p)}, \tag{4.118b}$$

and energy conservation ($P_i = P_r + P_t$) leads to

$$P_t(\theta_2; p) = \Upsilon_{1,2}(\theta_2; p) P_i(\theta_1; p)$$
$$= [1 - \Gamma_{1,2}(\theta_1; p)] P_i(\theta_1; p). \qquad (4.119)$$

The reflectivity is equal to the square of the magnitude of the Fresnel reflection coefficient, $R_{1,2}(\theta_1; p)$:

$$\Gamma_{1,2}(\theta_1; p) = |R_{1,2}(\theta_1; p)|^2$$
$$= \left| \frac{Z_2 - Z_1}{Z_2 + Z_1} \right|^2, \qquad (4.120)$$

where Z_1 and Z_2 are the normalized (relative) impedances of media 1 and 2, respectively:

$$Z_i = \begin{cases} \eta_i \cos \theta_i & \text{for } p = v, \\ \eta_i \sec \theta_i & \text{for } p = h, \end{cases} \qquad (4.121)$$

with $i = 1$ or 2. The refraction angle θ_2 is related to the angle of incidence θ_1 via the expression

$$\sin \theta_2 = \sqrt{\frac{\mu_1 \epsilon_1}{\mu_2 \epsilon_2}} \sin \theta_1. \qquad (4.122)$$

Now consider Fig. 4.18(b), where a wave in medium 2 is shown incident upon the boundary at an angle of incidence θ_2. The reflection coefficient $R_{2,1}(\theta_2; p)$ is given by

$$R_{2,1}(\theta_2; p) = (-1)^n \left(\frac{Z_1 - Z_2}{Z_1 + Z_2} \right) = -R_{1,2}(\theta_1; p); \ n = \begin{cases} 0 \text{ for } p = h, \\ 1 \text{ for } p = v, \end{cases}$$

which leads to

$$\Gamma_{2,1}(\theta_2; p) = \Gamma_{1,2}(\theta_1; p). \qquad (4.123)$$

That is, the reflectivity in medium 2 at θ_2 is equal to the reflectivity in medium 1 at θ_1 if θ_1 and θ_2 are related by (4.122).

Therefore, $P_t(\theta_1; p)$ in Fig. 4.18(b) may be written as

$$P_t(\theta_1; p) = \Upsilon_{2,1}(\theta_2; p) P_i(\theta_2; p)$$

$$= [1 - \Gamma_{2,1}(\theta_2; p)] P_i(\theta_2; p)$$

$$= [1 - \Gamma_{1,2}(\theta_1; p)] P_i(\theta_2; p). \qquad (4.124)$$

The above expression relates the power transmitted into medium 1 at an angle θ_1 to the power incident from medium 2 at θ_2 in terms of the reflectivity $\Gamma_{1,2}(\theta_1; p)$ in medium 1, which will prove useful in the treatment below. For brevity, $\Gamma_{1,2}(\theta_1; p)$ will henceforth be designated $\Gamma_1(\theta_1; p)$.

4-12 HOMOGENEOUS TERRAIN MEDIUM WITH UNIFORM TEMPERATURE PROFILE

We shall now use the quantities defined above to derive expressions for the brightness temperature $T_B(\theta_1; p)$ and the scattered temperature $T_{SC}(\theta_1; p)$ that would be observed at a point above the boundary between medium 1 (air) and medium 2 (terrain). The terrain is assumed to be homogeneous, both in terms of its constitutive parameters and in terms of its physical temperature. Thus, $\varepsilon_1 = 1$, $\mu_1 = 1$, $\eta_1 = 1$, and ε_2, μ_2, η_2, and κ_{a2} are constants for $z < 0$. Also, $T(z) = T_g$ for $z < 0$.

Since power is directly proportional to temperature, the brightness temperature $T_B(\theta_1; p)$ is related to the upwelling apparent temperature $T_{AP}(\theta_2; 0^-; p)$ of medium 2 (Fig. 4.19) according to the form of (4.124):

$$T_B(\theta_1; p) = [1 - \Gamma_1(\theta_1; p)] T_{AP}(\theta_2; 0^-; p), \qquad (4.125)$$

where $T_{AP}(\theta_2; 0^-; p)$ is the p-polarized (h or v) apparent temperature of medium 2 (incident upon the boundary from the direction θ_2) at a point just below the surface ($z = 0^-$).

The upwelling apparent temperature of the terrain medium is analogous to the downwelling apparent temperature of the infinite atmosphere considered earlier. Defining $\zeta = -z$ for convenience, we have

$$T_{AP}(\theta_2; \zeta = 0^+; p) = \sec\theta_2 \int_{0^+}^{\infty} \kappa_a(\zeta') T(\zeta') e^{-\tau(0^+, \zeta')\sec\theta_2} d\zeta', \qquad (4.126)$$

where κ_a is the absorption coefficient of medium 2. For a homogeneous

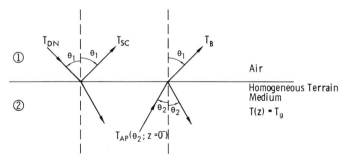

Fig. 4.19 Geometry associated with scattered (reflected) radiometric temperature T_{SC} and the terrain brightness temperature T_B.

medium, the above expression reduces to

$$T_{AP}(\theta_2; z=0^-; p) = T_{AP}(\theta_2; \zeta=0^+; p) = T_g, \tag{4.127}$$

and therefore T_B becomes

$$T_B(\theta_1; p) = [1 - \Gamma_1(\theta_1; p)] T_g. \tag{4.128}$$

The above result is valid if medium 2 is semiinfinite and $\kappa_a \neq 0$. In practice (4.128) holds with good accuracy for a medium with finite thickness (or depth) H, provided its optical thickness $\tau(0, H) \gg 1$.

The emissivity of such a semiinfinite homogeneous isothermal medium is given by

$$e(\theta_1; p) = \frac{T_B(\theta_1; p)}{T_g}$$

$$= 1 - \Gamma_1(\theta_1; p). \tag{4.129}$$

In accordance with Snell's law, the scattered temperature is given by

$$T_{SC}(\theta_1; p) = \Gamma_1(\theta_1; p) T_{DN}(\theta_1), \tag{4.130}$$

where $T_{DN}(\theta_1)$ is the downward-emitted atmospheric apparent temperature, given by (4.97).

In conclusion, the p-polarized apparent temperature of a homogeneous terrain medium bounded by a specular surface is given by (4.105), with the above results incorporated:

$$T_{AP}(\theta_1; H; p) = \frac{1}{L_a(\theta_1; H)} \left\{ [1 - \Gamma_1(\theta_1; p)] T_g + \Gamma_1(\theta_1; p) T_{DN}(\theta_1) \right\}$$

$$+ T_{UP}(\theta_1; H), \tag{4.131}$$

where H is the height above the terrain and θ_1 is the observation angle (Fig. 4.20). The atmospheric loss factor $L_a(\theta_1; H)$, downward atmospheric apparent temperature $T_{DN}(\theta_1)$, and upward atmospheric apparent temperature $T_{UP}(\theta_1; H)$ are given by (4.101), (4.97), and (4.95), respectively. $\Gamma_1(\theta_1; p)$ is given by

$$\Gamma_1(\theta_1; h) = \left| \frac{\mu_2 \cos\theta_1 - \sqrt{\mu_2 \varepsilon_2 - \sin^2\theta_1}}{\mu_2 \cos\theta_1 + \sqrt{\mu_2 \varepsilon_2 - \sin^2\theta_1}} \right|^2, \tag{4.132a}$$

$$\Gamma_1(\theta_1; v) = \left| \frac{\varepsilon_2 \cos\theta_1 - \sqrt{\mu_2 \varepsilon_2 - \sin^2\theta_1}}{\varepsilon_2 \cos\theta_1 + \sqrt{\mu_2 \varepsilon_2 - \sin^2\theta_1}} \right|^2, \tag{4.132b}$$

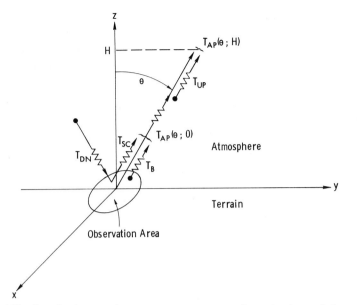

Fig. 4.20 Contributions to the apparent temperature of terrain observed through a plane-stratified atmosphere.

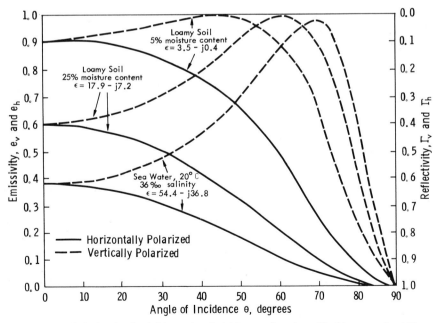

Fig. 4.21 Calculated reflectivities and emissivities as a function of incidence angle at 10 GHz. Calculation based on plane-surface model.

where ε_2 is the relative complex dielectric constant and μ_2 is the relative magnetic permeability of medium 2. For nonmagnetic materials, $\mu_2 = 1$. The angular variations of $\Gamma_1(\theta_1; h)$ and $\Gamma_1(\theta_1; v)$ are shown in Fig. 4.21 for several types of material media.

4-13 HOMOGENEOUS TERRAIN MEDIUM WITH NONUNIFORM TEMPERATURE PROFILE

If ε_2 and μ_2 are everywhere constant in medium 2, but $T(z)$ is not, then $T_{SC}(\theta_1; p)$ is again given by (4.130) and $T_B(\theta_1; p)$ is given by (4.125):

$$T_B(\theta_1; p) = [1 - \Gamma_1(\theta_1; p)] T_{AP}(\theta_2; 0^-; p),$$

but now

$$T_{AP}(\theta_2; z = 0^-; p) = T_{AP}(\theta_2; \zeta = 0^+; p)$$

$$= \sec \theta_2 \int_{0^+}^{\infty} \kappa_a T(\zeta') e^{-\kappa_a \zeta' \sec \theta_2} \, d\zeta'. \tag{4.133}$$

For a given temperature profile $T(\zeta')$, the above integral can be evaluated analytically or numerically. The resultant expression can then be used to replace T_g in (4.131).

4-14 TERRAIN MEDIUM WITH NONUNIFORM DIELECTRIC PROFILE

For a terrain medium characterized by

$$\left. \begin{array}{l} T(x, y, \zeta) = T_g, \\ \mu_r(x, y, \zeta) = 1, \\ \varepsilon_r(x, y, \zeta) = \varepsilon_r(\zeta), \end{array} \right\} \quad \zeta = -z > 0,$$

the apparent temperature $T_{AP}(\theta_1; H; p)$ is given again by (4.131) except that $\Gamma_1(\theta_1; p)$ should be replaced with $\Gamma_e(\theta_1; p)$, the effective reflectivity of the medium. The reflectivity $\Gamma_1(\theta_1; p)$ is defined for a semiinfinite homogeneous medium in which no reflections occur except at the surface boundary. By definition, $\Gamma_1(\theta_1; p)$ is the instantaneous power reflection coefficient at a boundary between two dissimilar media. If the permittivity profile $\varepsilon_r(\zeta)$ is not uniform with ζ, reflections occur whenever $\partial \varepsilon_r(\zeta)/\partial \zeta \neq 0$. The effective reflectivity $\Gamma_e(\theta_1; p)$ is a steady-state solution incorporating all the multiple reflections within the medium.

Two basic approaches have been adopted in the literature to compute $\Gamma_e(\theta_1; p)$; these are the *coherent approach*, which accounts for both the amplitudes and phases of the fields reflected within the medium, and the *incoherent approach*, which relies on amplitudes only. Each of these two approaches is discussed next.

4-14.1 Coherent Approach

A medium is considered horizontally homogeneous if its dielectric constant $\varepsilon_r(x, y, \zeta)$ is a function only of ζ, in which case no scattering occurs within a thin vertical layer of approximately constant dielectric. This condition is satisfied if the spatial wavelength describing the variations of ε_r in the xy-plane is much smaller than the electromagnetic wavelength in the medium, λ_g, which is related to the free-space wavelength λ_0 by the relation $\lambda_g = \lambda_0 / \sqrt{\varepsilon_r'}$. If this is not the case, we have volume scattering.

In the absence of volume scattering, the phase change associated with the field of a wave traveling between two points in the medium is accounted for by the phase shift due to propagation between the two points and the phase shifts associated with reflection and transmission due to the nonuniform dielectric vertical profile. This phase accountability mandates the use of field quantities to compute the effective field reflection coefficient $R_e(\theta_1; p)$ at the air-terrain boundary, and then squaring its magnitude to obtain the *coherent reflectivity* $\Gamma_c(\theta_1; p)$:

$$\Gamma_c(\theta_1; p) = |R_e(\theta_1; p)|^2. \tag{4.134}$$

The above approach is called a coherent approach because $R_e(\theta_1; p)$ accounts for both the amplitudes and phases of the reflections in the medium. For the case of a continuous dielectric profile $\varepsilon_r(\zeta)$, $R_e(\theta_1; p)$ is a solution of a differential equation known as the *Riccati equation* (Section 2-10), which, except for some simple profile shapes, has no closed-form solution.

Because of the coherent nature of the computation, approximating a continuous profile with discrete layers may lead to erroneous results, since it is not only the magnitude of the reflection coefficient at a boundary that is important, but the phase as well. The result of the computation becomes very dependent upon the choice of layer thicknesses.

If the terrain medium is indeed composed of uniform layers with distinct boundaries, $R_e(\theta_1; p)$ can be calculated using the procedure outlined in Section 2-9, or alternatively the equivalent transmission-line formulation (Moore, 1960) may be employed. To illustrate the latter with a simple example, consider the three-layer case shown in Figure 4.22(a). Layer 1 is air, layer 2 extends from $\zeta = 0$ to $\zeta = d$, and layer 3 extends from $\zeta = d$ to $\zeta = \infty$. The transmission line analog is shown in Fig. 4.22(b). Since layer 3 extends to infinity, it presents an impedance Z_3 at $\zeta = d$. Layer 2 is characterized by the impedance Z_2, and air by the impedance Z_1. The impedance of the transmission line looking into the medium at $\zeta = 0$ is obtained by transforming the impedance Z_3 through layer 2 to the input at $\zeta = 0$:

$$Z_{in} = Z_2 \left[\frac{1 + R_2 e^{-j2\gamma_2 d}}{1 - R_2 e^{-j2\gamma_2 d}} \right], \tag{4.135}$$

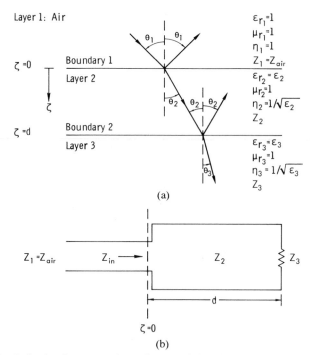

Fig. 4.22 Reflection from a terrain medium consisting of a layer of thickness d above a semiinfinite layer: (a) geometry of the three-layer problem; (b) transmission-line equivalent.

where

$$R_2 = (-1)^n \left(\frac{Z_3 - Z_2}{Z_3 + Z_2} \right); \quad n = \begin{cases} 0 \text{ for } h \text{ polarization,} \\ 1 \text{ for } v \text{ polarization,} \end{cases} \tag{4.136}$$

$$\gamma_2' = \gamma_2 \sec \theta_2, \tag{4.137}$$

$$j\gamma_2 = j\frac{2\pi}{\lambda_0}\sqrt{\varepsilon_2}. \tag{4.138}$$

Here R_2 is the reflection coefficient for a wave in medium 2 incident upon boundary 2; Z_1, Z_2, and Z_3 are as defined by (4.121); and λ_0 is the free-space wavelength. For a lossy medium, ε_2 is complex; therefore γ_2 is complex:

$$j\gamma_2 = j\beta_2 + \alpha_2, \tag{4.139}$$

where

$$\beta_2 = \frac{2\pi}{\lambda_0} \text{Re}\left[\sqrt{\varepsilon_2}\right], \tag{4.140a}$$

$$\alpha_2 = \frac{2\pi}{\lambda_0} \left| \text{Im}\left[\sqrt{\varepsilon_2}\right] \right|. \tag{4.140b}$$

Recalling the definition of the (power) loss factor L, we write for layer 2

$$L_2 = e^{\kappa_{a2} d \sec \theta_2}$$

$$= e^{2\alpha_2 d \sec \theta_2}, \tag{4.141}$$

where the (power) absorption coefficient $\kappa_{a2} = 2\alpha_2$. Rewriting (4.135) in terms of L_2 and $\beta_2' \,(\triangleq \beta_2 \sec \theta_2)$, we obtain

$$Z_{in} = Z_2 \left[\frac{1 + (R_2/L_2) e^{-j2\beta_2' d}}{1 - (R_2/L_2) e^{-j2\beta_2' d}} \right]. \tag{4.142}$$

Since the relative permeability is assumed unity for all media, the *relative* intrinsic impedances η_2 and η_3 are given in terms of only the *relative* complex dielectric constants ε_2 and ε_3:

$$\eta_2 = \frac{1}{\sqrt{\varepsilon_2}}, \qquad \eta_3 = \frac{1}{\sqrt{\varepsilon_3}}, \tag{4.143}$$

and for air, $\eta_1 = 1$.

To calculate Z_{in}, we need the angles θ_2 and θ_3. If the desired calculation is for reflection at the angle θ_1, at the air-medium interface (Fig. 4.22a), the angles θ_2 and θ_3 are found by applying Snell's law successively:

$$\sin \theta_3 = \sqrt{\frac{\varepsilon_2}{\varepsilon_3}} \sin \theta_2, \tag{4.144a}$$

$$\sin \theta_2 = \sqrt{\frac{1}{\varepsilon_2}} \sin \theta_1. \tag{4.144b}$$

Since the quantities of interest are $\cos \theta_2$ and $\cos \theta_3$, the above relations can be manipulated to yield

$$\cos \theta_2 = \sqrt{1 - \frac{1}{\varepsilon_2} \sin^2 \theta_1}, \tag{4.145a}$$

$$\cos \theta_3 = \sqrt{1 - \frac{1}{\varepsilon_3} \sin^2 \theta_1}. \tag{4.145b}$$

In the general case, ε_2 and ε_3 are complex quantities, and therefore the above relations lead to complex values for $\cos \theta_2$ and $\cos \theta_3$. For low-loss media such that $\varepsilon_2''/\varepsilon_2' \ll 1$ and $\varepsilon_3''/\varepsilon_3' \ll 1$, the imaginary parts of ε_2 and ε_3 may be neglected in the computation of θ_2 and θ_3. However, if these conditions are not satisfied, the real angles of transmission χ_1 and χ_2 should be found using the formulation given in Section 2-8.

After computing Z_{in}, $R_e(\theta_1; p)$ is obtained from

$$R_e(\theta_1; p) = (-1)^n \left(\frac{Z_{in} - Z_1}{Z_{in} + Z_1} \right); \quad n = \begin{cases} 0 \text{ for } p = h, \\ 1 \text{ for } p = v. \end{cases} \qquad (4.146)$$

Inserting (4.142) into (4.146) and simplifying leads to

$$R_e = \frac{R_1 + \dfrac{R_2}{L_2} e^{-j2\beta_2' d}}{1 + \dfrac{R_1 R_2 e^{-j2\beta_2' d}}{L_2}}, \qquad (4.147)$$

and the coherent reflectivity Γ_c is therefore given by

$$\begin{aligned}
\Gamma_c &= |R_e|^2 = R_e R_e^* \\
&= \left| \frac{\Gamma_1 + \dfrac{\Gamma_2}{L_2^2} + \dfrac{2\sqrt{\Gamma_1 \Gamma_2}}{L_2} \cos(2\beta_2' d + \phi_1 - \phi_2)}{1 + \dfrac{\Gamma_1 \Gamma_2}{L_2^2} + \dfrac{2\sqrt{\Gamma_1 \Gamma_2}}{L_2} \cos(2\beta_2' d + \phi_1 - \phi_2)} \right|,
\end{aligned} \qquad (4.148)$$

where $\Gamma_1 = |R_1|^2$, $\Gamma_2 = |R_2|^2$, and ϕ_1 and ϕ_2 are the phase angles of R_1 and R_2,

$$R_1 = |R_1| e^{j\phi_1}, \qquad (4.149a)$$

$$R_2 = |R_2| e^{j\phi_2}. \qquad (4.149b)$$

The presence of the cosine function in (4.148) causes Γ_c to oscillate as a function of d. If the loss factor L_2 is very large, Γ_c reduces to Γ_1, the reflectivity of boundary 1.

   Figure 4.23 shows the coherent reflectivity Γ_c at normal incidence ($\theta_1 = 0$) for a soil layer on top of a metal plate, plotted as a function of d, the depth of the soil layer. The calculation is for a free-space wavelength $\lambda_0 = 21$ cm and dry soil characterized by a relative dielectric constant $\varepsilon_2 = 4 - j0.3$. The metal plate, being a perfect conductor, with $\varepsilon_2 = 0 - j\infty$, has a reflection coefficient $R_2 = -1$. The oscillatory behavior is caused by the coherent addition of the multiple reflections at the soil-plate and the air-soil boundaries. The distance between successive maxima (or minima) is equal to $\lambda_2/2$, where λ_2 is the wavelength in medium 2 (soil) and is related to λ_0 by $\lambda_2 = \lambda_0/\sqrt{\varepsilon_1'}$. In this case, $\lambda_2 = 21/\sqrt{4} \simeq 10$ cm. As d is increased, the attenuation through the soil medium increases, thereby reducing the magnitude of the reflections from the metal plate relative to the reflection at the air-soil boundary. In the limit as d becomes very large, Γ_c approaches Γ_1, the air-soil reflectivity. The damped oscillatory behavior of Γ_c leads to a correspondingly similar behavior for

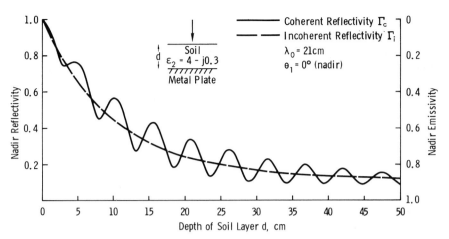

Fig. 4.23 The nadir reflectivity of a soil layer over a metal plate as a function of the layer thickness d. The oscillatory curve is the coherent reflectivity calculated according to (4.148), while the dashed curve is the incoherent reflectivity calculated according to (4.167).

$T_B = (1 - \Gamma_c)T_g$, which has been observed experimentally for sand over a metal plate (Blinn et al., 1972) and for oil films on water (Hollinger and Manella, 1973).

In addition to a plot of Γ_c, Fig. 4.23 shows a plot of the incoherent reflectivity Γ_i (discussed in the next section), which does not exhibit the oscillatory behavior of the coherent reflectivity, because it does not account for phase interference effects.

The formulation used in this section to compute Γ_c for the three-layer case may be extended to n layers by following the same procedure. The value thus obtained can then be used to replace Γ_1 in (4.131).

Nonuniform Temperature Profile

If the layers are not at the same physical temperature, a more elaborate procedure is required to compute the brightness-temperature term, since T_g is not a constant any more. For this case, the reader is referred to the paper by Wilheit (1978) which describes a procedure for computing the brightness temperature $T_B(\theta_1; p)$ of n layers in terms of their dielectric properties and physical temperatures. The next order of complexity is that of a flat surface between air and a terrain medium with continuous nonuniform temperature and dielectric profiles. Solutions are available in the papers by Stogryn (1970) and Njoku and Kong (1977).

4-14.2 Incoherent Approach (Nonuniform Temperature Profile)

The magnitude and phase of the reflection coefficient for a medium consisting of two layers is a function of the dielectric gradient across the boundary. In the examples considered above, the gradient was represented by a step function.

Except for some special cases such as an ice layer or an oil film over water, most terrain media are characterized by continuous dielectric profiles. Approximating a continuous profile with discrete layers leads to the oscillatory behavior caused by phase interference of the multiple reflections. Phase effects can be avoided by treating the reflections as an incoherent process, whereby all calculations are made on the basis of power rather than computing the field reflection coefficient R_e first and then squaring its magnitude to obtain Γ. The justification for the incoherent approach relies on the assumption that the medium consists of a large number of scatterers with dimensions comparable to the wavelength in the medium. These randomly distributed scatterers introduce a randomly distributed phase factor to the wave propagating between two points in the medium. Consequently, propagation becomes an incoherent process described solely by the power density of the wave.

To illustrate the mechanics of the incoherent approach for computing the brightness temperature $T_B(\theta_1; p)$ and the effective reflectivity $\Gamma_e(\theta_1; p)$, let us consider the three-layer case considered earlier. Use is made of the radiative transfer theory to compute the net emission into medium 1 (air). The brightness temperature $T_B(\theta_1; p)$ consists of two contributions:

$$T_B(\theta_1; p) = T_{B2}(\theta_1; p) + T_{B3}(\theta_1; p), \tag{4.150}$$

where T_{B2} and T_{B3} are the net apparent temperature contributions due to emission by layers 2 and 3, respectively. By *net* we mean that all multiple reflections at the two boundaries are incorporated.

Each of the two bottom layers is assumed to radiate isotropically. However, we are interested only in the radiation that is emitted into medium 1 at the angle θ_1. Hence, for the contribution from layer 2, the only radiation of interest is that incident upon boundary 1 at the angle θ_2 (Fig. 4.24), which

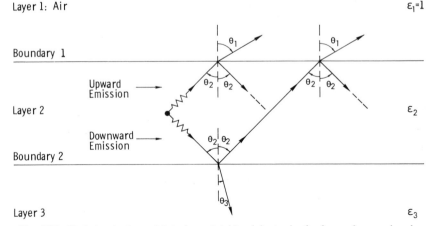

Fig. 4.24 Emission by layer 2 into layer 1 (air) originates in the form of upward and downward self-emission by layer 2.

consists of upward-emitted radiation as well as downward-emitted radiation that gets partially reflected by boundary 2 towards boundary 1. We shall designate the net contributions of these two components to T_{B2} by T_{2U} and T_{2D}:

$$T_{B2}(\theta_1; p) = T_{2U}(\theta_1; p) + T_{2D}(\theta_1; p). \tag{4.151}$$

Figure 4.25(a) and (b) illustrates the multiple reflections that the above components undergo.

Consider a thin horizontal stratum in layer 2 at depth ζ and of thickness $d\zeta$. The differential energy emitted by such a stratum in the direction θ_2 toward boundary 1 in Fig. 4.25(a) is represented by (see Section 4-9.2)

$$dT_{S2}(\theta_2; \zeta) = \sec \theta_2 \, \kappa_{a2} T_2 \, d\zeta, \tag{4.152}$$

where κ_{a2} and T_2 are the absorption coefficient and thermometric temperature of layer 2, both assumed constant within layer 2. At $\zeta = 0^+$ (just below boundary 1), the energy received due to emission by this stratum is

$$dT_{S2}(\theta_2; 0^+) = dT_{S2}(\theta_2; \zeta) e^{-\kappa_{e2}\zeta \sec \theta_2}$$

$$= \sec \theta_2 \, \kappa_{a2} T_2 e^{-\kappa_{e2}\zeta \sec \theta_2} \, d\zeta, \tag{4.153}$$

where the exponential term accounts for extinction between the stratum at depth ζ and boundary 1 along the path of length $\zeta \sec \theta_2$. Since both absorption and scattering are involved, the extinction coefficient κ_{e2} $(= \kappa_{a2} + \kappa_{s2})$ is used in (4.153). In the general case, if scattering exists in the medium, it influences the extinction of energy propagating between two points (as in (4.153)) as well as adding a second term to (4.152) due to diffuse scatter. This general case is treated in Chapter 13. Here, we shall assume that the single-scattering albedo $a_2 = \kappa_{s2}/\kappa_{e2}$ is sufficiently small that diffuse scatter may be ignored. The brightness-temperature expression obtained on the basis of the above assumption often is referred to as the *direct term* (England, 1975), and it is used as the source function for computing the *diffuse term*.

The total energy received at $\zeta = 0^+$ due to emission by all strata in layer 2 is given by

$$T_{S2}(\theta_2; 0^+) = \int_0^d dT_{S2}(\theta_2; 0^+). \tag{4.154}$$

Inserting (4.153) inside the above integral and integrating leads to

$$T_{S2}(\theta_2; 0^+) = (1 - a_2) T_2 \left[1 - \frac{1}{L_2} \right], \tag{4.155}$$

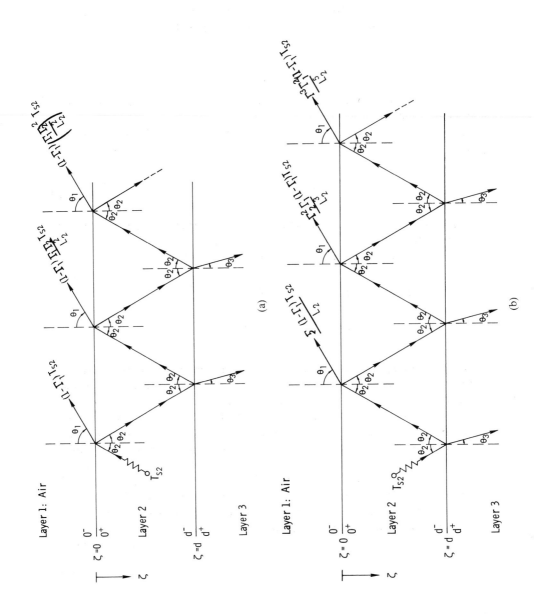

(a)

(b)

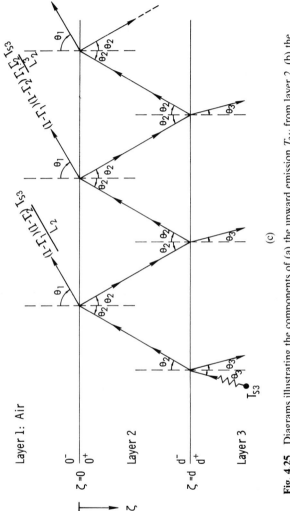

(c)

Fig. 4.25 Diagrams illustrating the components of (a) the upward emission T_{2U} from layer 2, (b) the downward emission T_{2D} from layer 2 and (c) the upward emission T_{B3} from layer 3.

where

$$a_2 = \kappa_{s2}/\kappa_{e2}, \tag{4.156}$$

$$L_2 = e^{\kappa_{e2}d \sec \theta_2}. \tag{4.157}$$

At boundary 1, a fraction of T_{S2} is transmitted across the boundary and the remainder is reflected. The transmitted portion is $(1-\Gamma_1)T_{S2}$, and the reflected portion is $\Gamma_1 T_{S2}$. The reflected part suffers a loss L_2 as it travels to boundary 2 and gets partly reflected towards boundary 1 and partly transmitted into layer 3. With the understanding that $\Gamma_1 = \Gamma_1(\theta_1; p)$ and $\Gamma_2 = \Gamma_2(\theta_2; p)$, the sum of all the components transmitted into layer 1 is

$$T_{2U} = (1-\Gamma_1)T_{S2} + (1-\Gamma_1)\frac{\Gamma_1\Gamma_2}{L_2^2}T_{S2} + (1-\Gamma_1)\left(\frac{\Gamma_1\Gamma_2}{L_2^2}\right)^2 T_{S2} + \cdots$$

$$= (1-\Gamma_1)T_{S2}[1 + x + x^2 + x^3 + \cdots], \tag{4.158}$$

where

$$x = \frac{\Gamma_1\Gamma_2}{L_2^2}.$$

The series inside the square brackets is the binomial series of the function

$$(1-x)^{-1} = 1 + x + x^2 + x^3 + \cdots \qquad \text{for} \quad x^2 < 1.$$

Since $\Gamma_1 \leqslant 1$, $\Gamma_2 \leqslant 1$, and $L_2 \leqslant 1$, we have $x^2 < 1$ unless layer 2 is a lossless dielectric bounded by perfectly reflecting surfaces, in which case no emission reaches Layer 1. The above form of the binomial series leads to

$$T_{2U} = \frac{(1-\Gamma_1)T_{S2}}{1 - \Gamma_1\Gamma_2/L_2^2}. \tag{4.159}$$

Since layer 2 radiates isotropically, its downwelling self-emitted radiation at $\zeta = d^-$ (just above boundary 2) in the direction θ_2 also is given by T_{S2}, as defined by (4.155). Following its multiple reflections between boundaries 1 and 2, its net contribution to the energy transmitted into Layer 1 is

$$T_{2D} = \frac{\Gamma_2(1-\Gamma_1)T_{S2}}{L_2} + \frac{\Gamma_2^2\Gamma_1(1-\Gamma_1)T_{S2}}{L_2^3} + \frac{\Gamma_2^3\Gamma_1^2(1-\Gamma_1)T_{S2}}{L_2^5} + \cdots$$

$$= \frac{\Gamma_2(1-\Gamma_1)T_{S2}}{L_2}[1 + x + x^2 + x^3 + \cdots], \tag{4.160}$$

which leads to the closed form

$$T_{2D} = \frac{\Gamma_2(1-\Gamma_1)T_{S2}}{L_2(1-\Gamma_1\Gamma_2/L_2^2)}.$$

Adding (4.159) and (4.160), we obtain

$$T_{B2} = \frac{\left(1+\dfrac{\Gamma_2}{L_2}\right)(1-\Gamma_1)T_{S2}}{1-\dfrac{\Gamma_1\Gamma_2}{L_2^2}}. \tag{4.161}$$

The contribution of layer 3, T_{B3}, can be computed in a manner similar to T_{B2}. Since layer 3 is semiinfinite in depth, its upwelling self-emission temperature at $\zeta = d^+$ (just below boundary 2) is equal to its thermometric temperature T_3:

$$T_{S3} = T_3.$$

The sum of its components that are transmitted into Layer 1 (Fig. 4.25(c)) is given by:

$$T_{B3} = \frac{(1-\Gamma_1)(1-\Gamma_2)T_3}{L_2(1-\Gamma_1\Gamma_2/L_2^2)} \tag{4.162}$$

Inserting (4.161) and (4.162) into (4.150), we have

$$T_B(\theta_1; p) = \frac{1-\Gamma_1}{1-\Gamma_1\Gamma_2/L_2^2}$$

$$\times \left[\left(1+\frac{\Gamma_2}{L_2}\right)\left(1-\frac{1}{L_2}\right)(1-a)T_2 + \frac{1-\Gamma_2}{L_2}T_3\right]. \tag{4.163}$$

The above expression gives the brightness temperature T_B at a point above the boundary between air (layer 1) and a medium consisting of two layers with thermometric temperatures T_2 and T_3. Layer 3 is assumed semiinfinite in depth, and layer 2 is of thickness d and characterized by an extinction coefficient κ_{e2} and a small single-scattering albedo, $a < 0.1$. The dependence of T_B on the observation angle θ_1 and the polarization configuration p is embedded in the expressions for Γ_1, Γ_2, and L_2. The factor $1-\Gamma_1\Gamma_2 L_2^{-2}$ in (4.163) accounts for the multiple reflections at boundaries 1 and 2.

In the above derivation of $T_B(\theta_1; p)$, the temperatures of layers 2 and 3 were intentionally chosen to be different, to illustrate how the procedure may be extended to n layers with different dielectric properties, thicknesses, and physical temperatures. Details of such a procedure are available in a paper by

Burke et al. (1979) for $a=0$, where second- and higher-order reflection terms are neglected to simplify the computation.

Incoherent Reflectivity

The radiometric scattered temperature is given by

$$T_{SC}(\theta_1; p) = \Gamma_i(\theta_1; p)T_{DN}(\theta_1), \tag{4.164}$$

where $\Gamma_i(\theta_1; p)$, called the *incoherent reflectivity*, is the reflectivity of the medium derived on the basis of the incoherent-phase assumption. The incoherent reflectivity may be obtained by noting that for the isothermal case, $T_2 = T_3 \triangleq T_g$, the brightness temperature T_B has to be given by

$$T_B(\theta_1; p) = [1 - \Gamma_i(\theta_1; p)]T_g \tag{4.165}$$

in order to satisfy the condition of energy conservation, which previously led to a similar expression, (4.128), for the semiinfinite homogeneous layer case. Upon setting $T_2 = T_3 = T_g$ in (4.163) and equating it to (4.165), we obtain

$$\Gamma_i(\theta_1; p) = 1 - \frac{1 - \Gamma_1}{1 - \Gamma_1\Gamma_2/L_2^2}\left[\left(1 + \frac{\Gamma_2}{L_2}\right)\left(1 - \frac{1}{L_2}\right)(1-a) + \frac{1 - \Gamma_2}{L_2}\right]$$

$$\triangleq 1 - e_i(\theta_1; p), \tag{4.166}$$

where $e_i(\theta_1; p)$ is defined as the *incoherent emissivity*. If $a \ll 1$, the above expression reduces to

$$\Gamma_i(\theta_1; p) = \frac{\Gamma_1 + \dfrac{\Gamma_2}{L_2^2}(1 - 2\Gamma_1)}{1 - \dfrac{\Gamma_1\Gamma_2}{L_2^2}}. \tag{4.167}$$

A plot of Γ_i at nadir ($\theta_1 = 0$) is compared in Fig. 4.23 with the coherent reflectivity Γ_c for a sand layer above a metal plate. If the loss factor of layer 2 is large, the above expression reduces to

$$\Gamma_i = \Gamma_1, \qquad L_2 \gg 1,$$

in which case the emission of layer 3 is masked completely by the loss in layer 2.

Apparent Temperature

The apparent temperature at a height H above the ground is then given by

$$T_{AP}(\theta_1; H; p) = \frac{1}{L_a(\theta_1; H)} \left[T_B(\theta_1; p) + \Gamma_i(\theta_1; p) T_{DN}(\theta_1) \right]$$
$$+ T_{UP}(\theta_1; H), \tag{4.168}$$

where T_B is given by (4.163) and Γ_i is given by (4.166).

4-15 EMISSIVITY OF A DIELECTRIC SLAB

Consider the case of a lossy dielectric slab of thickness d as shown in Fig. 4.26. This is a special case of the three-layer problem treated earlier in that layers 1 and 3 are both air. In practice, such a dielectric may represent a radome placed in front of a radiometer antenna. The radome modifies the incoming radiation by its *effective transmissivity* Υ_e and emits radiation of its own into the antenna. If the radome material is approximately lossless, the emitted radiation will be negligible, and if the thickness is chosen properly, as shown below, Υ_e can be made approximately unity.

To examine quantitatively the interaction of radiation with a dielectric slab, we shall derive expressions for the *effective reflectivity* Γ_e, the *effective transmissivity* Υ_e and the *effective absorptivity* α_e, where the adjective "effective" refers to the steady-state solution incorporating all multiple reflections within the slab. If P_i is the power incident upon boundary 1 (Figure 4.26), the steady-state reflected and transmitted powers are

$$P_r = \Gamma_e P_i, \tag{4.169a}$$
$$P_t = \Upsilon_e P_i, \tag{4.169b}$$

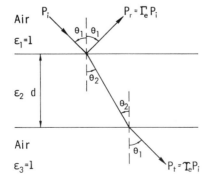

Fig. 4.26 Reflection from and transmission through a dielectric slab of thickness d. The quantities Γ_e and Υ_e are the effective reflectivity and transmissivity incorporating all multiple reflections within the dielectric slab.

and therefore the absorbed power P_a is

$$P_a = P_i - P_r - P_t$$
$$= P_i - \Gamma_e P_i - \Upsilon_e P_i. \tag{4.170}$$

Normalizing the above expression to P_i and defining the effective absorptivity a_e as

$$a_e = \frac{P_a}{P_i}, \tag{4.171}$$

we obtain

$$1 = a_e + \Gamma_e + \Upsilon_e. \tag{4.172}$$

If the material is to remain in thermodynamic equilibrium, its effective emissivity e_e should be equal to a_e. Hence,

$$1 = e_e + \Gamma_e + \Upsilon_e, \tag{4.173}$$

which is a statement of energy conservation. For an opaque material $\Upsilon_e = 0$, in which case (4.173) reduces to

$$1 = e_e + \Gamma_e, \qquad \text{opaque}; \tag{4.174}$$

and for a lossless material $a_e = e_e = 0$, so

$$1 = \Gamma_e + \Upsilon_e, \qquad \text{lossless}. \tag{4.175}$$

If the medium has nonreflective boundaries, as a cloud or the atmosphere, then $\Gamma_e = 0$, and therefore

$$1 = e_e + \Upsilon_e, \qquad \text{nonreflective}. \tag{4.176}$$

The parameters Γ_e, Υ_e, and e_e may be computed using the coherent or the incoherent approaches discussed earlier. The coherent approach is applicable to homogeneous dielectric media such as radome materials, while the incoherent approach is applicable to media with some degree of inhomogeneity at a scale comparable to the wavelength in the medium, thereby causing the phases of the propagating fields to become random in nature.

4-15.1 Coherent Approach

The effective coherent reflectivity Γ_c of the dielectric slab can be computed from the results obtained previously for the three-layer problem of Fig. 4.22 by setting $\varepsilon_3 = 1$, which leads to $|R_2| = |R_1|$ and $\phi_2 = \phi_1 + \pi$. Equation (4.148) becomes

$$\Gamma_c = \Gamma_1 \left[\frac{\left(1 + \dfrac{1}{L_2^2}\right) - \dfrac{2}{L_2}\cos(2\beta_2' d)}{\left(1 + \dfrac{\Gamma_1^2}{L_2^2}\right) - \dfrac{2\Gamma_1}{L_2}\cos(2\beta_2' d)} \right] \qquad (4.177)$$

The coherent transmissivity Υ_c can be shown to have the expression

$$\Upsilon_c = \frac{(1-\Gamma_1)^2}{L_2} \frac{1}{\left(1 + \dfrac{\Gamma_1^2}{L_2^2}\right) - \dfrac{2\Gamma_1}{L_2}\cos(2\beta_2' d)}. \qquad (4.178)$$

With Γ_c and Υ_c known, use of (4.173) leads to

$$e_c = \frac{(1-\Gamma_1)\left(1 - \dfrac{\Gamma_1}{L_2^2}\right) - \dfrac{1}{L_2}(1-\Gamma_1)^2}{\left(1 + \dfrac{\Gamma_1^2}{L_2^2}\right) - \dfrac{2\Gamma_1}{L_2}\cos(2\beta_2' d)}. \qquad (4.179)$$

For a lossless medium, $L_2 = 1$, which leads to $e_c = 0$. If in addition, the slab (or radome) thickness d is chosen so that the argument of the cosine factor in (4.178) and (4.179) is equal to $2n\pi$ where n is an integer, the expressions reduce to $\Gamma_c = 0$ and $\Upsilon_c = 1$.

4-15.2 Incoherent Approach

Following the same procedure used earlier in connection with the three-layer problem of Figs. 4.24 and 4.25, the incoherent reflectivity and transmissivity for $a \simeq 0$ can be shown to be given by

$$\Gamma_i = \Gamma_1 \left\{ 1 + \left[\left(\frac{(1-\Gamma_1)^2}{L_2^2}\right) \Big/ \left(1 - \frac{\Gamma_1^2}{L_2^2}\right) \right] \right\} \qquad (4.180)$$

and

$$\Upsilon_i = \left(\frac{(1-\Gamma_1)^2}{L_2} \right) \Big/ \left(1 - \frac{\Gamma_1^2}{L_2^2}\right). \qquad (4.181)$$

Using (4.173), we obtain the incoherent emissivity

$$e_i = \left(1 - \frac{1}{L_2}\right)(1-\Gamma_1)\left(1 + \frac{\Gamma_1}{L_2}\right) \Big/ \left(1 - \frac{\Gamma_1^2}{L_2^2}\right). \qquad (4.182)$$

Alternatively, the above expression could have been obtained from (4.163) after setting $T_3 = 0$, $a = 0$, and $\Gamma_1 = \Gamma_2$ and defining $e_i = T_B / T_2$.

For a lossless medium ($L_2 = 1$),

$$
\left.
\begin{aligned}
\Gamma_i &= \frac{2\Gamma_1}{1+\Gamma_1}, \\[4pt]
\Upsilon_i &= \frac{1-\Gamma_1}{1+\Gamma_1}, \\[4pt]
e_i &= 0
\end{aligned}
\right\}
\qquad \text{for} \quad L_2 = 1.
\tag{4.183}
$$

4-16 EMISSIVITY OF A ROUGH SURFACE

A plane wave incident upon a perfectly flat surface of a homogeneous medium is specularly reflected as shown in Fig. 4.27(a), and the reflected power is given by

$$
P_r(\theta_1; p) = \Gamma(\theta_1; p) P_i(\theta_1; p)
\tag{4.184}
$$

where P_i is the incident power, Γ is the specular reflectivity given by (4.120), and p denotes the polarization state ($p = v$ or h). Now let us consider the surface shown in Fig. 4.27(b). Superimposed on the flat surface are small

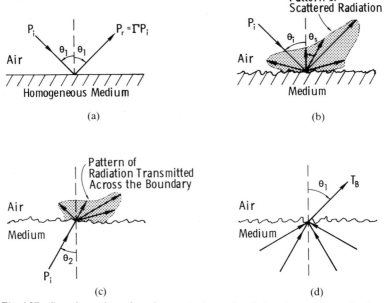

Fig. 4.27 Specular and rough surface scattering and emission: (a) specular reflection; (b) diffuse scattering; (c) Diffuse emission; (d) $T_B(\theta_1)$ is composed of contributions incident from below, along many directions.

height irregularities. If these are of the order of the wavelength λ or larger, the incident power will be scattered by the surface in many directions. Part of the scattered power will be in the specular direction and will retain the phase-coherence characteristic of reflection off a plane surface, and the remainder, known as the diffuse component, is phase-incoherent. Moreover, part of the diffuse scattering will bear the same polarization state as the incident power, and the remainder will be polarized in the orthogonal state. In like manner, the self-emitted radiation incident upon the surface from the underlying medium (Fig. 4.27(c)) is transmitted across the boundary into many different directions. Consequently, the brightness temperature $T_B(\theta_1; p)$ of the medium is composed of contributions that are incident upon the surface from below along many different directions (Fig. 4.27(d)).

For the specular surface, it was shown that, on the basis of Kirchhoff's energy conservation law, the specular emissivity e can be expressed in terms of the specular reflectivity Γ through

$$e(\theta_1; p) = 1 - \Gamma(\theta_1; p). \tag{4.185}$$

For the rough surface, the more general expressions given below are needed.

4-16.1 General Expressions

Scattering by a rough surface is characterized by the bistatic scattering cross-section per unit area $\sigma°(\theta_0, \phi_0; \theta_s, \phi_s; p_0, p_s)$ which relates the magnitude of the power scattered in the direction (θ_s, ϕ_s) with polarization p_s to the power incident upon the surface from the direction (θ_0, ϕ_0) with polarization p_0 (Fig. 4.28). $\sigma°$ is known also as the surface scattering coefficient. If p_0 and p_s are both v or h, $\sigma°$ is called the vertically polarized or horizontally polarized

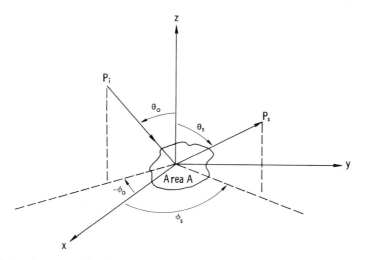

Fig. 4.28   Geometry of incident and scattered radiation.

scattering coefficient, respectively, and if p_0 and p_s are different, it is known as the cross-polarized scattering coefficient ($\sigma°(h, v) = \sigma°(v, h)$). Scattering by rough surfaces is discussed in detail in Chapter 11.

Applying Kirchhoff's radiation law to the rough-surface case, Peake (1959) developed expressions for the polarized emissivity $e(\theta_0, \phi_0; p_0)$ of a surface observed from the direction (θ_0, ϕ_0) and for the scattered temperature $T_{SC}(\theta_0, \phi_0; p_0)$ in terms of $\sigma°$:

$$e(\theta_0, \phi_0; p_0) = 1 - \frac{1}{4\pi \cos\theta_0} \int \left[\sigma°(\theta_0, \phi_0; \theta_s, \phi_s; p_0, p_0) \right.$$
$$\left. + \sigma°(\theta_0, \phi_0; \theta_s, \phi_s; p_0, p_s) \right] d\Omega_s \qquad (4.186)$$

and

$$T_{SC}(\theta_0, \phi_0; p_0) = \frac{1}{4\pi \cos\theta_0} \int \left[\sigma°(\theta_0, \phi_0; \theta_s, \phi_s; p_0, p_0) \right.$$
$$\left. + \sigma°(\theta_0, \phi_0; \theta_s, \phi_s; p_0, p_s) \right] T_{DN}(\theta_s, \phi_s) \, d\Omega_s, \quad (4.187)$$

where the integration is carried over the upper half space. When the polarization index p_0 stands for v (vertical), then p_s stands for h (horizontal), and vice versa.

4-16.2 Simple Models

Specular Surface

Scattering from a perfectly flat surface consists of only the specularly reflected, coherent part. Thus, the cross-polarized scattering coefficient $\sigma°(h, v)$ is zero, and the like-polarized scattering coefficient is given by delta functions:

$$\sigma°(\theta_0, \phi_0; \theta_s, \phi_s; p_0, p_0) = 4\pi\Gamma(\theta_0; p_0) \frac{\cos\theta_0}{\sin\theta_{sp}} \delta(\theta_s - \theta_{sp}) \delta(\phi_s - \phi_{sp}),$$

$$(4.188)$$

where (θ_{sp}, ϕ_{sp}) is the specular direction. That is,

$$\theta_{sp} = \theta_0, \qquad (4.189a)$$
$$\phi_{sp} = \pi - \phi_0. \qquad (4.189b)$$

Introducing (4.188) into (4.186) and (4.187) leads to

$$e(\theta_0, \phi_0; p_0) = 1 - \Gamma(\theta_0; p_0) \qquad (4.190a)$$

and

$$T_{SC}(\theta_0, \phi_0; p_0) = \Gamma(\theta_0; p_0) T_{DN}(\theta_0). \qquad (4.190b)$$

Perfectly Rough Surface

The other extreme from a specular surface is the perfectly rough surface, known as the *Lambertian* surface after Lambert's law, which states that the angular variation of $\sigma°$ is solely dependent on the product $\cos\theta_0\cos\theta_s$;

$$\sigma°(\theta_0, \phi_0; \theta_s, \phi_s; p_0, p_0) + \sigma°(\theta_0, \phi_0; \theta_s, \phi_s; p_0, p_s)$$

$$= \sigma_0°\cos\theta_0\cos\theta_s,$$

$$(4.191)$$

where $\sigma_0°$ is a constant related to the dielectric properties of the scattering surface. The corresponding emissivity is

$$e(\theta_0, \phi_0; p) = 1 - \frac{1}{4\pi\cos\theta_0}\int_{\phi_s=0}^{2\pi}\int_{\theta_s=0}^{\pi/2}\sigma_0°\cos\theta_0\cos\theta_s\sin\theta_s\,d\theta_s\,d\phi_s$$

$$= 1 - \frac{\sigma_0°}{4}, \qquad\qquad (4.192)$$

which is polarization- and angle-independent.

For the cases in between the perfectly smooth and perfectly rough surfaces, the scattering coefficient, and hence the emissivity, is related to the dielectric and geometrical properties of the surface. These cases are treated in Chapters 11-12.

PROBLEMS

4.1. Solar emission is characterized by a blackbody temperature of 5800 K. Of the total brightness radiated by such a body, what percentage is radiated over the frequency band between $f_m/2$ and $2f_m$, where f_m is the frequency at which the spectral brightness B_f is maximum?

4.2. Verify Eq. (4.40a).

4.3. From the earth, the (planar) angle subtended by the sun is 0.5°. A 1-cm-wavelength radio-telescope antenna pointed at the sun measured an antenna temperature of 1174 K. The antenna effective area is 0.4 m², its physical temperature is 300 K, and its radiation efficiency is 0.8.

(a) What is the apparent temperature of the sun?

(b) What would the percentage error in the measured value of the solar apparent temperature be had the antenna been assumed lossless?

(c) Using the answer obtained in (a), calculate the antenna temperature that a 3-m² lossless antenna would measure.

4.4. A radiometer is used to observe terrain surfaces with apparent temperatures in the range between 100 and 300 K. The antenna radiation efficiency is 0.9, and its physical temperature T_0 is always measured. The side-lobe apparent temperature $\overline{T}_{SL}$ is unknown but has been calculated to be somewhere between 100 and 200 K. Corresponding to this uncertainty in $\bar{T}_{SL}$, what should the minimum value of the main-beam efficiency be in order that the percentage error in the estimated value of the terrain apparent temperature be less than 3 percent?

4.5. Consider a downward-looking, nadir-pointing radiometer observing the ocean surface from an airborne platform above a 2-km-thick cloud with a water content of 1.5 gm^{-3}. The absorption coefficient of a water cloud is given by the approximate expression

$$\kappa_a \simeq 2.4 \times 10^{-4} f^{1.95} m_v \ Np\,km^{-1},$$

where f is in GHz and m_v and the water content in gm^{-3}. Assuming that the ocean has an apparent temperature $T_{AP}(0;0) = 150$ K, calculate and plot the apparent temperature observed by the radiometer as a function of frequency between 1 and 30 GHz. The cloud may be assumed to have a physical temperature of 275 K.

4.6. Repeat Problem 5 for $\theta = 60°$ and $T_{AP}(60°;0) = 100$ K.

4.7. A water cloud with a 2-km vertical thickness is characterized by a thermometric temperature profile of the form

$$T(z) = 300(1 - 4 \times 10^{-2}z)$$

where z is the height in km above the base of the cloud. Calculate T_{UP} and T_{DN} for $\theta = 60°$ and

(a) $\kappa_a = 10^{-4} \ Np\,km^{-1}$
(b) $\kappa_a = 10^{-3} \ Np\,km^{-1}$
(c) $\kappa_a = 10^{-2} \ Np\,km^{-1}$.

Are T_{UP} and T_{DN} the same? If not, why not?

4.8. What should the optical thickness of a constant-temperature cloud be in order for its apparent temperature to be within 1 percent of its thermometric temperature? Assume $\theta = 0°$.

4.9. Water vapor has an absorption maximum at 22 GHz. An approximate expression for the absorption coefficient of atmospheric water vapor at 22 GHz is

$$\kappa_a \simeq 6 \times 10^{-3} \rho_v \left(\frac{300}{T} \right)^2 \ Np\,km^{-1},$$

where ρ_v is the water-vapor density in gm^{-3}, and T is the temperature in kelvins. A commonly used standard atmosphere defines the vertical profiles of ρ_v and T as follows:

$$\rho_v = \rho_0 e^{-0.5z},$$
$$T = T_0 - 6.5z,$$

where z is the altitude in km, and ρ_0 and T_0 are sea-level values. Assuming the bulk of the earth's atmosphere to consist of the lowermost 10 km, calculate T_{DN} and T_{UP} for $\theta = 0°$, $\rho_0 = 7.5 \text{ gm}^{-3}$, and $T_0 = 300$ K.

4.10. One of the sensors flown aboard Skylab was a nadir-looking, 21-cm-wavelength radiometer. The radiometer antenna had approximately a Gaussian radiation pattern given by

$$F_n(\theta_a) = \exp\left[-2.77(\theta_a/\beta)^2\right],$$

where β, the half-power beamwidth, is 15°. The ground track of one of Skylab's passes was a line perpendicular to the South Carolina coastline, as shown in Fig. 4.29. Assuming T_{AP} to be 250 K for land and 90 K for the Atlantic Ocean, plot the observed antenna temperature as a function of time between 27.5 and 29.5 minutes. You may assume that (1) the antenna is lossless, (2) the atmosphere is lossless, (3) side-lobe contributions are negligible, and (4) T_{AP} is angle-of-incidence independent for both land and ocean. Skylab's orbit was at an altitude of 435 km above sea level and its ground velocity was 7.65 kms^{-1}. *Hint*: Assume the radiation pattern to consist of one main lobe 30° wide, and no side lobes. Also, for small angles, use the approximations $\sin \theta \simeq \theta$ and $\cos \theta \simeq 1$.

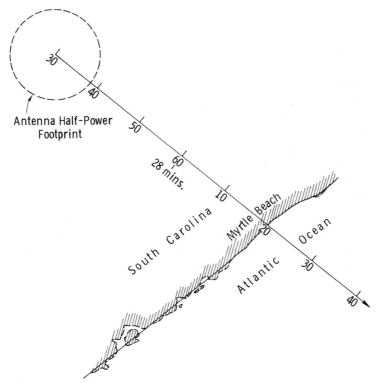

Fig. 4.29 Problem 4.10: Skylab ground track over Carolina coastline.

4.11. A soil medium characterized by a relative dielectric constant

$$\varepsilon_s = 8 - j1$$

is covered by a dry snow layer d cm thick. If the relative dielectric constant of dry snow is

$$\varepsilon_{ds} = 2 - j2 \times 10^{-3},$$

calculate and plot the nadir coherent reflectivity Γ_c as a function of d (in 1-cm increments between $d=0$ and $d=100$ cm) at:

(a) $f = 1$ GHz,
(b) $f = 30$ GHz.

4.12. Repeat Problem 4.11 for wet snow with a relative dielectric constant

$$\varepsilon_{ws} = 2.2 - j0.1.$$

4.13. Repeat Problem 4.11 for the incoherent reflectivity Γ_i.
4.14. Repeat Problem 4.12 for the incoherent reflectivity Γ_i.
4.15. A 10-cm-thick dielectric slab has a relative dielectric constant

$$\varepsilon = 2 - j0.02.$$

Calculate and plot the coherent transmissivity for normal incidence as a function of frequency over the range between 1 and 20 GHz.

4.16. Consider a vegetation canopy over a soil medium. The canopy is modeled as a dielectric layer with an extinction coefficient κ_e and an albedo a. The nonhomogeneous nature of the plants' geometry supports the following two assumptions: (1) the incoherent model for computing the brightness temperature is applicable, and (2) a "diffuse" type of boundary (no discontinuity) exists between the air and the vegetation layer, which means that the reflectivity at the air-canopy boundary may be assumed equal to zero.

(a) Using the above assumptions, derive an expression for the brightness temperature of a canopy of height d above a semiinfinite homogeneous soil medium. The thermometric temperatures of the canopy and soil are T_c and T_s, respectively.
(b) Show that for $T_c = T_s = T_0$ and $a \ll 1$,

$$T_B = \left(1 - \frac{\Gamma_2}{L_2^2}\right) T_0,$$

where Γ_2 is the reflectivity of the canopy-soil boundary and L_2 is the canopy loss factor.

References

Blinn, J. C., III, J. E. Conel, and J. G. Quade (1972), Microwave Emission from Geological Materials: Observations of Interference Effects, *J. Geophys. Res.*, 77, pp. 4366–4378.

Burke, W. J., T. Schmugge, and J. F. Paris (1979), Comparison of 2.8- and 21-cm Microwave Radiometer Observations over Soils with Emission Model Calculations, *J. Geophys. Res.*, 84, C1, pp. 287–294.

Chandrasekhar, S. (1960), *Radiative Transfer*, Dover Publications, Inc., New York.

England, A. W. (1975), Thermal Microwave Emission from a Scattering Layer, *J. Geophys. Res.*, 80, pp. 4484–4496.

Hollinger, J. P., and R. A. Manella (1973), Oil Spills: Measurements of Their Distributions and Volumes by Multifrequency Microwave Radiometry, *Science*, 181, pp. 54–56.

Kraus, J. D. (1966), *Radio Astronomy*, McGraw-Hill, New York, Chapter 3.

Moore, R. K. (1960), *Traveling-Wave Engineering*, McGraw-Hill, New York.

Njoku, E. G., and J. A. Kong (1977), Theory for Passive Microwave Sensing of Near-Surface Soil Moisture, *J. Geophys. Res.*, 82, pp. 3108–3118.

Peake, W. H. (1959), Interaction of Electromagnetic Waves with Some Natural Surfaces, *IRE Trans.*, AP-7, p. 5342.

Stogryn, A. (1970), Brightness Temperature of a Vertically Structured Medium, *Radio Science*, 5, pp. 1397–1406.

Wilheit, T. T. (1978), Radiative Transfer in a Plane Stratified Dielectric, *IEEE Trans. Geosci. Elec.*, GE-16, pp. 138–143.

Microwave Interaction with Atmospheric Constituents

5-1 INTRODUCTION

The earth's atmosphere plays an important role in microwave remote sensing. Through an understanding of the scattering, absorption, and emission behavior of atmospheric constituents, microwave remote-sensing techniques can be employed to monitor atmospheric parameters and weather conditions. Such an understanding also will provide the means to factor out the influence of the atmosphere on observations of land and ocean surfaces. The microwave spectrum offers a wide range of transmission conditions. In the 1–15-GHz region, the atmosphere is practically transparent even in the presence of clouds and moderate rainfall rates, which makes this band especially attractive for terrain and ocean observations from satellite platforms. Absorption (and therefore emission) resonances due to water vapor (at 22.2 and 183.3 GHz) and oxygen (in the 50–70-GHz region and at 118.7 GHz) can be used to determine the height profiles of atmospheric water vapor and temperature through radiometric measurements at and near the absorption maxima. Between the absorption maxima, a number of low-attenuation "atmospheric windows" exist that are suitable for terrain observations, most notably the 35-GHz window. Cloud heights and water content can be measured by radar through the relation between reflectivity and cloud water content. Similarly, rainfall rate is related to radar reflectivity and to radiometric emission. The spectral behavior of microwave interaction with atmospheric constituents is the subject of this chapter.

Following a section on the physical properties of the atmosphere and on models for the vertical profiles of air density, pressure, temperature, and water-vapor density, the material in this chapter is divided into two major groups of sections. The first group treats the absorption (and emission) characteristics of atmospheric gases, while the second group relates to absorption and scattering by clouds, fog, rain, and snow.

Fawwaz T. Ulaby, Richard K. Moore, and Adrian K. Fung,
Microwave Remote Sensing: Active and Passive,
Vol. I: Microwave Remote Sensing Fundamentals and Radiometry   ISBN 0-201-10759-7

5-2 PHYSICAL PROPERTIES OF THE ATMOSPHERE

The atmospheric pressure and density decrease approximately exponentially with increasing height, as does the water-vapor density, although its variation with height is somewhat irregular and is strongly dependent on time of day, season, geographic location, and atmospheric activity. The variation of atmospheric temperature with height exhibits a cyclic pattern, which can be used to

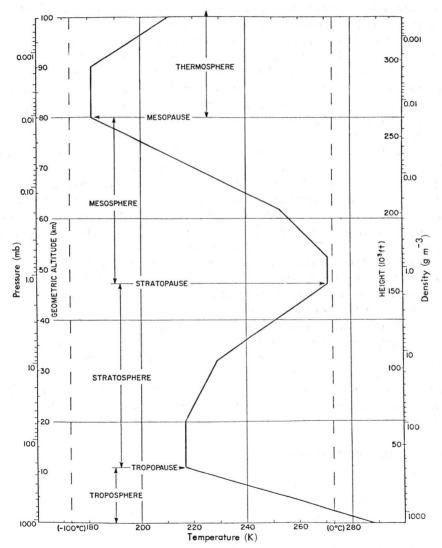

Fig. 5.1 Temperature-height profile to 100 km of U.S. Standard Atmosphere, 1962. The names shown for atmospheric shells and boundaries are those adopted by the World Meteorological Organization (Cole et al., 1965).

subdivide the earth's atmosphere into a number of atmospheric layers according to their thermal structure. As a guide, use will be made of the 1962 U. S. Standard Atmosphere (Cole et al., 1965), which describes the variation with height of atmospheric parameters of a "standard" or "reference" atmosphere (Fig. 5.1). In addition to the general model, specific supplements have also been defined for specific latitudes.

The boundaries of each atmospheric layer or shell are defined usually by the change in sign of the temperature gradient with height, dT/dz, where T is the atmospheric temperature and z is the geometrical height. If dT/dz is negative, the term *temperature lapse rate*, defined as $-dT/dz$, usually is used.

The lowermost layer of the earth's atmosphere is known as the *troposphere* (Figure 5.1), in which the temperature lapse rate is about 6.5 $K\,km^{-1}$. At its upper boundary, known as the *tropopause*, dT/dz changes abruptly to approximately zero. The tropopause varies in height according to latitude, season and weather activity, but in general, it is between 8 and 10 km in arctic regions in winter and between 16 and 18 km in the tropical and equatorial regions (Cole et al., 1965).

The next layer above the troposphere is the *stratosphere*, which extends from the tropopause to the *stratopause*, at a height of approximately 47 km. In the lower 10 km of the stratosphere the temperature is approximately constant, and then it increases with height between 20 and 32 km above sea level with a gradient of 1 $K\,km^{-1}$, followed by a faster rate of 2.8 $K\,km^{-1}$ between 32 and 47 km. According to the 1962 U. S. Standard Atmosphere, the atmospheric temperature is 270.5 K ($= -2.5°C$) at the stratopause.

The third layer, extending between the stratopause and approximately 80 to 90 km, is the *mesosphere*. In this layer, the temperature decreases to the lowest value of the atmospheric temperature profile. This value, typically 183 K ($= -90°C$), occurs at the *mesopause*.

The atmospheric composition and the molecular weight of air are approximately constant up to the mesopause. Above the mesopause, the density becomes very small and the composition changes due to dissociation, which makes direct measurements of air temperature impossible. The temperature profile shown in Fig. 5.1 for this layer, known as the *thermosphere*, is modeled according to temperature values inferred from measurements of other atmospheric parameters. No upper limit is defined for the thermosphere.

5-2.1 Atmospheric Composition

Except for water-vapor variations, the relative composition of the atmosphere essentially is constant up to 90 km above sea level. The sea-level composition of the 1962 U. S. Standard Atmosphere is given in Table 5.1 for contaminant-free air containing no water vapor. The principal constituents are molecular nitrogen and molecular oxygen, the molecular weight of the standard atmosphere is 28.9644, and the sea-level density of dry air is $\rho_{air}(0) = 1.225$ $kg\,m^{-3}$.

TABLE 5.1
Normal Composition of Clean, Dry Atmospheric Air near Sea Level[a]

Constituent gas	Gas symbol	Content (% by volume)	Molecular weight[b]
Nitrogen	N_2	78.084	28.0134
Oxygen	O_2	20.9476	31.9988
Argon	Ar	0.934	39.948
Carbon dioxide[c]	CO_2	0.0314	44.00995
Neon	Ne	0.001818	20.183
Helium	He	0.000524	4.0026
Krypton	Kr	0.000114	83.80
Xenon	Xe	0.0000087	131.30
Hydrogen	H_2	0.00005	2.01594
Methane[c]	CH_4	0.0002	16.04303
Nitrous oxide	N_2O	0.00005	44.0128
Ozone[c]	O_3	Summer: 0 to 0.000007	47.9982
		Winter: 0 to 0.000002	47.9982
Sulfur dioxide[c]	SO_2	0 to 0.0001	64.0628
Nitrogen dioxide[c]	NO_2	0 to 0.000002	46.0055
Ammonia[c]	NH_3	0 to trace	17.03061
Carbon monoxide[c]	CO	0 to trace	28.01055
Iodine[c]	I_2	0 to 0.000001	253.8088

[a] From Hering (1965).
[b] On basis of ^{12}C isotope scale for which ^{12}C equals 12.0000.
[c] The content of these gases may undergo significant variations from time to time or from place to place relative to the normal.

5-2.2 1962 U. S. Standard Atmosphere

The 1962 U. S. Standard Atmosphere (Cole et al., 1965) is a generalized model of the vertical structure of the earth's atmosphere. It provides temperature, pressure, and density profiles that represent average conditions in mid latitudes around 45° N. Most of the material presented in this section is adapted from the *Handbook of Geophysics and Space Environment*, edited by Valley (1965). In addition to the generalized model, supplemental models are provided in the *Handbook* for several different latitudes.

Table 5.2 provides numerical values for several atmospheric parameters for altitudes between 5 km below sea level and 90 km above sea level. For most microwave remote-sensing observations, the region of interest is the lower part of the atmosphere, because it contains the bulk of the total atmospheric mass, and therefore exercises the greatest influence upon earth-pointing remote-sensing observations. Exceptions are studies that are concerned specifically with the temperature and magnetic-field profiles and the concentration of gases in the upper part of the atmosphere (mesosphere and lower part of the thermosphere). The atmospheric density decreases exponentially with altitude;

TABLE 5.2
Properties of the U.S. Standard Atmosphere, 1962[a]

Geom. alt. (m)	Temperature (K)	Temperature (°C)	Pressure P (mbar)	Density ρ_{air} (kg m^{-3})	Density ρ_{air} (no. m^{-3})	Particle speed (m s^{-1})
−5000	320.676	47.526	1.77762+3	1.9311+0	4.0154+25	484.15
−4000	314.166	41.016	1.59598	1.7697	3.6798	479.22
−3000	307.659	34.509	1.42973	1.6189	3.3662	474.23
−2000	301.154	28.004	1.27783	1.4782	3.0735	469.19
−1000	294.651	21.501	1.13931	1.3470	2.8009	464.09
0	288.150	15.000	1.01325+3	1.2250+0	2.5471+25	458.94
1000	281.651	8.501	8.98762+2	1.1117+0	2.3115+25	453.74
2000	275.154	2.004	7.95014	1.0066	2.0929	448.48
3000	268.659	−4.491	7.01211	9.0925−1	1.8906	443.15
4000	262.166	−10.984	6.16604	8.1935	1.7037	437.76
5000	255.676	−17.474	5.40482	7.3643	1.5313	432.31
6000	249.187	−23.963	4.72176+2	6.6011−1	1.3726+25	426.79
7000	242.700	−30.450	4.11052	5.9002	1.2268	421.20
8000	236.215	−36.935	3.56516	5.2579	1.0933	415.53
9000	229.733	−43.417	3.08007	4.6706	9.7116+24	409.79
10000	223.252	−49.898	2.64999	4.1351	8.5981	403.97
11000	216.774	−56.376	2.26999+2	3.6480−1	7.5853+24	398.07
12000	216.650	−56.500	1.93994	3.1194	6.4861	397.95
13000	216.650	−56.500	1.65796	2.6660	5.5433	397.95
14000	216.650	−56.500	1.41704	2.2786	4.7378	397.95
15000	216.650	−56.500	1.21118	1.9475	4.0495	397.95
16000	216.650	−56.500	1.03528+2	1.6647−1	3.4614+24	397.95
17000	216.650	−56.500	8.84971+1	1.4230	2.9589	397.95
18000	216.650	−56.500	7.56522	1.2165	2.5294	397.95
19000	216.650	−56.600	6.46748	1.0400	2.1624	397.95
20000	216.650	−56.500	5.52930	8.8910−2	1.8487	397.95
21000	217.581	−55.569	4.72893+1	7.5715−2	1.5743+24	398.81
22000	218.574	−54.576	4.04749	6.4510	1.3414	399.71
23000	219.567	−53.583	3.46686	5.5006	1.1437	400.63
24000	220.560	−52.590	2.97174	4.6938	9.7598+23	401.53
25000	221.552	−51.598	2.54922	4.0084	8.3346	402.43
26000	222.544	−50.606	2.18837+1	3.4257−2	7.1230+23	403.33
28000	224.527	−48.623	1.61619	2.5076	5.2141	405.12
30000	226.509	−46.641	1.19703	1.8410	3.8280	406.91
32000	228.490	−44.660	8.89063+0	1.3555	2.8185	408.68
34000	233.743	−39.407	6.63412	9.8874−3	2.0559	413.35
36000	239.282	−33.868	4.98522+0	7.2579−3	1.5091+23	418.22
38000	244.818	−28.332	3.77138	5.3666	1.1159	423.03
40000	250.350	−22.800	2.87143	3.9957	8.3082+22	427.78
42000	255.878	−17.272	2.19967	2.9948	6.2270	432.38
44000	261.403	−11.747	1.69496	2.2589	4.6968	437.13
46000	266.925	−6.225	1.31340+0	1.7141−3	3.5642+22	441.72
48000	270.650	−2.500	1.02296	1.3167	2.7378	444.79
50000	270.650	−2.500	7.97790−1	1.0269	2.1352	444.79
52000	270.650	−2.500	6.22283	8.0097−4	1.6655	444.79

TABLE 5.2 (*continued*)

Collision frequency (s^{-1})	Mean free path (m)	Molecular weight	Sound speed ($m\,s^{-1}$)	Coefficient of viscosity ($kg\,m^{-1}\,s^{-1}$)	Kinematic viscosity ($m^2\,s^{-1}$)	Thermal conductivity ($kcal\,m^{-1}\,s^{-1}\,K^{-1}$)
$1.1507+10$	$4.2075-8$	28.964	358.986	$1.9422-5$	$1.0058-5$	$6.6545-6$
1.0438	4.5912	28.964	355.324	1.9123	1.0806	6.5356
$9.4488+9$	5.0189	28.964	351.625	1.8820	1.1625	6.4161
8.5356	5.4968	28.964	347.888	1.8515	1.2525	6.2958
7.6939	6.0320	28.964	344.111	1.8206	1.3516	6.1748
$6.9193+9$	$6.6328-8$	28.964	340.294	$1.7894-5$	$1.4607-5$	$6.0530-6$
$6.2079+9$	$7.3090-8$	28.964	336.435	$1.7579-5$	$1.5813-5$	$5.9305-6$
5.5558	8.0723	28.964	332.532	1.7260	1.7147	5.8073
4.9591	8.9361	28.964	328.583	1.6938	1.8628	5.6833
4.4144	9.9166	28.964	324.589	1.6612	2.0275	5.5586
3.9183	$1.1033-7$	28.964	320.545	1.6282	2.2110	5.4331
$3.4674+9$	$1.2309-7$	28.964	316.452	$1.5949-5$	$2.4162-5$	$5.3068-6$
3.0586	1.3771	28.964	312.306	1.5612	2.6461	5.1798
2.6889	1.5453	28.964	308.105	1.5271	2.9044	5.0520
2.3556	$1.7396-7$	28.964	303.848	1.4926	3.1957	4.9235
2.0559	1.9649	28.964	299.532	1.4577	3.5251	4.7942
$1.7872+9$	$2.2273-7$	28.964	295.154	$1.4223-5$	$3.8988-5$	$4.6642-6$
1.5278	2.6047	28.964	295.069	1.4216	4.5574	4.6617
1.3057	3.0477	28.964	295.069	1.4216	5.3325	4.6617
1.1160	3.5659	28.964	295.069	1.4216	6.2391	4.6617
$9.5386+8$	4.1720	28.964	295.069	1.4216	7.2995	4.6617
$8.1533+8$	$4.8808-7$	28.964	295.069	$1.4216-5$	$8.5397-5$	$4.6617-6$
6.9696	5.7098	28.964	295.069	1.4216	9.9902	4.6617
5.9580	6.6793	28.964	295.069	1.4216	$1.1686-4$	4.6617
5.0935	7.8130	28.964	295.069	1.4216	1.3670	4.6617
4.3546	9.1387	28.964	295.069	1.4216	1.5989	4.6617
$3.7163+8$	$1.0731-6$	28.964	295.703	$1.4267-5$	$1.8843-4$	$4.6804-6$
3.1735	1.2595	28.964	296.377	1.4322	2.2201	4.7004
2.7121	1.4772	28.964	297.049	1.4376	2.6135	4.7204
2.3196	1.7310	28.964	297.720	1.4430	3.0743	4.7403
1.9853	2.0270	28.964	298.389	1.4484	3.6135	4.7602
$1.7005+8$	$2.3719-6$	28.964	299.056	$1.4538-5$	$4.2439-4$	$4.7800-6$
1.2503	3.2402	28.964	300.386	1.4646	5.8105	4.8197
$9.2197+7$	4.4134	28.964	301.709	1.4753	8.0134	4.8593
6.8180	5.9942	28.964	303.025	1.4859	$1.0962-3$	4.8988
5.0300	8.2177	28.964	306.489	1.5140	1.5312	5.0031
$3.7358+7$	$1.1195-5$	28.964	310.099	$1.5433-5$	$2.1264-3$	$5.1125-6$
2.7941	1.5140	28.964	313.665	1.5723	2.9298	5.2213
2.1037	2.0335	28.964	317.189	1.6009	4.0067	5.3295
1.5940	2.7131	28.964	320.672	1.6293	5.4404	5.4370
1.2152	3.5970	28.964	324.116	1.6573	7.3371	5.5438
$9.3118+6$	$4.7401-5$	28.964	327.521	$1.6851-5$	$9.8305-3$	$5.6501-6$
7.2079	6.1709	28.964	329.799	1.7037	$1.2939-2$	5.7214
5.6214	7.9125	28.964	329.799	1.7037	1.6591	5.7214
4.3847	$1.0144-4$	28.964	329.799	1.7037	2.1270	5.7214

TABLE 5.2 *(continued)*

Geom. alt. (m)	Temperature (K)	Temperature (°C)	Pressure P (mbar)	Density ρ_{air} (kg m^{-3})	Density ρ_{air} (no. m^{-3})	Particle speed (ms^{-1})
54000	267.560	−5.590	4.84917	6.3137	1.3128	442.24
56000	263.628	−9.522	3.76572 −1	4.9762 −4	1.0347 +22	438.98
58000	259.699	−13.451	2.91373	3.9086	8.1271 +21	435.70
60000	255.772	−17.378	2.24606	3.0592	6.3610	432.39
62000	251.046	−22.104	1.72457	2.3931	4.9760	428.38
64000	243.202	−29.948	1.31504	1.8837	3.9168	421.63
66000	235.363	−37.787	9.94067 −2	1.4713 −4	3.0594 +21	414.78
68000	227.529	−45.621	7.44483	1.1399	2.3701	407.82
70000	219.700	−53.450	5.52047	8.7535 −5	1.8201	400.74
72000	211.876	−61.274	4.05013	6.6593	1.3847	393.54
74000	204.057	−69.093	2.93758	5.0151	1.0428	386.21
76000	196.24	−76.91	2.1045 −2	3.736 −5	7.768 +20	378.7
78000	188.43	−84.72	1.4877	2.750	5.719	371.1
80000	180.65	−92.50	1.0366	1.999	4.157	363.4
85000	180.65	−92.50	4.1250 −3	7.955 −6	1.654 +20	363.4
90000	180.65	−92.50	1.6438	3.170	6.591 +19	363.4

[a] Condensed from the complete tabulations. Numbers following the plus or minus sign are the power of ten by which that entry and each following entry should be multiplied. (From Cole et al., 1965.)

at 30-km altitude, the density is only 1.5 percent of its sea-level value. Hence, for computational purposes, only the lowermost 30 km of the atmosphere needs to be considered. For this region, simple expressions can be developed for the atmospheric parameters of interest in microwave remote sensing. These expressions are based on the numerical listings given in Table 5.2 and on the equation of state for an ideal gas.

Temperature Profile

At a height z in km above sea level, the atmospheric temperature $T(z)$ is given by

$$T(z) = \begin{cases} T_0 - az, & 0 \leqslant z \leqslant 11 \text{ km}, \\ T(11), & 11 \text{ km} \leqslant z \leqslant 20 \text{ km}, \\ T(11) + (z - 20), & 20 \text{ km} \leqslant z \leqslant 32 \text{ km}, \end{cases} \tag{5.1}$$

where T_0 is the sea-level atmospheric temperature and $T(11)$ is the atmospheric temperature at $z = 11$ km, both in kelvins, and a is the temperature lapse rate in the lower 11 km of the atmosphere. For the 1962 U. S. Standard Atmosphere, $T_0 = 288.15$ K and $a = 6.5$ K km^{-1}.

Collision frequency (s^{-1})	Mean free path (m)	Molecular weight	Sound speed $(m s^{-1})$	Coefficient of viscosity $(kg m^{-1} s^{-1})$	Kinematic viscosity $(m^2 s^{-1})$	Thermal conductivity $(Kcal m^{-1} s^{-1} K^{-1})$
3.4365	1.2869	28.964	327.911	1.6883	2.6740	5.6622
2.6885+6	1.6328−4	28.964	325.492	1.6686−5	3.3531−2	5.5867−6
2.0959	2.0788	28.964	323.058	1.6487	4.2182	5.5109
1.6280	2.6560	28.964	320.606	1.6287	5.3241	5.4349
1.2617	3.3952	28.964	317.630	1.6045	6.7047	5.3431
9.7749+5	4.3134	28.964	312.628	1.5638	8.3020	5.1896
7.5111+5	5.5223−4	28.964	307.549	1.5226−5	1.0348−1	5.0352−6
5.7213	7.1218	28.964	302.387	1.4808	1.2991	4.8796
4.3174	9.2821	28.964	297.139	1.4383	1.6431	4.7230
3.2254	1.2201−3	28.964	291.800	1.3953	2.0952	4.5654
2.3838	1.6202	28.964	286.365	1.3515	2.6949	4.4067
1.741+5	2.175−3	28.964	280.83	1.307−5	3.499−1	4.247−6
1.256	2.954	28.964	275.18	1.262	4.588	4.086
8.940+4	4.065	28.964	269.44	1.216	6.085	3.925
3.558+4	1.021−2	28.964	269.44	1.216−5	1.529+0	3.925−6
1.418	2.563	28.96	269.44	1.216	3.837	3.925

Density Profile

The density of dry air, ρ_{air}, decreases exponentially with altitude:

$$\rho_{air}(z) = 1.225 e^{-z/H_1} \quad kg\,m^{-3},\tag{5.2}$$

where z is the altitude (km) and $H_1 = 9.5$ km is the *density scale height*. The above expression is in excellent agreement (less than 3-percent error) with the density values given in Table 5.2 for the lowermost 10 km of the atmosphere, but deviates from the tabulated values at higher altitudes. A better fit to the tabulated values for altitudes up to 30 km is provided by the expression

$$\rho_{air}(z) = 1.225 e^{-z/H_2}[1 + 0.3\sin(z/H_2)] \quad kg\,m^{-3},\tag{5.3}$$

where $H_2 = 7.3$ km.

Pressure Profile

Assuming air to be an ideal gas, its equation of state is

$$P = \rho_{air} RT/M = \rho_{air} R_a T,\tag{5.4}$$

where P is the atmospheric pressure in millibars, R is the universal gas constant, T is the kinetic (actual) temperature in kelvins, and M is the molecular weight of air. If the density ρ_{air} is in $kg\,m^{-3}$, the gas constant for air is $R_a = 2.87$. Thus, using

$$P = 2.87 \rho_{air} T, \tag{5.5}$$

$P(z)$ can be found for any altitude z between sea level and 30 km via (5.1) and (5.3).

Alternatively, the pressure profile can be fitted with an exponential of the form

$$P(z) = P_0 e^{-z/H_3} \qquad \text{mbar}, \tag{5.6}$$

where P_0 is the sea-level pressure and H_3 is the *pressure scale height*. For the 1962 U. S. Standard Atmosphere, $P_0 = 1013.25$ mbar and $H_3 = 7.7$ km. The above expression provides values that are within 3 percent of the tabulated values for $z \leqslant 10$ km.

Water-Vapor Density Profile

The amount of water vapor contained in the atmosphere is a function of several weather parameters, but it is especially dependent on the atmospheric temperature. At sea level, the water-vapor density ρ_v can vary from 10^{-2} g m^{-3} in very cold, dry climates to as much as 30 g m^{-3} in hot, humid climates. The average surface value used by the 1962 U. S. Standard Atmosphere is $\rho_0 = 7.72$ g m^{-3} for middle latitudes. The altitude profile of $\rho_v(z)$ is usually described by a decreasing exponential,

$$\rho_v(z) = \rho_0 e^{-z/H_4} \qquad \text{g m}^{-3}, \tag{5.7}$$

where the scale height H_4 is typically chosen to be between 2 and 2.5 km. The total mass of water vapor contained in a vertical column of unit cross section is

$$M_v = \int_0^\infty \rho_v(z)\, dz$$
$$= \rho_0 H_4. \tag{5.8}$$

For $\rho_0 = 7.72$ g m^{-3} and $H_4 = 2$ km, $M_v = 15.44$ kg m^{-2} or 1.54 g cm^{-2}.

5-3 ABSORPTION AND EMISSION BY GASES

5-3.1 Electromagnetic Interaction with Individual Molecules

The total internal energy $\mathcal{E}$ of an isolated molecule consists of three types of energy states,

$$\mathcal{E} = \mathcal{E}_e + \mathcal{E}_v + \mathcal{E}_r \tag{5.9}$$

where $\mathcal{E}_e = electronic$ energy,
        $\mathcal{E}_v = vibrational$ energy,
        $\mathcal{E}_r = rotational$ energy.

These energy states are quantized; they can assume discrete values that are specified by one or more quantum numbers. Corresponding to each possible electronic state, there are a number of possible vibrational states, and corresponding to each possible vibrational state there are a number of possible rotational states. Rotational energy is associated with rotational motions of the atoms of the molecule about the molecule's center of mass, and vibrational energy is associated with vibrational motions of the atoms about their equilibrium positions.

Radiation is absorbed (or emitted) when a transition takes place from a lower (or higher) energy state to a higher (or lower) energy state. The frequency f_{lm} of the absorbed (or emitted) quantum is given by the Bohr formula,

$$f_{lm} = \frac{\mathcal{E}_m - \mathcal{E}_l}{h}, \tag{5.10}$$

where h is Planck's constant and $\mathcal{E}_m$ and $\mathcal{E}_l$ are the internal energies of the higher and lower molecular states, respectively. The transition may involve changes of electronic, vibrational, or rotational energy, or any combination of the three types. The absorption spectrum due to a single transition is called an absorption line. The energy differences are largest between different electronic states, being typically from 2 to 10 eV,* followed by differences between vibrational states of the same electronic state, which typically vary between 0.1 and 2 eV; and the smallest energy differences are associated with differences between rotational states belonging to the same electronic and vibrational state. Changes in rotational energy alone are usually of the order of 10^{-4} to 5×10^{-2} eV. Transition between pure rotational states (same $\mathcal{E}_e$ and $\mathcal{E}_v$ but different $\mathcal{E}_r$'s) gives rise to rotation lines that occur in the microwave and far-infrared portions of the spectrum. Since energy changes between pure vibrational states (same $\mathcal{E}_e$) are several orders of magnitude larger than energy changes between pure rotational states, vibrational transitions never occur alone, but are always accompanied by many rotational transitions. This condition gives rise to a group of lines, usually referred to as a vibration-rotation band. Such bands, corresponding to values of $\Delta\mathcal{E}$ in the 0.1–2-eV range, occur betwen the red part of the visible spectrum and the thermal infrared region.

The large energy differences associated with electronic transitions (compared to pure vibrational or rotational transitions) usually result in complex band systems (in the visible and ultraviolet parts of the spectrum) involving simultaneous changes of all three types of energy.

Absorption of electromagnetic energy by molecules in the gaseous state usually involves the interaction of the electric or magnetic field of the incident

*1 eV $= 1.6 \times 10^{-19}$ J.

wave with an electric or magnetic dipole or quadrupole moment of the molecules. Of the various gases in the earth's atmosphere, oxygen and water vapor are the only constituents that exhibit significant absorption bands in the microwave spectrum. The oxygen molecule has a permanent magnetic moment. Magnetic interaction with the incident field produces a family of rotation lines in the vicinity of 60 GHz and an isolated line at 118.8 GHz. Water vapor, on the other hand, is a polar molecule with an electric dipole. Electric interaction with the incident field produces rotation lines at 22.2 GHz, 183.3 GHz, and several frequencies in the far-infrared region (above 300 GHz).

5-3.2 The Shape of a Spectral Line

According to the preceding discussion, the absorption (or emission) spectrum of a molecule consists of sharply defined frequency lines (Fig. 5.2(a)) corresponding to transitions between sharply defined (quantized) energy levels of

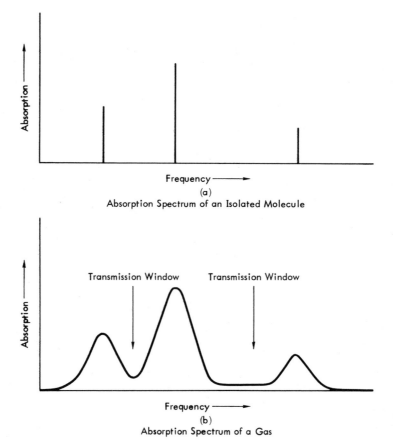

Fig. 5.2 Absorption spectrum of (a) a single isolated molecule, and (b) a gas containing many molecules.

the molecule. Such a spectrum would be characteristic of an isolated, undisturbed, and stationary molecular system. In reality, however, the molecules are in constant motion, interacting and colliding with one another, and colliding with other material objects (such as dust particles). These disturbances cause the energy levels to vary in width, which results in spectral lines with finite widths, as illustrated in Fig. 5.2(b). The increase in linewidth is called *line broadening*. Among the various sources of spectral line broadening (Townes and Schawlow, 1955; Gordy and Cook, 1970), *pressure broadening*, which arises from collisions between molecules, is the most important for atmospheric absorption in the microwave region of the spectrum. The absorption spectrum for transitions between energy states $\mathcal{E}_l$ and $\mathcal{E}_m$ may be written in the following form:

$$\kappa_a(f, f_{lm}) = \frac{4\pi f}{c} S_{lm} F(f, f_{lm}),\tag{5.11}$$

where $\kappa_a = $ *power absorption coefficient*, $\mathrm{Np\,m^{-1}}$,
  $f = $ frequency, Hz,
  $f_{lm} = $ *molecular resonance frequency* for transitions between energy states
    $\mathcal{E}_l$ and $\mathcal{E}_m$, Hz,
  $c = $ velocity of light, $3 \times 10^8 \mathrm{~m\,s^{-1}}$,
  $S_{lm} = $ *line strength* of the lm line, Hz,
  $F = $ *line-shape function*, $\mathrm{Hz^{-1}}$.

The *line strength* S_{lm} of the lm line of a specific atmospheric gas is governed by the number of absorbing molecules of that gas per unit volume, the temperature of the gas, and the molecular parameters associated with that transition. Expressions for S_{lm} are given in future sections for water-vapor and oxygen absorption lines.

The *line-shape function* $F(f, f_{lm})$ describes the shape of the absorption spectrum with respect to the resonance frequency f_{lm}. Several different line-shape functions, based on different models for the nature of the collision between the molecules, have been derived and used in connection with gaseous microwave spectra. The simplest is the *Lorentzian* function,

$$F_L(f, f_{lm}) = \frac{1}{\pi} \frac{\gamma}{(f_{lm} - f)^2 + \gamma^2},\tag{5.12}$$

where γ, usually called the *linewidth parameter* is defined as half the frequency width at half peak intensity (Fig. 5.3). At the line center, $f = f_{lm}$, the line-shape function simplifies to $F_L = 1/(\pi\gamma)$. As will be discussed later, the linewidth parameter γ is proportional to the pressure of the gas under consideration. The Lorentzian function is generally valid for sharp lines whose values of γ are much smaller than the transition frequencies f. This has been confirmed for the 22.2-GHz water vapor line at pressures between 1 and 17 millibars (Liebe et al., 1969; Liebe and Dillon, 1969). To accommodate pressure levels corre-

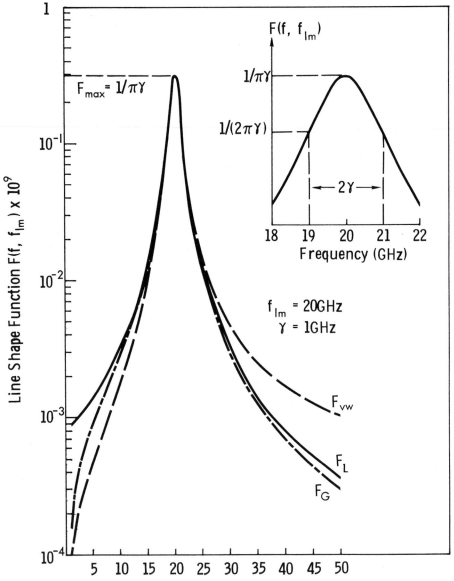

Fig. 5.3 Comparison of different line-shape functions: F_L = Lorentzian function, F_{VW} = Van Vleck–Weisskopf function, and F_G = Gross function. The line center is at 20 GHz, and the line-width parameter $\gamma = 1$ GHz (see inset).

sponding to atmospheric conditions, for which γ is comparable in magnitude to f_{lm}, Van Vleck and Weisskopf (1945) developed the function

$$F_{vw}(f, f_{lm}) = \frac{1}{\pi}\left(\frac{f}{f_{lm}}\right)\left[\frac{\gamma}{(f_{lm}-f)^2+\gamma^2} + \frac{\gamma}{(f_{lm}+f)^2+\gamma^2}\right]. \qquad (5.13)$$

For $f=f_{lm}$, the second term inside the square brackets may be neglected in favor of the first, in which case (5.13) reduces to $F_{vw} \simeq 1/(\pi\gamma)$. Measurements have shown good agreement with calculations based on the above line-shape function for frequencies near the resonant frequency f_{lm}, but have indicated significant deviations in the far wings.

Based on a different set of assumptions (from those made by Van Vleck and Weisskopf) characterizing the statistics of the collision process, Gross (1955) derived a line-shape function that takes the same form as $F_{vw}(f, f_{lm})$ near resonance but seems to provide better agreement with measurements in the far wings (Zhevakin and Naumov, 1963, 1967; Hall, 1967). Gross's line-shape formula, which was independently derived by Zhevakin and Naumov (1963) and is sometimes referred to as the *kinetic* line shape, is given by

$$F_G(f, f_{lm}) = \frac{1}{\pi}\frac{4ff_{lm}\gamma}{(f_{lm}^2-f^2)^2+4f^2\gamma^2}. \qquad (5.14)$$

Again, at the line center, $F_G = 1/(\pi\gamma)$. Although the Gross line-shape function has been shown to provide a better fit to absorption data than the Van Vleck–Weisskopf line-shape function, the latter continues to enjoy wide use in microwave absorption calculations. This is because for microwave absorption lines, the difference between the two functions is small in the microwave region (Section 5.5). The difference becomes appreciable, however, in the thermal infrared region, where the absorption is partly due to contributions by the high-frequency wings of the many water-vapor absorption lines in the submillimeter part of the spectrum. Zhevakin and Naumov (1963) point out that in the well-known infrared window at a wavelength of approximately 10 μm, the Van Vleck–Weisskopf line-shape function predicted an attenuation of 20 dB km^{-1}, while the Gross form gave a value in closer agreement with the measured value of 0.55 dB km^{-1}.

For further discussion of line-shape functions, the reader is referred to Gross (1955), Hall (1967), Liebe (1969), Ulaby and Straiton (1970), and Waters (1976).

5-4 WATER-VAPOR ABSORPTION

From (5.11), the absorption coefficient of a spectral line is given by

$$\kappa(f, f_{lm}) = \left(\frac{4\pi}{c}f\right)S_{lm}F_G(f, f_{lm}) \qquad \text{Np m}^{-1}, \qquad (5.15)$$

where the Gross line-shape function is used because it provides better agreement with experimental observations than the other line-shape functions. For a water-vapor line, S_{lm} can be written as

$$S_{lm} = S_{lm0} f_{lm} \rho_v T^{-5/2} e^{-\mathcal{E}_l/kT}, \tag{5.16}$$

where S_{lm0} is a constant characteristic of the lm transition, f_{lm} is the resonance frequency, ρ_v is the water-vapor density, $\mathcal{E}_l$ is the energy level of the lower state, and k is Boltzmann's constant. Inserting (5.16) into (5.15) and multiplying by $10^4 \log e = 4.34 \times 10^3$ to convert the units of the absorption coefficient from $\mathrm{Np\,m^{-1}}$ to $\mathrm{dB\,km^{-1}}$, we have

$$\kappa(f, f_{lm}) = 4.34 \times 10^3 \left(\frac{4\pi}{c} \right)$$
$$\times S_{lm0} \left[f f_{lm} \rho_v T^{-5/2} e^{-\mathcal{E}_l/kT} F_G(f, f_{lm}) \right] \mathrm{dB\,km^{-1}}. \tag{5.17}$$

In the microwave region (1–300 GHz), water vapor has rotational absorption lines at 22.235 and 183.31 GHz. There are, however, numerous other lines at frequencies just above this region that also contribute to the microwave absorption spectrum. For calculations at frequencies below approximately 100 GHz, the practice has been to group the contributions of the 183.31-GHz line and the submillimeter (above 300 GHz) lines together into a "residual" term through the use of low-frequency approximations. Since the majority of microwave remote-sensing studies are today conducted at frequencies below 100 GHz, we shall consider this region first, and then outline the formulation for the 100–300-GHz region. The material presented below is extracted from review articles by Liebe (1969) and Waters (1976).

5-4.1 Below 100 GHz

At a frequency f below 100 GHz, the total water vapor absorption coefficient κ_{H_2O} may be written as

$$\kappa_{H_2O}(f) = \kappa(f, 22) + \kappa_r(f) \qquad \mathrm{dB\,km^{-1}}, \tag{5.18}$$

where $\kappa(f, 22)$ is the absorption coefficient of the 22.235-GHz line and $\kappa_r(f)$ is the *residual* term representing the contributions of all higher-frequency water-vapor absorption lines.

Using the values tabulated by Waters (1976) for the transition parameters of the 22.235-GHz line, (5.17) assumes the form

$$\kappa(f, 22) = 2f^2 \rho_v \left(\frac{300}{T} \right)^{5/2} e^{-644/T} \left[\frac{\gamma_1}{\left(494.4 - f^2\right)^2 + 4f^2 \gamma_1^2} \right] \mathrm{dB\,km^{-1}}$$

$$\tag{5.19}$$

where the linewidth parameter γ_1 is given by

$$\gamma_1 = 2.85 \left(\frac{P}{1013} \right) \left(\frac{300}{T} \right)^{0.626} \left[1 + 0.018 \frac{\rho_v T}{P} \right] \text{ GHz.} \qquad (5.20)$$

In the above formulas, f and γ_1 are in GHz, T is in kelvins, ρ_v is in gm^{-3}, and P is the atmospheric pressure in millibars.

The residual absorption coefficient $\kappa_r(f)$ is given by

$$\kappa_r(f) = 2.4 \times 10^{-6} f^2 \rho_v \left(\frac{300}{T} \right)^{3/2} \gamma_1 \qquad \text{dB km}^{-1}. \qquad (5.21)$$

The constant coefficient in the above expression was empirically determined (Waters, 1976) to fit experimental data; it is approximately six times larger than the value that would be obtained from a summation of the low-frequency contributions of the 183.31-GHz and higher-frequency lines if the Van Vleck–Weisskopf line-shape function were used, and approximately three times larger than the value that would be obtained using the Gross line-shape function. This empirical approach, of increasing the magnitude of the residual absorption coefficient to bring the calculated absorption in closer agreement with measured values, has been widely used in the literature (Westwater and Strand, 1967; Barrett and Chung, 1962).

Adding (5.19) and (5.21), we obtain the total water-vapor absorption coefficient at frequencies below 100 GHz:

$$\kappa_{H_2O}(f) = 2f^2 \rho_v \left(\frac{300}{T} \right)^{3/2} \gamma_1$$

$$\times \left[\left(\frac{300}{T} \right) e^{-644/T} \frac{1}{(494.4 - f^2)^2 + 4f^2 \gamma_1^2} + 1.2 \times 10^{-6} \right] \text{dB km}^{-1}. \qquad (5.22)$$

Figure 5.4 shows the 1–100-GHz water-vapor absorption spectrum for typical sea-level conditions ($T = 300$ K, $P = 1013$ mbar, and $\rho_v = 7.5$ gm^{-3}). The formula needed for calculating the absorption coefficient at frequencies above 100 GHz is discussed next.

5-4.2 100–300 GHz

In the previous section, where considerations were limited to frequencies below 100 GHz, the contributions of the 183.31-GHz and higher-frequency water-vapor absorption lines were approximated by a simple "residual" absorption term. Above approximately 100 GHz, this approach is no longer valid. Indeed, complete expressions should be used for the 22.235- and 183.31-GHz lines, as

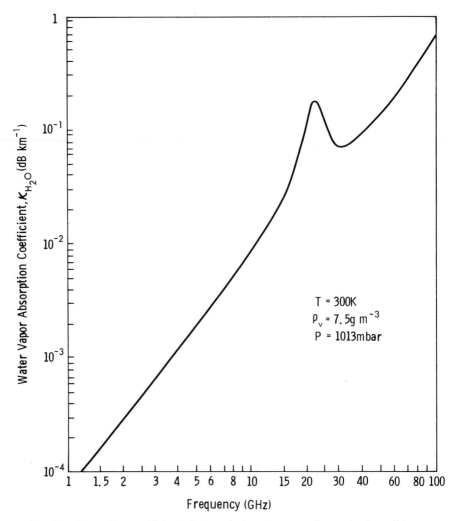

Fig. 5.4 Attenuation coefficient of atmospheric water vapor for sea-level conditions, calculated using (5.22).

well as for some of the major submillimeter lines. Waters (1976) states that "for the frequency range up to 300 GHz it is sufficiently accurate to make the summation over the ten lowest frequency transitions." Thus, $\kappa_{H_2O}(f)$ is given by

$$\kappa_{H_2O}(f) = \sum \kappa(f, f_{lm}),\tag{5.23}$$

where the summation is over the ten lowest-frequency lines. Using (5.17), we have

$$\kappa_{H_2O}(f) = 4.34 \times 10^3 \left(\frac{4\pi}{c}\right) f\rho_v T^{-5/2}$$

$$\times \sum S_{lm0} f_{lm} e^{-\mathscr{E}_l/kT} F_G(f, f_{lm}) \qquad \text{dB km}^{-1}. \qquad (5.24)$$

If we designate $lm=1$ to represent the 22.235-GHz line, $lm=2$ to represent the 183.31-GHz line, and so on, upon introducing the Gross line-shape function F_G and normalizing T to 300 K, the above expression becomes

$$\kappa_{H_2O}(f) = 1.5 \times 10^{-10} f^2 \rho_v \left(\frac{300}{T}\right)^{5/2} \sum_{i=1}^{10} S_{i0} f_i^2 e^{-\mathscr{E}_i/kT}$$

$$\times \left[\frac{\gamma_i}{\left(f_i^2 - f^2\right)^2 + 4f^2\gamma_i^2}\right]. \qquad (5.25)$$

If we further define

$$\mathscr{E}_i' = \mathscr{E}_i/k, \qquad (5.26)$$

$$A_i = S_{i0} f_i^2 / S_{10} f_1^2, \qquad (5.27)$$

and introduce the appropriate conversion factor so that f, f_i, and γ_i are in GHz, (5.25) becomes

$$\kappa_{H_2O}(f) = 2f^2 \rho_v \left(\frac{300}{T}\right)^{5/2} \sum_{i=1}^{10} A_i e^{-\mathscr{E}_i'/T}$$

$$\times \left[\frac{\gamma_i}{\left(f_i^2 - f^2\right)^2 + 4f^2\gamma_i^2}\right] \text{dB km}^{-1}. \qquad (5.28)$$

Table 5.3 lists the values of A_i, $\mathscr{E}_i'$, and f_i for $i=1$ to 10. These values were extracted from more detailed information tabulated by Waters (1976). The linewidth parameter γ_i is given by

$$\gamma_i = \gamma_{i0} \left(\frac{P}{1013}\right)\left(\frac{300}{T}\right)^x \left[1 + 10^{-2} a_i \frac{\rho_v T}{P}\right] \text{GHz}, \qquad (5.29)$$

where γ_{i0}, a_i, and x are also listed in Table 5.3. In the above, P is in millibars, T is in kelvins, and ρ_v is in grams per cubic meter.

Figure 5.5 shows three calculated water-vapor absorption spectra for the 10–300-GHz region. The curve labeled "Gross line shape" corresponds to the expression for $\kappa_{H_2O}(f)$ given by (5.28). For the purpose of comparison, the

TABLE 5.3
Line Parameters of the Ten Lowest
Water-Vapor Absorption Transitions[a]

i	f_i^{b} (GHz)	$\mathcal{E}_i'$ (K^{-1})	A_i	γ_{i0} (GHz)	a_i	x
1	22.23515	644	1.0	2.85	1.75	0.626
2	183.31012	196	41.9	2.68	2.03	0.649
3	(323.)	1850	334.4	2.30	1.95	0.420
4	325.1538	454	115.7	3.03	1.85	0.619
5	380.1968	306	651.8	3.19	1.82	0.630
6	(390.)	2199	127.0	2.11	2.03	0.330
7	(436.)	1507	191.4	1.50	1.97	0.290
8	(438.)	1070	697.6	1.94	2.01	0.360
9	(442.)	1507	590.2	1.51	2.02	0.332
10	448.0008	412	973.1	2.47	2.19	0.510

[a] Extracted from a more detailed list prepared by Waters (1976).
[b] Transition frequencies in parentheses are calculated values.

absorption spectrum calculated using the Van Vleck–Weisskopf line shape is shown also. The solid curve is a plot of $\kappa'_{H_2O}(f)$, which is equal to $\kappa_{H_2O}(f)$ of (5.28) plus a correction term $\Delta\kappa(f)$:

$$\kappa'_{H_2O}(f) = \kappa_{H_2O}(f) + \Delta\kappa(f) \qquad dB\,km^{-1}. \tag{5.30}$$

The correction term $\Delta\kappa(f)$ was empirically derived by Gaut and Reifenstein (1971) through a comparison of calculated values of the absorption coefficient with measured data, and is given by

$$\Delta\kappa(f) = 4.69 \times 10^{-6}\rho_v \left(\frac{300}{T}\right)^{2.1}\left(\frac{P}{1000}\right)f^2 \qquad dB\,km^{-1}, \tag{5.31}$$

where all quantities are in the same units stated earlier. The insets in Fig. 5.5, which compare the three theoretical curves with measured data for the regions around the 22.235- and 183.31-GHz lines, clearly show the improved agreement obtained using the additive correction term. Therefore, the reader is advised to use (5.30) for computing the absorption coefficient of water vapor in the 100–300-GHz region. Although the formulation is also valid for frequencies below 100 GHz, the simpler expression given by (5.22) is quite adequate and gives results in close agreement with values computed according to (5.30).

5-5 OXYGEN ABSORPTION

The microwave absorption spectrum of oxygen consists of a large number of absorption lines spread out over the 50–70-GHz frequency range (known as

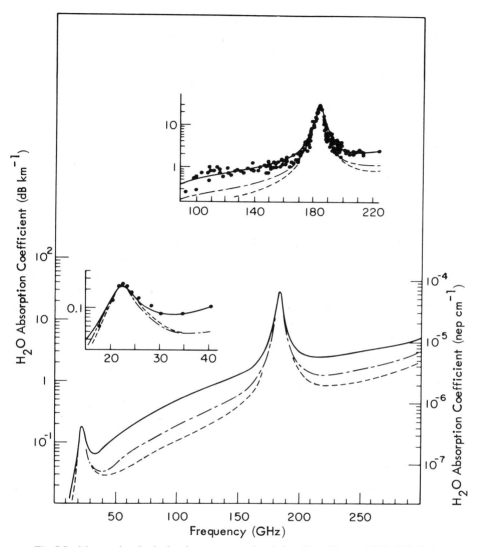

Fig. 5.5 Measured and calculated water-vapor absorption (from Waters, 1976). Calculations are shown for the Van Vleck–Weisskopf line shape (---), the Gross line shape (—·—), and the Gross line shape with the added empirical correction discussed in the text (—), with $T = 300$ K, $P = 1013$ mbar, and $\rho_v = 7.5$ g m^{-3}. Points in the 20–40-GHz inset are measurements of Becker and Autler (1946), where $T = 318$ K, $P = 1013$ mbar, and $\rho_v = 10$ g m^{-3}. Points in the 100–200-GHz inset are measurements quoted by Dryagin et al. (1966), where $T = 300$ K, $P = 1013$ mbar, and $\rho_v = 7.5$ g m^{-3}.

the 60-GHz oxygen complex) and an additional line at 118.75 GHz. At pressures characteristic of the lower part of the earth's atmosphere, pressure broadening causes the complex of lines to blend together, forming a continuous absorption band centered around 60 GHz.

The traditional approach used for computing the absorption spectrum of the 60-GHz oxygen complex has been to sum the absorption coefficients due to the individual lines (Meeks and Lilley, 1963; Tolbert and Straiton, 1963; Carter et al., 1968) using the Van Vleck–Weisskopf (1945) line-shape factor. Similar computations also have been made (Reber, 1972; Zhevakin and Naumov, 1965) using the Gross (1955) line-shape factor. According to the theory of collision broadening, the linewidth parameter γ of an isolated oxygen line should be proportional to the partial pressure of oxygen,

$$\gamma = \gamma_0 P_{O_2} \tag{5.32}$$

where γ_0 is the linewidth at $P_{O_2} = 1$ mbar and P_{O_2} is the partial pressure of oxygen. In order to fit calculated absorption values to experimental measurements made in the neighborhood of 1 atmosphere of pressure (1013 mbar), it was found necessary to use values of γ_0 that are 2 to 3 times smaller than the spectroscopic value measured at low pressures (Artman and Gordon, 1954) where the individual lines can be resolved.

To resolve this nonconstant linewidth dependence on pressure, Rosenkranz (1975) applied the theory of bands composed of overlapping lines to the 60-GHz oxygen complex and employed reasonable approximations to reduce the complexity of the computation for practical use in remote sensing, radio astronomy, and communications. The material presented below is based on Rosenkranz's (1975) formulation; some of the units and symbols have been changed to retain consistency with previous sections.

5-5.1 Complete Solution

For an atmospheric oxygen concentration of 0.21 by volume, the oxygen absorption coefficient in air is given by

$$\kappa_{O_2}(f) = 1.61 \times 10^{-2} f^2 \left(\frac{P}{1013} \right) \left(\frac{300}{T} \right)^2 F' \qquad \text{dB km}^{-1}, \tag{5.33}$$

where f is frequency (GHz), P is atmospheric pressure (mbar), and T is atmospheric temperature (K).

The function F' incorporates the line strengths and determines (together with the factor f^2) the shape of the absorption spectrum. It is given as a summation over odd values of the rotational quantum number N for $N \leq 39$ (contributions of lines with $N > 39$ are considered insignificant):

$$F' = \frac{0.7\gamma_b}{f^2 + \gamma_b^2} + \sum_{\substack{N=1 \\ N \text{ odd}}}^{39} \Phi_N \left[g_{N^+}(f) + g_{N^+}(-f) + g_{N^-}(f) + g_{N^-}(-f) \right],$$

$$\tag{5.34}$$

where

$$g_{N^\pm}(f) = \frac{\gamma_N(d_{N^\pm})^2 + P(f - f_{N^\pm})Y_{N^\pm}}{(f - f_{N^\pm})^2 + \gamma_N^2}, \tag{5.35}$$

$$\Phi_N = 4.6 \times 10^{-3} \left(\frac{300}{T}\right)(2N+1)$$

$$\times \exp\left[-6.89 \times 10^{-3} N(N+1)\left(\frac{300}{T}\right)\right]. \tag{5.36}$$

The quantities γ_N and γ_b are known as the *resonant* and *nonresonant* linewidth parameters, respectively, and are given by

$$\gamma_N = 1.18\left(\frac{P}{1013}\right)\left(\frac{300}{T}\right)^{0.85} \text{GHz}, \tag{5.37}$$

$$\gamma_b = 0.49\left(\frac{P}{1013}\right)\left(\frac{300}{T}\right)^{0.89} \text{GHz}. \tag{5.38}$$

The quantities d_{N^+} and d_{N^-} are the amplitudes of the f_{N^+} and f_{N^-} lines, respectively, and are given by

$$d_{N^+} = \left[\frac{N(2N+3)}{(N+1)(2N+1)}\right]^{1/2}, \tag{5.39a}$$

$$d_{N^-} = \left[\frac{(N+1)(2N-1)}{N(2N+1)}\right]^{1/2}. \tag{5.39b}$$

The remaining quantities are the resonant frequencies f_{N^+} and f_{N^-} and the parameters Y_{N^+} and Y_{N^-}, (known as the *interference parameters*). These four quantities are given in Table 5.4 for $N=1$ to 39. Except for the $N=1^-$ line, whose resonant frequency is at 118.75 GHz, the resonant frequencies of the remaining 39 lines are distributed over the frequency range between approximately 50 and 70 GHz.

Following the above procedure, the oxygen absorption spectrum was computed and plotted in Fig. 5.6. The computations are for sea-level conditions characterized by $T=300$ K and $P=1013$ mbar.

5-5.2 Below 45 GHz

For frequencies outside the 50–70-GHz resonance region of the 60-GHz oxygen complex, the centroid approximation may be employed to replace all the resonance lines with a single line at 60 GHz (Van Vleck, 1947a). Below 45 GHz, the contribution of the 118.75-GHz oxygen absorption line may be

TABLE 5.4
Frequencies and Interference Coefficients[a]

N	Frequencies (GHz)		Interference coefficients[b] (mbar^{-1})	
	f_N^+	f_N^-	γ_N^+	γ_N^-
1	56.2648	118.7503	4.51−4	−2.14−5
3	58.4466	62.4863	4.94−4	−3.78−4
5	59.5910	60.3061	3.52−4	−3.92−4
7	60.4348	59.1642	1.86−4	−2.68−4
9	61.1506	58.3239	3.30−5	−1.13−4
11	61.8002	57.6125	−1.03−4	3.44−5
13	62.4112	56.9682	−2.23−4	1.65−4
15	62.9980	56.3634	−3.32−4	2.84−4
17	63.5685	55.7838	−4.32−4	3.91−4
19	64.1278	55.2214	−5.26−4	4.93−4
21	64.6789	54.6711	−6.13−4	5.84−4
23	65.2241	54.1300	−6.99−4	6.76−4
25	65.7647	53.5957	−7.74−4	7.55−4
27	66.3020	53.0668	−8.61−4	8.47−4
29	66.8367	52.5422	−9.11−4	9.01−4
31	67.3694	52.0212	−1.03−3	1.03−3
33	67.9007	51.5030	−9.87−4	9.86−4
35	68.4308	50.9873	−1.32−3	1.33−3
37	68.9601	50.4736	−7.07−4	7.01−4
39	69.4887	49.9618	−2.58−3	2.64−3

[a] From Rosenkranz, © 1975 IEEE. Frequencies for $N \leqslant 31$ are from Wilheit and Barrett (1970) and Wilheit (1970); for $N > 31$ from Liebe and Welch (1973). See also Welch and Mizushima (1972).
[b] Power of 10 given to right.

neglected and the contribution of the 60-GHz complex may be written as

$$
\kappa_{O_2}(f) = 1.1 \times 10^{-2} f^2 \left(\frac{P}{1013} \right) \left(\frac{300}{T} \right)^2
$$

$$
\times \gamma \left[\frac{1}{(f-f_0)^2 + \gamma^2} + \frac{1}{f^2 + \gamma^2} \right] \text{dB km}^{-1}, \tag{5.40}
$$

where f is in GHz and $f_0 = 60$ GHz. The linewidth parameter γ is given by (Meeks and Lilley, 1963)

$$
\gamma = \gamma_0 \left(\frac{P}{1013} \right) \left(\frac{300}{T} \right)^{0.85} \text{GHz}, \tag{5.41}
$$

where

$$
\gamma_0 = \begin{cases} 0.59, & P \geqslant 333 \text{ mbar}, \\ 0.59 \left[1 + 3.1 \times 10^{-3} (333 - P) \right], & 25 \leqslant P \leqslant 333 \text{ mbar}, \\ 1.18, & P \leqslant 25 \text{ mbar}. \end{cases} \tag{5.42}
$$

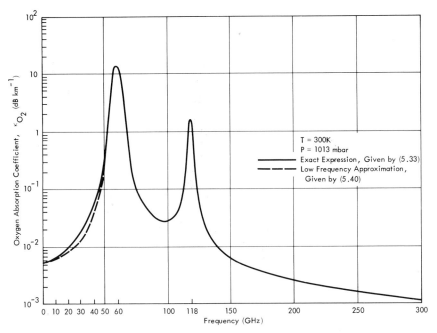

Fig. 5.6 Calculated oxygen absorption for sea-level conditions. The dashed curve is based on the low-frequency approximation given by (5.40).

The above formulation is quite adequate for computations at frequencies below 45 GHz (see Fig. 5.6).

5-6 TOTAL ATMOSPHERIC GASEOUS ABSORPTION AND EMISSION

In addition to oxygen and water vapor, other atmospheric gases and pollutants have absorption lines in the microwave spectrum. These include O_3, SO_2, NO_2, and N_2O, among others, but their relative concentrations at sea level are so small that their contributions to the microwave gaseous absorption spectrum is negligible in comparison to the contributions of oxygen and water vapor. The total gaseous absorption coefficient is therefore given by

$$\kappa_g(f) = \kappa'_{H_2O}(f) + \kappa_{O_2}(f), \qquad \text{dB km}^{-1}, \tag{5.43}$$

where $\kappa'_{H_2O}(f)$ is given by (5.30) [or (5.22) for $f \leqslant 100$ GHz] and $\kappa_{O_2}(f)$ is given by (5.33) [or (5.40) for $f \leqslant 45$ GHz]. A plot of $\kappa_g(f)$ as a function of f is shown in Fig. 5.7(a), together with measured values published in the literature.

5-6.1 Atmospheric Opacity

The expressions and plots of the absorption spectra presented thus far have been for propagation in a homogeneous medium, e.g. horizontally in a stratified, planar atmosphere. For microwave remote-sensing observations from a

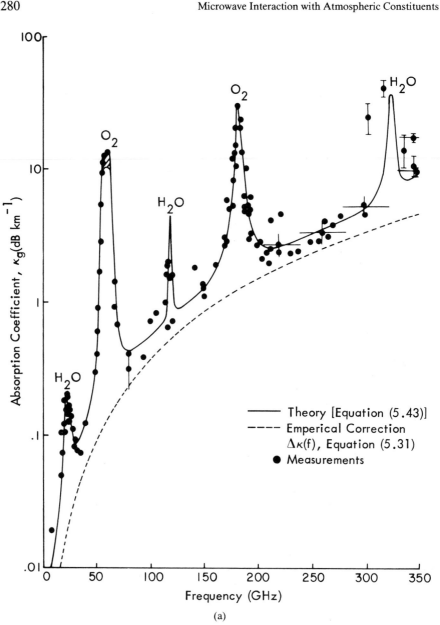

Fig. 5.7 Microwave absorption due to atmospheric gases: (a) gaseous absorption coefficient $\kappa_g(f)$ at sea level and (b) zenith opacity, both for the surface conditions $P_0 = 1013$ mbar, $T_0 = 293$ K, and $\rho_0 = 7.5$ g cm^{-3}. Solid curves are calculated according to theory, and dots are measured values (Crane, © 1981 IEEE).

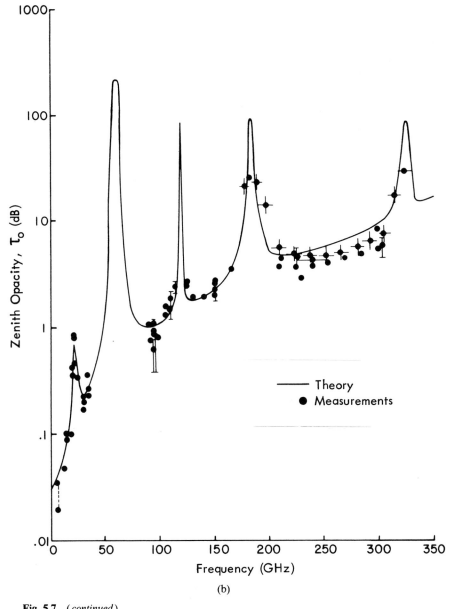

(b)

Fig. 5.7 (*continued*)

high-altitude aircraft or spacecraft platform, one of the quantities of interest is the *opacity* of the atmosphere, τ_θ, which is the optical depth (integrated attenuation) of the entire atmosphere along a path at a zenith angle θ. For θ less than 70°, a spherically stratified atmosphere may be approximated by a planar atmosphere and refraction effects may be ignored. Hence,

$$\tau_\theta = \int_0^\infty \kappa_e(z) \sec \theta \, dz, \tag{5.44}$$

where $\kappa_e(z)$ is the extinction coefficient at height z above the surface. Under clear-sky conditions, the atmosphere may be considered a nonscattering medium, in which case κ_e is equal to the gaseous absorption coefficient κ_g. If κ_g is in dB per kilometer and z is in kilometers,

$$\tau_\theta = \sec \theta \, \tau_0, \qquad \text{dB}, \tag{5.45}$$

where

$$\tau_0 = \int_0^\infty \kappa_g(z) \, dz, \qquad \text{dB}, \tag{5.46}$$

is the zenith opacity. For $\theta \leqslant 70°$, the $\sec \theta$ approximation yields results to an accuracy better than 1 percent. The zenith atmospheric opacity, calculated by Crane (1981) using a standard atmosphere with a surface water-vapor density of 7.5 $\mathrm{g\,m^{-3}}$, is compared in Fig. 5.7(b) with published data. The low-absorption regions around 35, 94, 140 and 225 GHz are called atmospheric *windows*.

The *total atmospheric loss factor* L_θ (due to propagation through the entire atmosphere) is defined by

$$L_\theta = e^{\tau_0 \sec \theta}, \tag{5.47}$$

where τ_0 is in nepers. The inverse of the loss factor is the atmospheric transmissivity, $\Upsilon_\theta = 1/L_\theta$, which was shown earlier in Fig. 1.10 for $\theta = 0$ (zenith direction). When expressed in dB, L_θ becomes

$$L_\theta(\text{dB}) = 4.34 \tau_0(\text{Np}) \sec \theta$$
$$= \tau_0(\text{dB}) \sec \theta. \tag{5.48}$$

At a given frequency f, the atmospheric absorption coefficient κ_g is a function of three atmospheric parameters, T, P, and ρ_v. Since the water-vapor absorption coefficient κ_{H_2O} is essentially directly proportional to ρ_v, and likewise the oxygen absorption coefficient κ_{O_2} is directly proportional to P, and since both ρ_v and P decrease approximately exponentially with increasing altitude, the major contribution to the integral defined by (5.44) is provided by the atmospheric layer closest to the surface. Among the two parameters, ρ_v exhibits a much wider range of relative variation as a function of atmospheric conditions and geographic location than does P. Hence it is reasonable to expect the zenith opacity τ_0 to vary approximately linearly with the surface water-vapor density ρ_0. This expectation is supported by the experimental observations shown in Fig. 5.8.

5-6.2 Atmospheric Emission

For a nonscattering atmosphere, the apparent (or brightness) temperature representing the downwelling atmospheric radiation is given by (4.97) as

$$T_{DN}(\theta) = \sec\theta \int_0^\infty \kappa_a(z') T(z') e^{-\tau(0,z')\sec\theta} \, dz', \qquad (5.49)$$

where θ is the zenith angle, $\kappa_a(z')$ and $T(z')$ are the atmospheric absorption coefficient (nepers per unit height) and kinetic temperature at height z', and $\tau(0, z')$ is the optical thickness of the vertical layer between the surface and height z',

$$\tau(0, z') = \int_0^{z'} \kappa_a(z) \, dz, \qquad \text{Np.} \qquad (5.50)$$

Under cloud-free conditions $\kappa_a = \kappa_g$, the gaseous absorption coefficient. For a given set of atmospheric temperature, pressure, and water-vapor-density height profiles, $\kappa_g(z)$ can be calculated for each height z according to the expressions given in the preceding sections. It should be noted, however, that in computing (5.49), $\kappa_g(z)$ should be expressed in nepers per unit height ($\kappa_g(\text{Np km}^{-1}) = 0.23\kappa_g(\text{dB km}^{-1})$). Fig. 5.9(a) shows a plot of $T_{DN}(0)$ as a function of frequency for the 1962 U.S. Standard Atmosphere with a surface water-vapor density of 10 g m^{-3}. Since emission is linked to absorption, the spectrum of the radiometric temperature $T_{DN}(0)$ is similar in shape to the atmospheric opacity spectrum of Fig. 5.7(b), particularly in those regions of the spectrum where τ_0 does not exceed 2 to 3 dB. However, in the high attenuation regions, around the 60-GHz oxygen complex and the 118.75- and 183.31-GHz lines, the atmosphere behaves like a blackbody with a radiometric temperature approximately equal to the weighted mean of the atmospheric temperature profile, where the weighting function accounts for the relative contributions of the various atmospheric layers to T_{DN}.

In addition to the downwelling radiation represented by T_{DN}, an upward-looking radiometer would receive a relatively small amount of energy due to cosmic and galactic radiation incident upon the atmosphere from the top. Thus, the apparent temperature of the sky, usually referred to as the *sky radiometric temperature*, T_{SKY}, consists of

$$T_{SKY}(\theta) = T_{DN}(\theta) + T_{EXTRA} e^{-\tau_0 \sec\theta}, \qquad (5.51a)$$

and

$$T_{EXTRA} = T_{COS} + T_{GAL}, \qquad (5.51b)$$

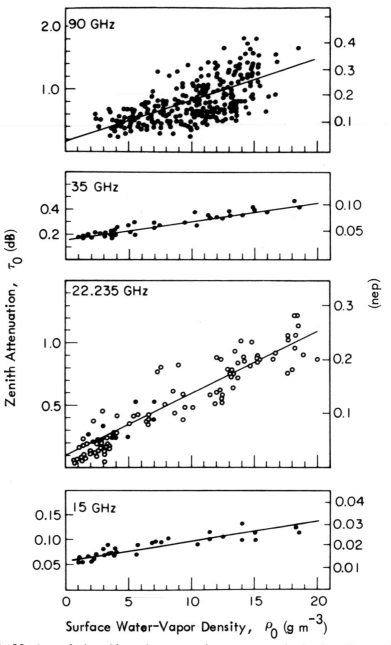

Fig. 5.8 Atmospheric zenith opacity versus surface water-vapor density (from Waters, 1976). The equations for the straight lines that best fit the points are: at 90 GHz, $\tau_0(dB) = 0.17 + 0.06\rho_0(g\,m^{-3})$; at 35 GHz, $\tau_0(dB) = 0.17 + 0.013\rho_0(g\,m^{-3})$; at 22.235 GHz, $\tau_0(dB) = 0.11 + 0.048\rho_0(g\,m^{-3})$; and at 15 GHz, $\tau_0(dB) = 0.055 + 0.004\rho_0(g\,m)^{-3}$). Open points are values calculated by Waters, and closed points are measured values reported in the literature and summarized in the above form by Waters (1976).

where τ_0 is the total zenith atmospheric opacity, and T_{COS} and T_{GAL} are the *cosmic* and *galactic* brightness temperatures, respectively, whose sum we call the *extraterrestrial brightness temperature*, T_{EXTRA}. The cosmic radiation contribution is independent of frequency and the zenith angle θ, and has the constant value $T_{COS} = 2.7$ K. The galactic contribution is due to radiation from our own galaxy. Its magnitude is direction-dependent due to the nonuniformity of radiation emitted by different parts of the galaxy; T_{GAL} is a maximum in the direction of the center of the galaxy and a minimum in the direction of the galactic pole. Plots of $T_{SKY}(\theta)$ are shown in Fig. 5.9(b) (solid curves) for several values of θ, calculated for minimum galactic emission. Also shown is a dashed line corresponding to $T_{GAL}(\text{max})$ which arises from a narrow belt extending about 3° in the galactic plane and concentrated toward the galactic center (Evans et al., 1968). The frequency dependence of T_{GAL} varies between $f^{-2.5}$ and f^{-3}, depending on the specific region of the galaxy. Above about 5 GHz, T_{GAL} may be neglected in comparison to T_{DN}. Below 1 GHz, however, the contribution of T_{GAL} may not be ignored. The wide range of values that T_{GAL} may assume (between $T_{GAL}(\text{min})$ and $T_{GAL}(\text{max})$) poses a serious problem for the use of microwave radiometry for earth observations at frequencies below 1 GHz. This factor, together with the problem of interference from manmade radio sources (primarily radio and television transmitters) and the poor spatial resolution attainable with reasonable-size antennas, is responsible for the very limited use of frequencies below 1 GHz for radiometric earth observations.

In the above discussion, contributions of point sources, such as the sun, were not included. The brightness temperature of the "quiet" sun decreases rapidly with increasing frequency from about 10^6 K at 100 MHz down to about 10^4 K at 10 GHz. Above 10 GHz, the solar brightness temperature decreases at a slower rate towards the value of 6000 K, which remains approximately constant above about 30 GHz. When sunspots and flares occur, the solar brightness temperature may increase by several orders of magnitude. The contribution received by an upward-looking radiometer depends on the direction of the sun relative to the antenna pattern and on the brightness temperature of the sun. If the sun is within the main beam of the radiometer antenna, the antenna temperature is given by (4.54).

The atmospheric emission plots shown in Fig. 5.9(a) and (b) are for downwelling radiation such as would be observed by an upward-looking radiometer located at sea level. Ignoring the cosmic and galactic contributions, which are quite small in comparison to atmospheric emission above 5 GHz, the plots of $T_{DN}(\theta)$ are within a few degrees of what would be calculated for $T_{UP}(\theta)$, the upwelling atmospheric radiation that would be observed by a downward-looking radiometer located above the earth's atmosphere (excluding emission from the earth's surface). Hence, the curves of Fig. 5.9 may be used as approximate representatives of $T_{UP}(\theta)$.

It was stated earlier that for computational purposes, the approximation of horizontal atmospheric stratification (which led to the $\sec\theta$ dependence in

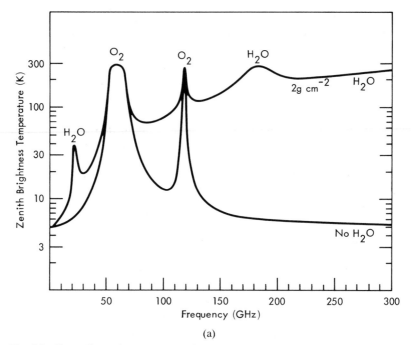

(a)

Fig. 5.9 Sky radiometric temperature that would be observed by an upward-looking radiometer. (a) In the zenith direction for frequencies between 1 and 300 GHz: brightness temperature of the downwelling atmospheric radiation, T_{DN}, plus 3 K of cosmic radiation incident on the atmosphere from the top (Waters, 1976). The upper and lower curves correspond to $M_v = 2$ $g\,cm^{-2}$ and 0 $g\,cm^{-2}$, respectively. (b) For several zenith angles θ in the 0.1–100-GHz region: calculated sky radiometric temperature, T_{SKY}, for a standard atmosphere with $\rho_0 = 7.5$ $g\,m^{-3}$. Included in the calculation are galactic contributions corresponding to directions away from the center of the galaxy. The dashed line shows the maximum galactic radiometric temperature, corresponding to the galactic center. The angle θ is relative to the zenith.

(5.44)) may be used up to about 70° from the zenith. This statement is verified by the excellent agreement shown in Fig. 5.10 between measured values of $T_{SKY}(\theta)$ and the results of computations based on the above approximation. The agreement is good even for angles as large as 82°.

5-7 EXTINCTION AND EMISSION BY CLOUDS AND PRECIPITATION

The treatment thus far has been limited to clear-sky conditions, where absorption and emission are due solely to atmospheric gases, and are the result of transitions between the energy levels of individual molecules. The interaction of electromagnetic radiation with particles (such as those in clouds, fog, snow, or rain) is different in nature and may involve both absorption and scattering. In the sections that follow, we first consider the interaction with a single particle and then proceed to treat the case of a large number of particles within

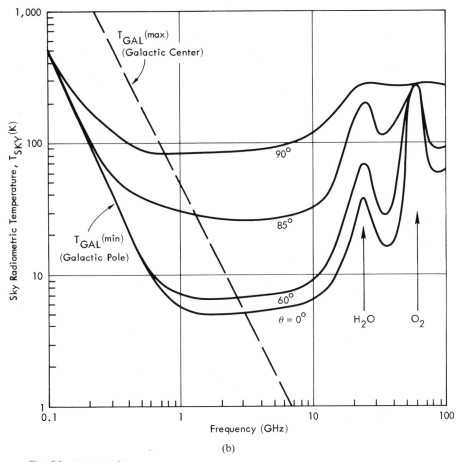

Fig. 5.9 (*continued*)

the volume of interest. The volume extinction coefficient is governed by the density, shape, size distribution, and dielectric properties of the particles contained in the volume. In extending the results for a single particle to the ensemble containing many particles, the particles usually are assumed to be randomly distributed within the volume, and therefore the contributions of the individual particles can be summed assuming an incoherent process (by considering the phases of the fields scattered by the particles as random). In addition to the above assumptions, one further assumption will be made in the discussions below, namely, that the particles are spherical, which is a reasonable assumption for most atmospheric water and ice droplets. Although models have been developed (Oguchi, 1973) to account for the nonspherical nature of raindrops, the differences between their results and those obtained for spherical droplets usually are smaller than the statistical uncertainties due to other parameters such as the drop-size distribution.

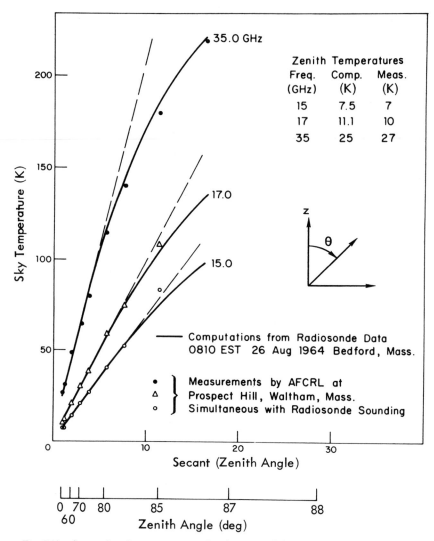

Fig. 5.10 Comparison between measured and computed sky temperature as a function of sec θ, where θ is the zenith angle (Crane, © 1971 IEEE).

5-8 ELECTROMAGNETIC INTERACTION WITH INDIVIDUAL SPHERICAL PARTICLES

If S_i is the power density ($\mathrm{W\,m^{-2}}$) of an electromagnetic wave incident upon a suspended material particle of geometrical cross-sectional area A, then a fraction of the incident power is absorbed by the particle, and an additional fraction is scattered by the particle in all directions. The ratio of absorbed power P_a to incident power density S_i is known as the *absorption cross-section*

Q_a:

$$Q_a = \frac{P_a}{S_i}, \quad m^2, \tag{5.52}$$

and the ratio of Q_a to the physical cross-section A is known as the *absorption efficiency factor* ξ_a. For a spherical particle of radius r, $A = \pi r^2$ and therefore

$$\xi_a = \frac{Q_a}{\pi r^2}. \tag{5.53}$$

If the incident plane wave is traveling in the z-direction and if $S_s(\theta, \phi)$ is the power density of the radiation scattered in the direction (θ, ϕ) at a distance R from the particle, the total power scattered by the particle is the integral of $S_s(\theta, \phi)$ over the spherical surface of radius R centered on the particle:

$$P_s = \iint_{4\pi} S_s(\theta, \phi) R^2 \, d\Omega. \tag{5.54}$$

The *scattering cross-section* Q_s and *scattering efficiency factor* ξ_s are defined as

$$Q_s = \frac{P_s}{S_i}, \quad m^2 \tag{5.55}$$

$$\xi_s = \frac{Q_s}{\pi r^2}. \tag{5.56}$$

The total power removed from the incident wave is $P_a + P_s$, and the corresponding *extinction* (or attenuation) cross-section Q_e and efficiency ξ_e are:

$$Q_e = Q_a + Q_s, \tag{5.57a}$$

$$\xi_e = \xi_a + \xi_s. \tag{5.57b}$$

The scattered power given by (5.54) is the total power scattered by the particle in all possible directions. Of particular interest in radar meteorology is the power density scattered in the backward direction towards the radiation source. This is S_s at $\theta = \pi$. In this connection, the *radar backscattering cross-section* σ_b is defined such that σ_b multiplied by the incident power density S_i would be equal to the total power radiated by an equivalent isotropic radiator, so that at a distance R from the scatterer, $S_s(\pi)$ is given by

$$S_s(\pi) = \frac{S_i \sigma_b}{4\pi R^2}. \tag{5.58}$$

From (5.58), σ_b is given by

$$\sigma_b = 4\pi R^2 \frac{S_s(\pi)}{S_i}, \qquad m^2. \tag{5.59}$$

5-8.1 Mie Scattering

The solution for the scattering and absorption of electromagnetic waves by a dielectric sphere of arbitrary radius r is due to Mie (1908). His derivation (which has been restated by several authors, including Stratton (1941) and van de Hulst (1957), among others) is formulated in terms of

$$\chi = k_b r = \frac{2\pi r}{\lambda_b} = \frac{2\pi r}{\lambda_0} \sqrt{\varepsilon'_{rb}} \tag{5.60a}$$

and

$$n = \frac{n_p}{n_b} = \left(\frac{\varepsilon_{cp}}{\varepsilon_{cb}} \right)^{1/2} \triangleq \varepsilon_c^{1/2} \tag{5.60b}$$

where k_b is the wave number in the background medium, ε'_{rb} is the real part of the relative dielectric constant of the background medium, λ_b is the wavelength in the background medium, λ_0 is the free-space wavelength, and n_p and n_b are the complex indices of refraction of the particle (sphere) material and of the background medium, respectively, and ε_{cp} and ε_{cb} are the corresponding complex dielectric constants. When the background medium is air, as is true in the atmosphere, we have $\varepsilon'_{rb} = 1$, $n_b = 1$, and $\lambda_b = \lambda_0$. However, for other remote-sensing applications of Mie scattering (Chapter 13), the background need not be air. Hence, the more general notation defined by (5.60) will be retained in the material presented in this section. The results of Mie's solution lead to expressions for the scattering and extinction efficiencies of the sphere in the form of converging series, given by

$$\xi_s(n, \chi) = \frac{2}{\chi^2} \sum_{l=1}^{\infty} (2l+1)\left(|a_l|^2 + |b_l|^2\right), \tag{5.61a}$$

$$\xi_e(n, \chi) = \frac{2}{\chi^2} \sum_{l=1}^{\infty} (2l+1)\,\mathrm{Re}\{a_l + b_l\}, \tag{5.61b}$$

where Re signifies "real part of" and a_l and b_l, known as the *Mie coefficients*, are functions of n and χ. The formal expressions for the Mie coefficients involve Bessel functions of complex argument. For computational purposes, Deirmendjian (1969, pp. 14–15) developed an iterative procedure using the recursion formulas for Bessel functions. His development leads to the expressions

$$a_l = \frac{\left(\dfrac{A_l}{n} + \dfrac{l}{\chi}\right) \mathrm{Re}\{W_l\} - \mathrm{Re}\{W_{l-1}\}}{\left(\dfrac{A_l}{n} + \dfrac{l}{\chi}\right) W_l - W_{l-1}} \tag{5.62}$$

and

$$b_l = \frac{\left(nA_l + \dfrac{l}{\chi}\right) \mathrm{Re}\{W_l\} - \mathrm{Re}\{W_{l-1}\}}{\left(nA_l + \dfrac{l}{\chi}\right) W_l - W_{l-1}}, \tag{5.63}$$

where

$$W_l = \left(\frac{2l-1}{\chi}\right) W_{l-1} - W_{l-2} \tag{5.64}$$

with

$$W_0 = \sin\chi + j\cos\chi, \tag{5.65}$$
$$W_{-1} = \cos\chi - j\sin\chi, \tag{5.66}$$

and

$$A_l = -\frac{l}{n\chi} + \left[\frac{l}{n\chi} - A_{l-1}\right]^{-1} \tag{5.67}$$

with

$$A_0 = \cot n\chi. \tag{5.68}$$

For n complex,

$$n = n' - jn'', \tag{5.69}$$

(5.68) can be expressed in the form

$$A_0 = \frac{\sin n'\chi \cos n'\chi + j\sinh n''\chi \cosh n''\chi}{\sin^2 n'\chi + \sinh^2 n''\chi}. \tag{5.70}$$

The above computational form of the Mie coefficients, which involves no approximations, is substantially simpler to use for machine processing than the

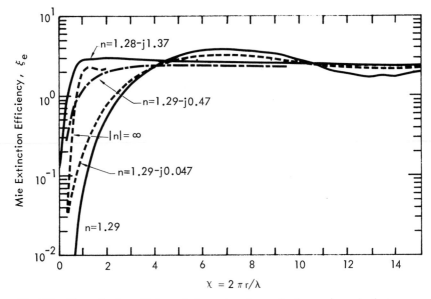

Fig. 5.11   The extinction efficiency ξ_e for various types of spheres, shown in the range $0 \leqslant \chi \leqslant 15$ (Deirmendjian, 1969, Chapter 2).

traditional expressions involving Bessel functions of the complex argument. Deirmendjian (1969, p. 24) notes, however, that when using the above recursion formulas for spheres with $\chi > 30$, inaccurate results are obtained unless double precision is used in the computer program.

The variations of the extinction efficiency ξ_e with χ were computed by Deirmendjian (1969, Chapter 2) for several types of spheres; Fig. 5.11 illustrates the behavior for four spheres (in air) having the same real part of n but differing imaginary parts. The perfect dielectric sphere ($n''=0$) is nonabsorbing ($\xi_a=0$), in which case the curve also is a plot of the scattering efficiency ξ_s. As the absorption is increased (by increasing n''), ξ_e increases rapidly for small particles with $\chi < 4$, and the peak-to-peak variation of the oscillatory behavior occurring for $\chi < 4$ is decreased. Also shown for comparison is a curve for the perfectly conducting sphere with $|n|=\infty$. Regardless of the magnitude of n, all spheres approach $\xi_e=2$ in the "optical" limit ($\chi \gg 1$).

The relative magnitudes of the scattering and absorption efficiencies of a strongly conducting sphere with $n=1.28-j1.37$ are illustrated in Fig. 5.12(a), also from Deirmendjian (1969). For $\chi \ll 1$, which is known as the Rayleigh region, $\xi_s \ll \xi_a$ and therefore $\xi_e \simeq \xi_a$. As χ is increased, the ξ_s curve exhibits a rapid increase, while the ξ_a curve decreases slowly for $\chi > 0.5$. At about $\chi=2.4$, $\xi_s \simeq \xi_a$, and beyond this point ξ_s exceeds ξ_a. Figure 5.12(b) shows the variation of the three efficiencies for values of χ between 1 and 1000.

In contrast to the strongly conducting sphere discussed above, the case of the weakly absorbing dielectric sphere is shown in Fig. 5.13. Here the

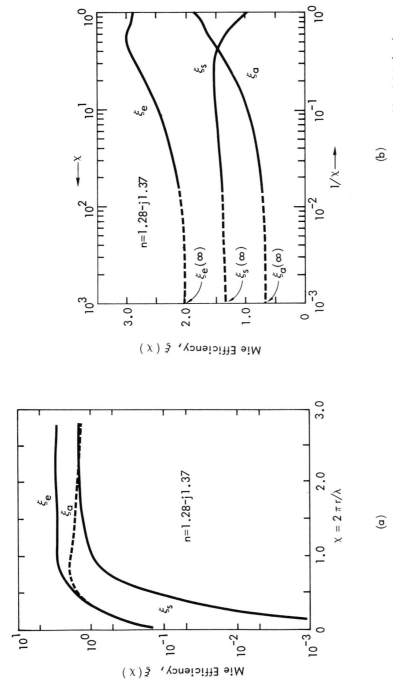

Fig. 5.12 (a) The three efficiencies for conducting spheres with $\chi<3$. (b) The same efficiencies plotted as a function of $\log(1/\chi)$ showing tendency toward the asymptotic values indicated by arrows (Deirmendjian, 1969, Chapter 2).

efficiencies are plotted in the range $0 \leq \chi \leq 0.35$ because the crossover of the ξ_s and ξ_a curves occurs at about $\chi = 0.06$, which is considerably smaller than the crossover value of $\chi = 2.4$ observed earlier in connection with the strongly absorbing sphere of Fig. 5.12. Over the range of χ shown in Fig. 5.13, $\xi_e \simeq \xi_a$ for $\chi < 0.025$ and $\xi_e \simeq \xi_s$ for $\chi > 0.15$. However, beyond $\chi = 0.35$ the curves will exhibit an oscillatory behavior, and as $\chi \to \infty$, $\xi_a \to 1$ and $\xi_s \to 1$ if $n'' \ll 1$ but not identically zero (Deirmendjian, 1969, Chapter 2; van de Hulst, 1957, p. 181).

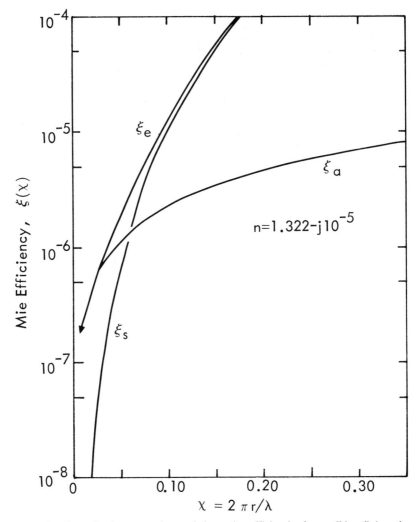

Fig. 5.13 The extinction, scattering, and absorption efficiencies for small but finite spheres composed of dielectric, weakly absorbing material (Deirmendjian, 1969, Chapter 2).

5-8.2 Rayleigh Approximation

If the particle size is much smaller than the wavelength of the incident wave, so that $|n\chi| \ll 1$, the Mie expression for ξ_s and ξ_e may be shown to reduce to simple well-known expressions, known as the Rayleigh approximations (van de Hulst, 1957, p. 270). Specifically, if only the most significant terms of the series expansion of ξ_s and ξ_e are retained, the Mie expressions take the form

$$\xi_s = \tfrac{8}{3}\chi^4 |K|^2 + \cdots \tag{5.71}$$

and

$$\xi_e = 4\chi \operatorname{Im}\{-K\} + \tfrac{8}{3}\chi^4 |K|^2 + \cdots, \tag{5.72}$$

where Im signifies "the imaginary part of" and K is a complex quantity defined in terms of the complex index of refraction n (of the droplet to the background medium)

$$K = \frac{n^2 - 1}{n^2 + 2} = \frac{\varepsilon_c - 1}{\varepsilon_c + 2}. \tag{5.73}$$

Here $\varepsilon_c = n^2$ is the complex dielectric constant of the droplet relative to the background medium. The absorption efficiency ξ_a is obtained from (5.71) and (5.72):

$$\begin{aligned} \xi_a &= \xi_e - \xi_s \\ &= 4\chi \operatorname{Im}\{-K\}. \end{aligned} \tag{5.74}$$

The corresponding scattering and absorption cross-sections are

$$Q_s = \frac{2\lambda^2}{3\pi}\chi^6 |K|^2 \tag{5.75}$$

and

$$Q_a = \frac{\lambda^2}{\pi}\chi^3 \operatorname{Im}\{-K\}. \tag{5.76}$$

Because Q_s varies as χ^6 and Q_a varies as χ^3, Q_a is usually much larger than Q_s in the Rayleigh region ($\chi \ll 1$) unless the particle is made of a very weakly absorbing material (i.e., $n'' \ll n'$ such that $\operatorname{Im}\{-K\} \ll |K|^2$).

For most computational purposes, the Rayleigh approximations yield acceptable accuracies if $|n\chi| < 0.5$. Comparison of the Rayleigh scattering values with the exact values obtained from the Mie expressions is discussed in a later section for water and ice droplets.

5-8.3 Backscattering Cross-Section

Mie's solution for the field scattered by a spherical particle leads to the following expression for the backscattering efficiency ξ_b (normalized radar backscattering cross-section):

$$\xi_b = \frac{\sigma_b}{\pi r^2} = \frac{1}{\chi^2} \left| \sum_{l=1}^{\infty} (-1)^l (2l+1)(a_l - b_l) \right|^2 . \tag{5.77}$$

The Mie coefficients a_l and b_l may again be computed using the procedure outlined in the previous section.

   The behavior of ξ_b as a function of χ is illustrated in Fig. 5.14 for three types of spheres. It is observed that the perfect dielectric nonabsorbing sphere ($n=1.29$) exhibits large oscillations for $\chi > 1$, whereas the strongly absorbing sphere with $n=1.28 - j1.37$ and the perfectly conducting sphere with $|n| = \infty$ show regularly damped oscillations as a function of χ. The limiting value of ξ_b as $\chi \to \infty$ (optical limit) is given by the power reflection coefficient for normal incidence,

$$\lim_{\chi \to \infty} \xi_b(n, \chi) = \left| \frac{n-1}{n+1} \right|^2 . \tag{5.78}$$

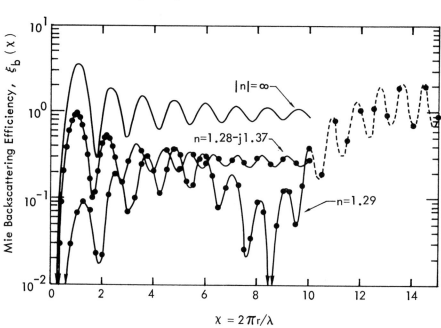

Fig. 5.14   The backscattering efficiency ξ_b for dielectric, conducting, and totally reflecting spheres. The dashed extension of the curve for $n=1.29$ is a freehand fit to the computed points shown (from Deirmendjian, 1969, Chapter 2).

Moving towards low values of χ takes us to the Rayleigh region, corresponding to $|n\chi|$ less than about 0.5. For sufficiently small χ and finite n, it can be shown (Kerr, 1951) that (5.77) reduces to

$$\xi_b = 4\chi^4|K|^2, \qquad |n\chi| < 0.5, \tag{5.79}$$

which is known as Rayleigh's backscattering law. Returning to (5.73), if $|n| \gg 1$ but finite, $|K| \simeq 1$. The corresponding expression for ξ_b from (5.79) is

$$\xi_b \simeq 4\chi^4 \qquad \text{for} \quad \text{finite } |n| \gg 1 \text{ and } |n\chi| < 0.5. \tag{5.80}$$

For a sphere of infinite n, such as a perfectly conducting metal sphere, (5.79) is not applicable, because it is the result of an approximation of the Mie expression for $|n\chi| < 0.5$. A solution obtained directly from the Mie coefficients a_l and b_l for $|n| = \infty$ and $\chi \ll 1$ leads to (Kerr, 1951)

$$\xi_b = 9\chi^4 \qquad \text{for} \quad |n| = \infty \text{ and } |\chi| \ll 1. \tag{5.81}$$

Although already included in Fig. 5.14, ξ_b of the perfectly conducting sphere is shown again in Fig. 5.15 with the χ-axis on a logarithmic scale. This

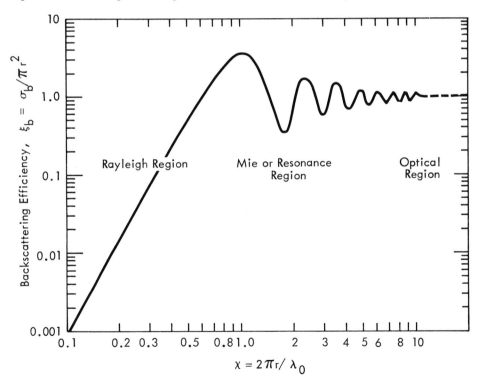

Fig. 5.15 Radar backscattering efficiency as a function of χ for a metal sphere of radius r (Skolnik, 1980).

type of presentation is useful in discerning the three regions shown in Fig. 5.15. In the low-frequency (Rayleigh) region, (5.81) provides accurate results for $\chi < 0.7$; in the intermediate (Mie) region, the Rayleigh approximations are no longer valid and therefore the complete Mie expression given by (5.77) should be used; and in the high-frequency region, the optical limit is $\xi_b = 1$ (from (5.78) with $n = \infty$).

5-9 SCATTERING AND ABSORPTION BY HYDROMETEORS

According to the previous section, the scattering and absorption characteristics of a spherical particle in air are governed by three parameters: (1) the electromagnetic wavelength λ_0, (2) the complex index of refraction n, and (3) the radius r of the particle. The microwave dielectric properties (from which n can be computed) of water and ice are summarized in Appendix E of Volume III. Using this information, the scattering and absorption efficiencies of individual hydrometeors, such as rain and hail, can be computed. The dielectric properties of snow particles can be expressed in terms of those for ice and of the snow density, as discussed below.

5-9.1 Water Particles

The real and imaginary parts of the refractive index of water are shown in Fig. 5.16 as a function of frequency at $0°$ and $20°C$. The curves are calculated from

$$n_w = n'_w - jn''_w = \sqrt{\varepsilon_w}$$
$$= \text{Re}\{\sqrt{\varepsilon_w}\} + j\,\text{Im}\{\sqrt{\varepsilon_w}\}$$

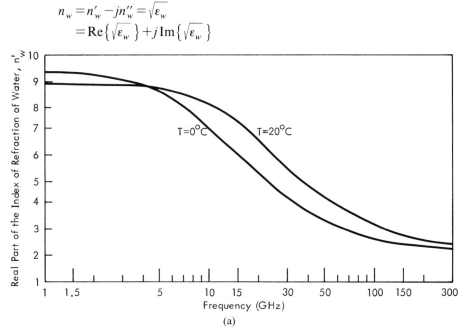

Fig. 5.16 Frequency variation of (a) real part of the index of refraction, n'_w, (b) the imaginary part n''_w, and (c) the magnitude $|n_w|$, for pure water.

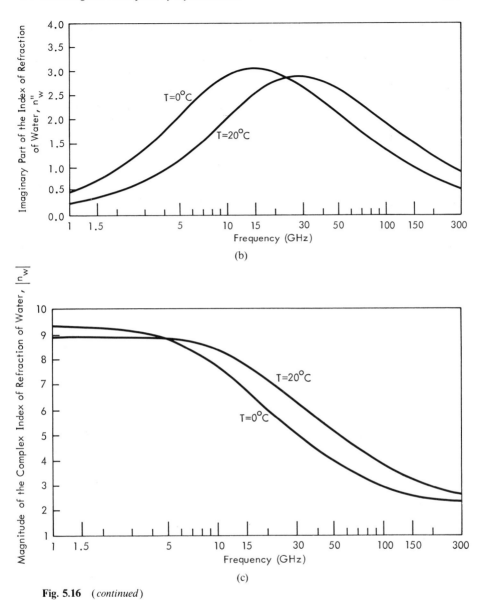

Fig. 5.16   (*continued*)

or

$$n'_w = \mathrm{Re}\{\sqrt{\varepsilon_w}\}$$

and

$$n''_w = \left|\mathrm{Im}\{\sqrt{\varepsilon_w}\}\right|,$$

where ε_w is the relative complex dielectric constant of pure water (see Appendix E of Volume III).

The Mie extinction and scattering efficiencies, ξ_e and ξ_s, are shown in Figures 5.17–5.19 (from Fraser et al., 1975) as a function of drop radius r between 10 μm and 10,000 μm ($= 10$ mm). The three figures, corresponding to 3, 30, and 300 GHz, also include dashed lines representing the Rayleigh extinction efficiency. The heavy horizontal lines indicate the ranges of drop radii characteristic of two types of water clouds and a rain cloud with a rain rate of 25.4 mmhr^{-1}. At 3 GHz, the Rayleigh approximation is certainly applicable for the water clouds and is approximately valid for the rain cloud, while at 30 GHz the Rayleigh approximation is valid for the water clouds only, and at 300 GHz, it is valid for the fair-weather cloud only.

A similar examination of the applicability of the Rayleigh approximation also has been conducted by Haddock (1948). His results are shown in Fig. 5.20, in which the ratio $\xi_e(\text{Mie})/\xi_e(\text{Rayleigh})$ is plotted as a function of $\chi = 2\pi r/\lambda_0$ for each of several values of λ_0, where $\xi_e(\text{Mie})$ is the extinction efficiency factor calculated according to the Mie expression given by (5.61) and

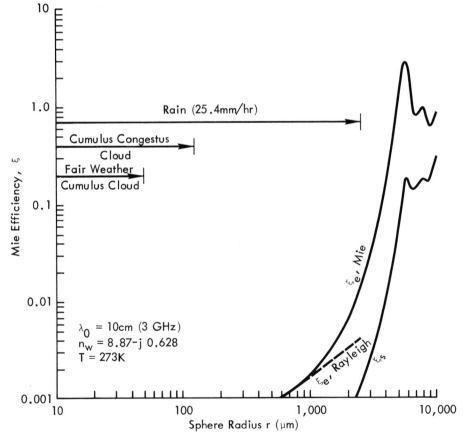

Fig. 5.17 Mie efficiency factors for scattering and extinction by a water sphere as a function of drop radius, at 3 GHz (Fraser et al., © 1975 Am. Soc. Photogram.). Horizontal arrows indicate range of drop radii.

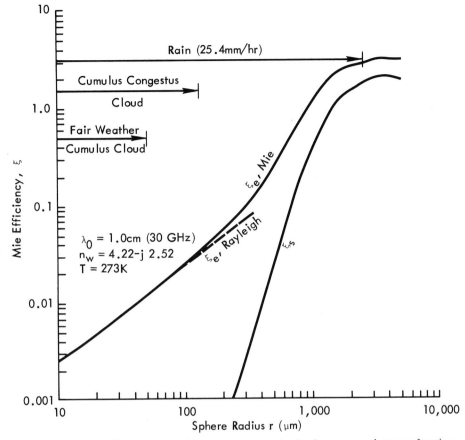

Fig. 5.18 Mie efficiency factors for scattering and extinction by a water sphere as a function of drop radius, at 30 GHz (Fraser et al., © 1975 Am. Soc. Photogram.). Horizontal arrows indicate drop radii.

ξ_e(Rayleigh) is the Rayleigh approximation calculated using (5.72). The Rayleigh approximation is valid for $|n|\chi$ less than about 0.5 (with air as the background medium, χ is real). From Fig. 5.16(c), we observe that $|n_w|$ decreases with increasing frequency between 1 and 300 GHz, and therefore the Rayleigh condition $|n_w|\chi < 0.5$, can be satisfied for increasingly larger values of χ as the frequency increases. Also shown are curves for a similarly defined ratio of the backscattering efficiency ξ_b. Comparison of the two sets of curves indicates that for the same level of relative accuracy, the Rayleigh approximation remains valid up to larger values of $|n_w|\chi$ for ξ_b than for ξ_e. For the backscattering efficiency, the Rayleigh approximation is within the range of 1 ± 0.3 times the Mie value at all wavelengths in the microwave region if $|n_w|\chi \leqslant 2$ (or $\chi \leqslant 0.2$, since the maximum value of $|n_w|$ is about 10 in the microwave region), whereas this condition is not quite sufficient for the extinction efficiency. As will be discussed in the next section, droplets in water

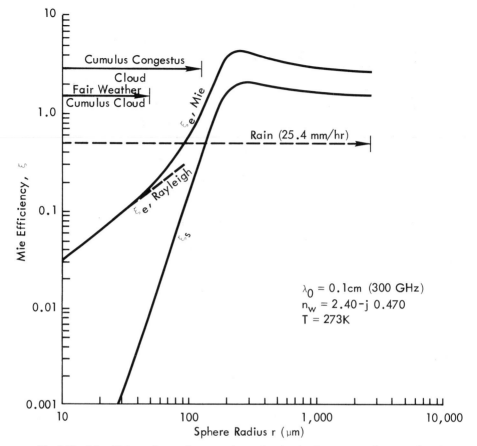

Fig. 5.19 Mie efficiency factors for scattering and extinction by a water sphere as a function of drop radius, at 300 GHz (Fraser et al., © 1975 Am. Soc. Photogram.). Horizontal arrows indicate range of drop radii.

clouds and rain clouds seldom exceed 3 mm in radius. At $\lambda_0 = 10$ cm, the condition $\chi \leqslant 0.2$ corresponds to approximately $r \leqslant 3$ mm, which means that the Rayleigh approximation for ξ_b may be used for most rain conditions with a worst-case accuracy of $10 \log 0.7 = -1.5$ dB. If the accuracy requirement is relaxed to ± 3 dB (or $\xi_b(\text{Mie})/\xi_b(\text{Rayleigh})$ between 0.5 and 2.0), the Rayleigh approximation may be used up to $\chi = 1$ at $\lambda_0 = 1$ cm, corresponding to approximately $r = 1.5$ mm, which includes all water clouds and light-to-moderate rainfall rates.

5-9.2 Ice Particles

The validity of the Rayleigh approximation depends on the magnitude of $|n|\chi$ relative to unity, which is clearly evident in Fig. 5.20: for a given value of χ, the relative accuracy of the Rayleigh approximation is best for the 3-mm-wavelength curve ($n_w = 3.41 - j1.94$) and worst for the 10-cm-wavelength curve

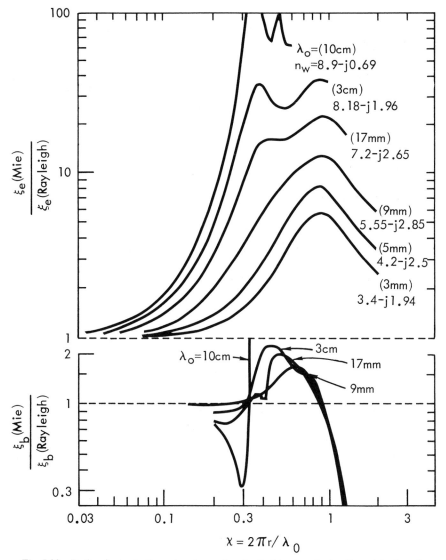

Fig. 5.20 Ratio of actual attenuation (upper) and actual backscattering (lower) to that given by the Rayleigh approximation for water at 18°C (from F. T. Haddock, U.S. Naval Research Laboratory, available in Gunn and East, 1954.).

$(n_w = 8.9 - j0.69)$. In the microwave region, the refractive index of ice, n_i, is smaller than that of water and is weakly dependent on frequency. The real part of n_i is approximately frequency- and temperature-independent and (from Appendix E of Volume III) is given by

$$n_i' \simeq \sqrt{\varepsilon_i'} = 1.78.$$

The imaginary part of n_i varies with frequency and temperature, but its magnitude is much smaller than n_i': $n_i''/n_i' < 10^{-2}$. With $|n_i| \simeq 1.78$, the Rayleigh approximation is valid for $\chi \leqslant 0.3$ for computing ξ_e and for $\chi \leqslant 1$ for computing ξ_b with small error. Thus, the Rayleigh expressions may be used for ice clouds (where r is typically $\leqslant 0.2$ mm) up to about 70 GHz for computing ξ_e, and up to about 200 GHz for computing ξ_b. Occasionally, however, ice crystals may attain radii of the order of 1 mm or larger, in which case the Rayleigh approximation would be limited to the lower microwave region.

5-9.3 Snowflakes

According to the review by Atlas (1964) on scattering by spheroids, the scattering and absorption efficiencies of an ice particle are only weakly dependent on the shape of the particle. Thus, a snowflake, although nonspherical in shape, may be treated using the Rayleigh expression for a spherical particle of the same mass provided the Rayleigh criterion applies.

Snowflakes consist of a mixture of air and ice crystals. The density of pure ice is $\rho_i = 0.916$ g cm^{-3}, and the density of a snowflake, ρ_s, is usually between about 0.05 and 0.3 g cm^{-3}. The relative dielectric constant of dry snow is given (from Appendix E of Volume III) as

$$\frac{\varepsilon_{ds}'-1}{3\varepsilon_{ds}'} = \frac{\rho_s}{\rho_i}\left(\frac{\varepsilon_i'-1}{\varepsilon_i'+2\varepsilon_{ds}'}\right), \tag{5.82}$$

where the imaginary parts of the relative dielectric constants of dry snow and ice have been ignored because their magnitudes are much smaller than the real parts, ε_{ds}' and ε_i'. In Rayleigh scattering, the dielectric properties of the scattering particle appear in the form of the factor K defined by (5.73). For dry snow, let us examine the magnitude of K_{ds}/ρ_s relative to K_i/ρ_i for ice:

$$\frac{K_{ds}/\rho_s}{K_i/\rho_i} = \frac{\rho_i}{\rho_s}\left(\frac{\varepsilon_{ds}'-1}{\varepsilon_{ds}'+2}\right)\left(\frac{\varepsilon_i'+2}{\varepsilon_i'-1}\right).$$

Incorporating (5.82) into the above expression leads to

$$\frac{K_{ds}/\rho_s}{K_i/\rho_i} = \left(\frac{\varepsilon_i'+2}{\varepsilon_{ds}'+2}\right)\left(\frac{3\varepsilon_{ds}'}{\varepsilon_i'+2\varepsilon_{ds}'}\right). \tag{5.83}$$

In the microwave region, $\varepsilon_i' = 3.15$ and is independent of frequency and temperature. The range of values that ε_{ds}' may take is between $\varepsilon_{ds}' = 1$ for $\rho_s = 0$ (air) and $\varepsilon_{ds}' = \varepsilon_i' = 3.15$ for $\rho_s = \rho_i$ (pure ice). At both extremes, the right-hand side of (5.83) is equal to unity, and over the range of interest, $0.05 \leqslant \rho_s \leqslant 0.3$

$g\,cm^{-3}$, it is less than 1.1. The ratio $K_i/\rho_i = 0.46$. Hence, the approximation

$$\frac{K_{ds}}{\rho_s} \simeq \frac{1.1 K_i}{\rho_i} \simeq 0.5 \tag{5.84}$$

may be used in the expressions that follow.

In the Rayleigh region, the backscattering cross-section of a snowflake of radius r_s is, from (5.79), given by

$$\sigma_{bs} = \pi r_s^2 \xi_b = \frac{64\pi^5}{\lambda_0^4} r_s^6 |K_{ds}|^2. \tag{5.85}$$

Marshall and Gunn (1952) proposed that σ_{bs} may be expressed in terms of the parameters of an equivalent ice crystal of radius r_i (and density of 1 $g\,cm^{-3}$) containing the same mass as the snowflake. That is, $r_s^3 = r_i^3/\rho_s$. Incorporating this conversion and the approximate relation given by (5.84) into (5.85) leads to

$$\sigma_{bs} \simeq \frac{16\pi^5}{\lambda_0^4} r_i^6. \tag{5.86}$$

5-10 VOLUME SCATTERING AND ABSORPTION COEFFICIENTS

In a cloud or rain volume, the scatterers (particles) usually are assumed to be randomly distributed within the volume, so that there are no coherent phase relationships between the fields scattered by the individual particles, thereby allowing the use of incoherent scattering theory for computing the absorption and scattering by a volume containing many particles. Additionally, the concentration of particles usually is small enough to support the assumption that shadowing of one particle by another may be ignored. These two assumptions lead to the conclusion that the total scattering cross-section of a given volume is equal to the algebraic sum of the scattering cross-sections of all the individual particles contained in that volume. Similar statements may be made regarding the absorption and backscattering cross sections.

The *volume scattering coefficient* κ_s is the total scattering cross-section per unit volume, and its units are $(Np\,m^{-3})\times m^2 = Np\,m^{-1}$. The range of sizes of the particles contained in a cloud or rain mass usually is described by a continuous function known as the *drop-size distribution* $p(r)$, which defines the partial concentration of particles per unit volume and per unit increment of the radius r. Hence κ_s is given by

$$\kappa_s = \int_{r_1}^{r_2} p(r) Q_s(r)\, dr \tag{5.87}$$

where κ_s = volume scattering coefficient, $\mathrm{Np\,m^{-1}}$,

$p(r)$ = drop-size distribution, number of drops per m^3 per unit increment of r,

$Q_s(r)$ = scattering cross-section of sphere of radius r, m^2,

r = drop radius, m,

r_1, r_2 = lower and upper limits, respectively, of drop radii contained in the cloud

It sometimes is convenient to express κ_s in terms of the scattering efficiency $\xi_s = Q_s/\pi r^2$ and the dimensionless parameter $\chi = 2\pi r/\lambda_0$:

$$\kappa_s = \frac{\lambda_0^3}{8\pi^2} \int_0^\infty \chi^2 p(\chi) \xi_s(\chi)\, d\chi \qquad (5.88)$$

where the limits on the integral cover the entire range of possible values of χ, it being understood that $p(\chi) = 0$ for $r < r_1$ or $r > r_2$. Similar expressions may be written for the volume *absorption*, *extinction*, and *backscattering* coefficients κ_a, κ_e, and σ_v by replacing ξ_s in (5.88) with ξ_a, ξ_e, and ξ_b, respectively. The volume backscattering coefficient σ_v often is called the *radar reflectivity*.

5-11 EXTINCTION AND BACKSCATTERING BY CLOUDS, FOG, AND HAZE

5-11.1 Drop-Size Distribution

Cloud nomenclature and models are defined according to several cloud parameters, the most significant of which are: (1) the liquid water content per unit volume, m_v (gm^{-3}), (2) the drop-size distribution $p(r)$, (3) the principal composition (water, ice, or rain), and (4) the height of the cloud base above the ground. Table 5.5 provides a list of properties for each of six cloud models,

TABLE 5.5
Properties of Standard Cloud Models[a]

Descriptive cloud name	Cloud base (m)	Height top (m)	Mass density liq. H_2O (gm^{-3})	Mode radius of distribution, r_c (μm)	Shape parameters α	γ	Principal composition
Cirrostratus, mid-lat.	5000.	7000.	0.10	40.0	6.0	0.5	Ice
Low-lying stratus	500.	1000.	0.25	10.0	6.0	1.0	Water
Fog layer	0.	50.	0.15	20.0	7.0	2.0	Water
Haze, heavy	0.	1500.	10^{-3}	0.05	1.0	0.5	Water
Fair-weather cumulus	500.	1000.	0.50	10.0	6.0	0.5	Water
Cumulus congestus	1600.	2000.	0.80	20.0	5.0	0.3	Water

[a]Additional models are available in Fraser et al. (1975).

which include ice and water clouds, fog, and haze. Three of the parameters listed relate to the drop-size distribution as formulated by Deirmendjian (1969, pp. 75–76),

$$p(r) = ar^\alpha \exp(-br^\gamma), \qquad 0 \leqslant r \leqslant \infty, \tag{5.89}$$

which vanishes at $r=0$ and $r=\infty$. Deirmendjian calls it a modified gamma distribution, since it reduces to the gamma distribution when $\gamma = 1$. For a given drop-size distribution, a, α, b, and γ are positive and real constants and are related to physical properties of the cloud. For convenience in mathematical manipulations, the constant α is specified to be an integer.

The total number of particles per unit volume, N_v, is obtained by integrating $p(r)$ over all values of r:

$$
\begin{aligned}
N_v &= \int_0^\infty p(r)\, dr \\
&= a \int_0^\infty r^\alpha \exp(-br^\gamma)\, dr \\
&= \frac{a\Gamma(\beta_1)}{\gamma b^{\beta_1}},
\end{aligned}
\tag{5.90}
$$

where $\Gamma(\ )$ is the standard gamma function and

$$\beta_1 = \frac{\alpha + 1}{\gamma}. \tag{5.91}$$

Another parameter of interest is the mode radius of the distribution, r_c. Upon differentiating $p(r)$ with respect to r and setting the result equal to zero, the solution of such an equation for r gives (Deirmendjian, 1969, pp. 75–76)

$$r_c^\gamma = \frac{\alpha}{b\gamma}, \tag{5.92}$$

and the corresponding maximum density of the distribution is

$$p(r_c) = ar_c^\alpha \exp\left(-\frac{\alpha}{\gamma}\right). \tag{5.93}$$

The water content (or mass density) of the cloud, m_v ($\mathrm{g\,m^{-3}}$), is equal to the total volume occupied by the particles per unit volume, V_p, multiplied by the density of water ($= 10^6 \ \mathrm{g\,m^{-3}}$). The volume fraction V_p is obtained by multiplying $p(r)$ by $4\pi r^3/3$ and integrating. Thus,

$$
\begin{aligned}
m_v &= \tfrac{4}{3} \times 10^6 a\pi \int_0^\infty r^{\alpha+3} \exp(-br^\gamma)\, dr \\
&= \frac{4 \times 10^6 a\pi}{3\gamma b^{\beta_2}} \Gamma(\beta_2) \qquad \mathrm{g\,m^{-3}},
\end{aligned}
\tag{5.94}
$$

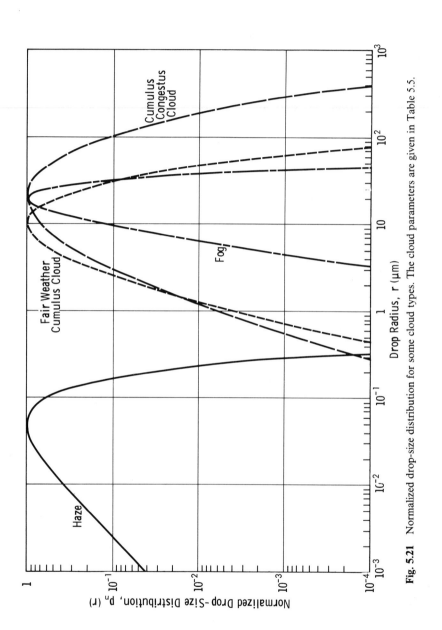

Fig. 5.21 Normalized drop-size distribution for some cloud types. The cloud parameters are given in Table 5.5.

where

$$\beta_2 = \frac{\alpha+4}{\gamma}. \qquad (5.95)$$

By virtue of (5.92) and (5.95), the distribution function $p(r)$ is completely specified by m_v, r_c, α, and γ. The normalized drop-size distribution $p_n(r)$ is the ratio of $p(r)$ to its peak value $p(r_c)$. From (5.89) and (5.93) we have

$$p_n(r) = \frac{p(r)}{p(r_c)} = \left(\frac{r}{r_c}\right)^\alpha \exp\left\{-\frac{\alpha}{\gamma}\left[\left(\frac{r}{r_c}\right)^\gamma - 1\right]\right\} \qquad (5.96)$$

Plots of $p_n(r)$ as a function of r are shown in Fig. 5.21 for two types of water clouds and for fog and haze. As formulated, the distributions are defined for all values of r between 0 and ∞, although clouds do not contain particles with radii much larger than r_c. The justification is based on the fact that $p_n(r)$ becomes very small for $r \gg r_c$. If desired, the distribution may be truncated at the largest value of r.

For a given drop-size distribution $p(r)$, the volume absorption, scattering and extinction coefficients, κ_a, κ_s, and κ_e ($=\kappa_a + \kappa_s$) and the volume back-scattering coefficient σ_v can be obtained through expressions of the form given by (5.88), namely,

$$\kappa = \frac{\lambda_0^3}{8\pi^2} \int_0^\infty \chi^2 p(\chi)\xi(\chi)\,d\chi, \qquad (5.97)$$

where $\chi = 2\pi r/\lambda_0$, and κ is κ_s, κ_a, κ_e, or σ_v corresponding to ξ_s, ξ_a, ξ_e, or ξ_b, respectively, in the integrand. In the general case, the ξ's are the Mie efficiencies defined in Section 5.8. However, if the wavelength λ_0 is such that the Rayleigh approximations are valid over the range of r of the droplets contained in the cloud, simpler expressions are obtained, as shown next.

5-11.2 Volume Extinction Coefficient

It was shown in Section 5.9 that, for individual particles, the Rayleigh approximation is applicable if $|n|\chi \leq 0.5$. Most water clouds (except rain-bearing clouds) do not contain particles with radii larger than 0.1 mm. For the values of $|n_w|$ given in Fig. 5.16(c), the Rayleigh approximation applies to frequencies up to about 50 GHz. Ice clouds may contain particles with radii up to about 0.2 mm, but the refractive index of ice is smaller than that of water. The combination of these two factors leads to the conclusion that the Rayleigh criterion is applicable up to about 70 GHz for ice clouds.

For water and ice spheres, the refractive index is such that the absorption cross-section Q_a is much larger than the scattering cross-section Q_s in the Rayleigh region (see Section 5-8.2). The cloud volume extinction coefficient κ_{ec}

is therefore approximately equal to the volume absorption coefficient, and is given by a summation of the absorption cross-sections of all particles contained in a unit volume of the cloud:

$$\kappa_{ec} = \sum_{i=1}^{N_v} Q_a(r_i), \tag{5.98}$$

where N_v is the number of particles per unit volume and r_i is the radius of the ith particle. Using (5.76) for $Q_a(r_i)$,

$$Q_a(r_i) = \frac{8\pi^2}{\lambda_0} r_i^3 \operatorname{Im}\{-K\}, \tag{5.99}$$

(5.98) becomes

$$\kappa_{ec} = \frac{8\pi^2}{\lambda_0} \operatorname{Im}\{-K\} \sum_{i=1}^{N_v} r_i^3. \tag{5.100}$$

The water content of the cloud, m_v (gm^{-3}), is equal to the volume fraction occupied by the particles, multiplied by the density of water ($=10^6$ gm^{-3}). For N_v particles per unit volume,

$$m_v = 10^6 \sum_{i=1}^{N_v} \frac{4\pi}{3} r_i^3. \tag{5.101}$$

By virtue of the form of the above expression, κ_{ec} simplifies to

$$\kappa_{ec} = \kappa_1 m_v, \qquad \mathrm{Np\,m^{-1}}, \tag{5.102}$$

where

$$\kappa_1 = \frac{6\pi}{\lambda_0} \operatorname{Im}\{-K\} \times 10^{-6} \tag{5.103}$$

is the volume extinction (or attenuation) coefficient in nepers per meter for a water content of 1 gm^{-3}. In (5.103) λ_0 is in meters. If λ_0 is expressed in cm and κ_{ec} is expressed in dBkm^{-1} by multiplying κ_{ec} (Np m^{-1}) by 4.34×10^3, (5.102) and (5.103) become

$$\kappa_{ec} = \kappa_1 m_v \qquad \mathrm{dB\,km^{-1}} \tag{5.104}$$

and

$$\kappa_1 = 0.434 \frac{6\pi}{\lambda_0} \operatorname{Im}\{-K\} \qquad \mathrm{dB\,km^{-1}\,g^{-1}\,m^3} \tag{5.105}$$

with λ_0 in cm. Plots of κ_1 as a function of frequency are shown in Fig. 5.22 for

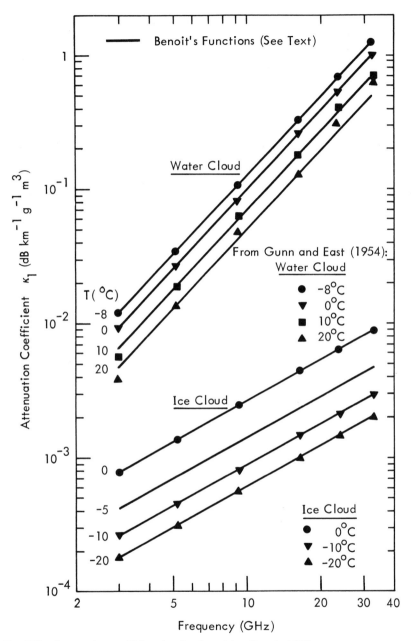

Fig. 5.22   Attenuation coefficient for clouds and fog (Benoit, 1968).

water and ice clouds at several temperatures. We note that κ_1 increases rapidly with increasing frequency f and increases slowly with decreasing temperature. The graphs also show that κ_1 of ice clouds is one to two orders of magnitude smaller than that of water clouds and fog. This difference is attributed to the fact that ice spheres are considerably less lossy than water spheres at the same frequency.

The factor K in (5.105) is a function of the complex dielectric constant of the material (water or ice), which in turn is a function only of the wavelength λ_0 (or microwave frequency f) and the physical temperature of the material, T. The solid lines shown in Fig. 5.22 are plots of empirical functions developed by Benoit (1968) which incorporate the dependence of κ_1 on frequency and temperature. The plots are observed to be in good agreement with the values calculated by Gunn and East (1954) on the basis of (5.105). Benoit's empirical expression is given by

$$\kappa_1 = \begin{cases} f^{a_1}\exp\left[a_2(1+a_3T)\right] \\ \qquad \text{for water clouds and fog,} \\ f^{b_1}\exp\left[b_2(1+b_3T+b_4T^2)\right] \\ \qquad \text{for ice clouds,} \end{cases} \qquad (5.106)$$

where κ_1 is in dB km^{-1} per gm^{-3}, f is the frequency in GHz, T is the temperature in degrees Celsius, and the a's and b's are constants having the following values:

$$a_1 = 1.95 \qquad\qquad b_1 = 1.006$$
$$a_2 = -6.866 \qquad\quad b_2 = -8.261$$
$$a_3 = 4.5 \times 10^{-3} \qquad b_3 = -1.767 \times 10^{-2}$$
$$b_4 = -4.374 \times 10^{-4}.$$

In (5.105), part of the frequency dependence of κ_1 is explicitly expressed in terms of the factor $1/\lambda_0$, but additionally, the factor K may depend on frequency. The empirical relationship given by (5.106) provides an explicit dependence on f. For water clouds and fog, the exponent of f is $a_1 = 1.95$, which means that $\text{Im}\{-K\}$ varies approximately as $f^{0.95}$. The factor K for ice, on the other hand, is approximately frequency-independent, which leads to $b_1 = 1.006$.

The form of (5.106) leads to a linear plot for κ_1 versus f on a log-log scale, as shown in Fig. 5.22. However, this expression is not valid for frequencies much higher than the range indicated in Fig. 5.22. Calculated values of the attenuation by water clouds and fog were reported by Haroules and Brown (1969) for the frequency range between 3 and 300 GHz, and are shown here in Fig. 5.23. It is observed that the linear dependence of κ_1 on f (on a log-log

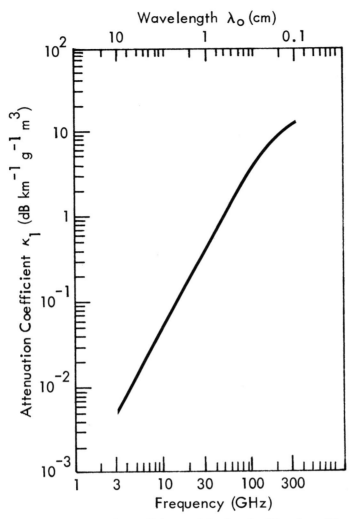

Fig. 5.23 Calculated attenuation coefficient κ_1 of clouds or fog (Haroules and Brown, 1969).

scale) continues with frequency up to about 100 GHz, but at higher frequencies κ_1 exhibits a shallower slope as a function of f due to the weaker frequency dependence of the dielectric constant of water. The curve shown in Fig. 5.23 is based on the Rayleigh approximation given by (5.105). Therefore, beyond about 50 GHz, Fig. 5.23 is representative of the attenuation by fair-weather water clouds only.

Before concluding this section, it is relevant to compare the attenuation by clouds and fog in the microwave region with the visible region of the electromagnetic spectrum. Figure 5.24 shows the attenuation coefficient κ_{ec} (dB km^{-1}) as a function of frequency for several values of the cloud water content m_v. Corresponding to each value of m_v, a "visibility" range R_v is indicated.

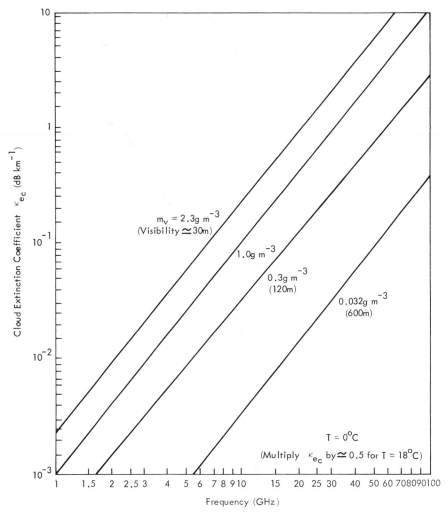

Fig. 5.24 Extinction coefficient of clouds or fog for several water contents (and corresponding visibilities) at 0°C (adapted from Barton, 1974).

Visibility is defined as the greatest distance at which it is possible to identify (with the unaided eye) a dark object against the sky at the horizon (in the daytime). Mathematically, R_v may be defined as the range over which the total attenuation in the visible region ($\lambda = 0.4$–0.7 μm) is approximately 18 dB, which corresponds to a transmission coefficient slightly larger than 1 percent. Thus,

$$\kappa_{ec} R_v \simeq 18 \text{ dB.} \tag{5.107}$$

For $R_v = 600$ m, $\kappa_{ec} \simeq 30$ dB km^{-1} in the visible region, compared to about 0.03 dB km^{-1} at 30 GHz.

5-11.3 Volume Backscattering Coefficient

In the Rayleigh region, the backscattering cross-section of an individual spherical particle of radius r is given by

$$\sigma_b = \pi r^2 \xi_b$$

$$= \frac{64\pi^5}{\lambda_0^4} r^6 |K|^2, \qquad m^2, \tag{5.108}$$

where (5.79) was used for ξ_b. Summing over N_v particles per unit volume, the cloud volume backscattering coefficient σ_{vc} is expressed as

$$\sigma_{vc} = \sum_{i=1}^{N_v} \sigma_b(r_1)$$

$$= \frac{64\pi^5}{\lambda_0^4} |K|^2 \sum_{i=1}^{N_v} r_i^6 \qquad m^{-1}. \tag{5.109}$$

The *reflectivity factor* Z is defined as

$$Z = \sum_{i=1}^{N_v} d_i^6, \tag{5.110}$$

where $d_i = 2r_i$ is the diameter of the ith particle. Use of (5.110) leads to

$$\sigma_{vc} = \frac{\pi^5}{\lambda_0^4} |K|^2 Z \tag{5.111}$$

With d_i expressed in meters, Z has the dimensions of meters to the sixth power per cubic meter. Upon converting Z from m^6 per m^3 to mm^6 per m^3 and expressing λ_0 in centimeters (rather than meters), (5.111) becomes

$$\sigma_{vc} = 10^{-10} \frac{\pi^5}{\lambda_0^4} |K|^2 Z \qquad m^{-1}. \tag{5.112}$$

For water clouds, the reflectivity factor Z_w was related by Atlas (1964) to the cloud water content m_v ($g\,m^{-3}$) through the expression

$$Z_w = 4.8 \times 10^{-2} m_v^2. \tag{5.113}$$

Ice crystals in ice clouds can attain sizes an order of magnitude larger than water droplets found in water clouds. Hence, the reflectivity factor Z_i of an ice cloud may be several orders of magnitude larger than that of a water cloud with the same liquid water content m_v. Atlas (1964) derived the following relation for the reflectivity Z_i of an ice cloud:

$$Z_i = 9.21 \times 10^3 m_v^4. \tag{5.114}$$

Upon inserting (5.113) in (5.112), and similarly inserting (5.114) in (5.112), we obtain the following expressions for the volume backscattering coefficients of water clouds and ice clouds:

$$\sigma_{vwc} = \frac{1.47}{\lambda_0^4} \times 10^{-9} |K_w|^2 m_v^2 \qquad \text{m}^{-1}, \tag{5.115a}$$

$$\sigma_{vic} = \frac{2.82}{\lambda_0^4} \times 10^{-4} |K_i|^2 m_v^4 \qquad \text{m}^{-1}. \tag{5.115b}$$

It should be noted that σ_v has the dimension of reciprocal length (m^{-1}), but it represents physically the backscattering cross-section (m^2) per unit volume (m^3). As can be seen from (5.115), the magnitude of σ_v is quite small in the microwave region. The water content of a cloud typically is less than 1 g m^{-3} and rarely exceeds 4 g cm^{-3}. The factor $|K|^2$ for water varies between 0.89 and 0.93 over the 0–20°C temperature range and 1–10-cm wavelength range. Hence, for $\lambda_0 = 1$ cm and $m_v = 1$ g m^{-3}, we have $\sigma_{vwc} \simeq 1.3 \times 10^{-9}$ m^{-1}. For ice, $|K_i|^2 \simeq 0.2$, which is about 4.5 times smaller than $|K_w|^2$, but because of the much larger value of Z_i (in comparison to Z_w), ice clouds are much more readily detectable by radar.

5-12 EXTINCTION AND BACKSCATTERING BY RAIN

Raindrops are typically two orders of magnitude larger in diameter than cloud droplets. Hence, whereas for clouds the Rayleigh approximation is valid up to about 50 GHz (most cloud types) or even up to 300 GHz (fair-weather clouds), for rain the validity of the Rayleigh approximation is limited to rainfall rates of less than 10 millimeters per hour in the centimeter wavelength range, and to very low rainfall rates at frequencies above 30 GHz (refer to Section 5.15 for further discussion). Hence, in the general case, Mie scattering should be employed for computing absorption and scattering in a rain volume even at the lower microwave frequencies.

5-12.1 Drop-Size Distribution

The drop-size distribution for rain has been determined by several investigators, including Laws and Parsons (1943), Wexler (1948), Marshall and Palmer

TABLE 5.6
Laws-Parsons Drop-Size Distributions for Various Precipitation Rates

Drop diam (cm)	Rain rate (mm hr^{-1})	Percent of Total Volume								
		0.25	1.25	2.5	5	12.5	25	50	100	150
0.05		28.0	10.9	7.3	4.7	2.6	1.7	1.2	1.0	1.0
0.1		50.1	37.1	27.8	20.3	11.5	7.6	5.4	4.6	4.1
0.15		18.2	31.3	32.8	31.0	24.5	18.4	12.5	8.8	7.6
0.2		3.0	13.5	19.0	22.2	25.4	23.9	19.9	13.9	11.7
0.25		0.7	4.9	7.9	11.8	17.3	19.9	20.9	17.1	13.9
0.3			1.5	3.3	5.7	10.1	12.8	15.6	18.4	17.7
0.35			0.6	1.1	2.5	4.3	8.2	10.9	15.0	16.1
0.4			0.2	0.6	1.0	2.3	3.5	6.7	9.0	11.9
0.45				0.2	0.5	1.2	2.1	3.3	5.8	7.7
0.5					0.3	0.6	1.1	1.8	3.0	3.6
0.55						0.2	0.5	1.1	1.7	2.2
0.6							0.3	0.5	1.0	1.2
0.65								0.2	0.7	1.0
0.7										0.3

(1948), and Best (1950). Among these, the most widely used in the literature are the Laws-Parsons and Marshall-Palmer distributions, which compare reasonably well with one another. Table 5.6 presents the distributions reported by Laws and Parsons (1943) based on observations made during 1938 and 1939 in the Washington, D.C. area. One of the major attributes of Laws and Parsons's set is that it covers a wide range of precipitation rates. Graphical presentations are given in Fig. 5.25 for three different rainfall rates.

Using drop-size distributions measured at the ground surface for rainfall intensities between 1 and 23 mm hr^{-1}, Marshall and Palmer (1948) developed the following expression for the distribution of drop-diameters d:

$$p(d) = N_0 e^{-bd}, \tag{5.116}$$

where $p(d)$ = number of drops of diameter d, per unit volume per unit drop-diameter interval, m^{-4},
   $N_0 = 8.0 \times 10^6$ m^{-4},
   d = drop diameter, m,

and $b(m^{-1})$ is related to the rainfall rate R_r (mm hr^{-1}) by

$$b = 4100 R_r^{-0.21}. \tag{5.117}$$

According to Crane (1971), measurements of raindrop size distributions show large variations for the same location, rain type, and rain rate. Consequently, drop-size distribution models should be regarded as representative of average, rather than individual, rainfall conditions.

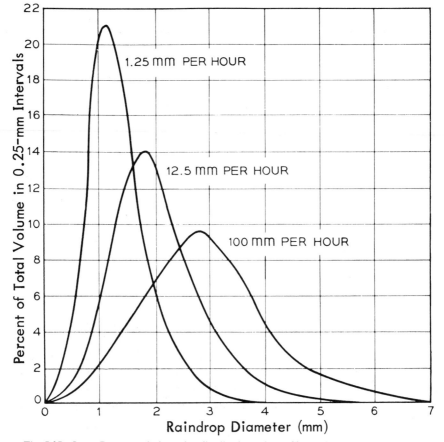

Fig. 5.25   Laws-Parsons raindrop size distributions (from Chu and Hogg, 1968).

5-12.2 Volume Extinction Coefficient

For a given drop-size distribution $p(r)$, where r is the drop radius, the volume extinction (attenuation) coefficient κ_{er} of rain can be computed using (5.97):

$$\kappa_{er} = \frac{\lambda_0^3}{8\pi^2} \int_0^\infty \chi^2 p(\chi) \xi_e(\chi) \, d\chi, \tag{5.118}$$

where, as previously defined, $\chi = 2\pi r/\lambda_0$, and $\xi_e(\chi)$ is the Mie extinction coefficient given by (5.61b).

Using the Laws-Parsons distribution of Table 5.6, Setzer (1970) computed κ_{er} as a function of rainfall rate R_r at 20°C for several microwave frequencies. His results are shown in Fig. 5.26. Similar computations have been reported by Ryde and Ryde (1945) and Medhurst (1965), among others.

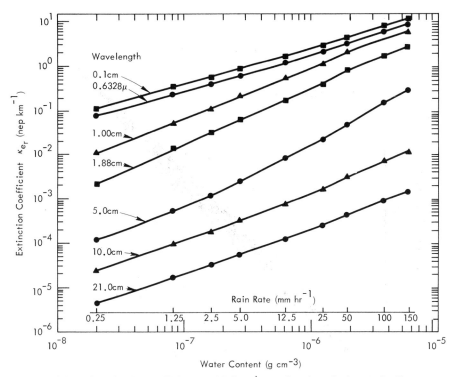

Fig. 5.26 Rain extinction coefficient κ_{er} (Np km^{-1}) as a function of rain rate R_r (Setzer, 1970).

Photographic observations indicate that falling raindrops tend to be flattened on the bottom side, and that this departure from the spherical shape assumed in the computation increases with the size of the drop. The nonspherical shape leads to a polarization dependence of the fields scattered by the raindrop. According to Oguchi's (1964) computations of the attenuation due to distorted raindrops for vertical and horizontal polarizations, the difference in attenuation from the values obtained for spherical particles is less than 16 percent for rain rates up to 150 mm hr^{-1}. The computations were performed for $\lambda_0 = 8.6$ mm. Crane (1971) notes that this difference is small in comparison with the statistical variation of attenuation (at the same rain rate and microwave frequency) due to variations in the drop-size distribution, and therefore the effects of departure from perfect sphericity can be ignored. This conclusion is supported by computations of the attenuation coefficient κ_{er} for 4741 drop-size distributions recorded over a two-year period at Franklin, North Carolina (Crane, 1971). Figure 5.27 is a scattergram of these computations (expressed in dB km^{-1}) as a function of rain rate.

From a practical standpoint, it is desirable to relate the extinction coefficient κ_{er} directly to the rain rate R_r. The relationship commonly used in

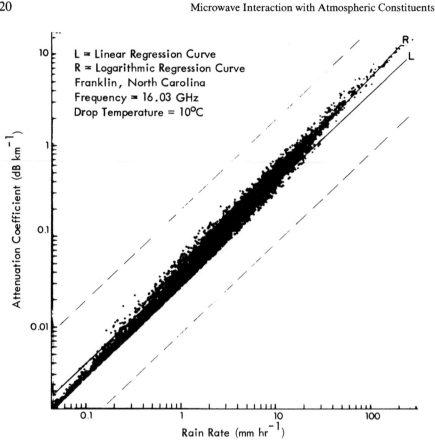

Fig. 5.27 Scattergram of attenuation coefficient versus rain rate at 16 GHz (Crane, © 1971 IEEE).

the literature (Gunn and East, 1954; Crane, 1971; de Bettencourt, 1974) is of the form

$$\kappa_{er} = \kappa_1 R_r^b, \qquad dB\,km^{-1}, \tag{5.119}$$

where κ_1 is in $dB\,km^{-1}$ per $mm\,hr^{-1}$, R_r is the precipitation rate in $mm\,hr^{-1}$, and b is a dimensionless parameter. κ_1 and b, which are functions of the wavelength λ_0, are determined by fitting (5.119) to computed values of κ_{er} for known drop-size distributions. The drop-size distribution determines in turn the precipitation rate R_r through the relation

$$R_r = 6\pi \times 10^{-4} \sum_{i=1}^{N_v} v_i d_i^3 \qquad mm\,hr^{-1}, \tag{5.120}$$

where v_i ($m\,s^{-1}$) is the terminal velocity and d_i (mm) the diameter of the ith raindrop, and N_v (m^{-3}) is the total number of drops per unit volume. Medhurst (1965) gives a curve relating v_i to d_i.

TABLE 5.7
Values of Parameters in the Relationships
$\kappa_{er} = \kappa_1 R_r^b$ **(Logarithmic Model) and** $\kappa_{er} = \kappa_1 R_r$ **(Linear Model)**

Frequency (GHz)	Logarithmic model[a] κ_1 V	Logarithmic model[a] κ_1 H	Logarithmic model[a] b V	Logarithmic model[a] b H	Linear model κ_1	Comments[b]
2.8	0.000459		0.954		—	(1)
7.5	0.00459		1.06		0.00481	(1)
9.4	0.0087		1.10		0.00932	(1)
11.0	0.012	0.014	1.23	1.24	—	(2)
16.0	0.0374		1.10	1.24	0.0403	(1)
18.0	0.053	0.061	1.07	1.10	—	(2)
24.0	0.10	0.11	1.03	1.06	—	(2)
30.0	0.17	0.19	0.98	1.00	—	(2)
34.9	0.225		1.05		0.234	(1)
40.0	0.31	0.38	0.91	0.93	—	(2)
60.0	0.63	0.71	0.81	0.82	—	(2)
69.7	0.729		0.893		—	(1)
80.0	0.86	0.93	0.76	0.77	—	(2)
100.0	1.06	1.15	0.73	0.73	—	(2)

[a] The symbols V and H refer to vertical and horizontal polarizations.
[b] (1) Computed for spherical particles by Crane (1971); (2) computed for oblate spheroidal drops, reported by Harden et al. (1978).

Table 5.7 provides a list of values for κ_1 and b at each of several microwave frequencies between 2.8 and 100 GHz. The values due to Crane (1971) are based on regression fits of computed values of κ_{er} for a large number of measured drop-size distributions and rain rates, as shown by the curve labeled R in Fig. 5.27. The computations were performed for spherical raindrops, and therefore the entries in Table 5.7 are the same for both polarizations. For a horizontally propagating wave through rain, Harden et al. (1978) provide values of κ_1 and b for horizontal and for vertical polarizations, based on theoretical computations of κ_{er} for oblate spheroidal raindrops and a Laws-Parsons (1943) drop-size distribution. The computations were performed by Bell Laboratories researchers (Lin, 1975; Morrison and Cross, 1974). Table 5.7 is by no means a comprehensive list of values reported in the literature; it includes only recent studies representing "normal" rain conditions. The attenuation by intense rain of the order of 100 mm hr^{-1} has been discussed by Hogg (1969); the effects of variations in rainfall rate along the transmission path were examined by Semplak and Turrin (1969) and Goldhirsh (1975); and the depolarization effects caused by rain are discussed by McCormick and Hendry (1975, 1979) and Oguchi (1975).

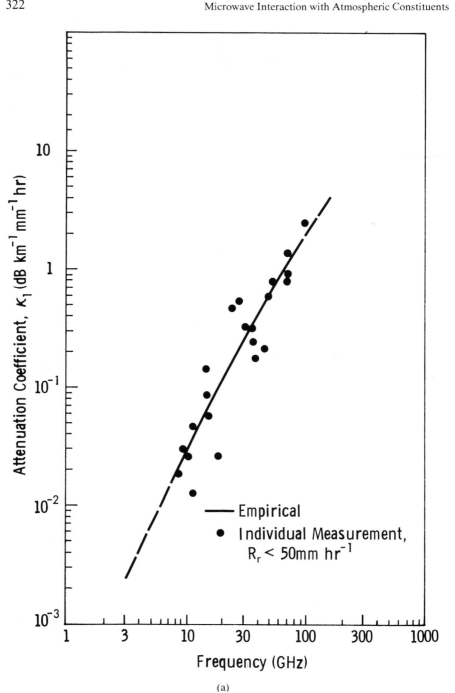

(a)

Fig. 5.28 Empirical averaged rainfall attenuation $\kappa_{er} = \kappa_1 R_r^b$ for the range $2 \leqslant R_r \leqslant 150$ mm hr^{-1}. (a) κ_1 as a function of frequency; (b) the exponent b as a function of frequency (de Bettencourt, 1974).

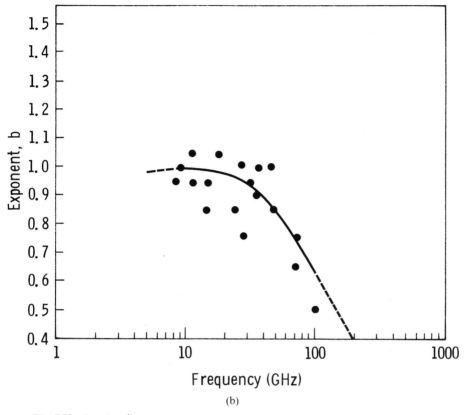

Fig. 5.28 (*continued*)

In addition to the "logarithmic" form given by (5.119), Table 5.7 gives the values of κ_1 for a linear equation ($b=1$) due to Crane (1971). The linear model is simpler to use, but the rms variation about the linear regression curve is slightly larger than the rms variation about the logarithmic regression curve (28 percent compared to 22 percent, respectively, at 16 GHz).

We conclude this section with "averaged" curves (Fig. 5.28) showing regression fits of κ_1 and b as a function of frequency. These curves were generated by de Bettencourt (1973, 1974) on the basis of over 25 literature references to experimental measurements of attenuation by rain. He states that these curves apply to frequencies between 8 and 100 GHz and for R_r between 2 and 150 mm hr^{-1}. Application of these averaged curves, together with curves reported by Haroules and Brown (1968) and by Treussart et al. (1970), results in the family of curves shown in Figure 5.29 (from Schanda, 1976).

5-12.3 Volume Backscattering Coefficient

Formally, the volume backscattering coefficient of rain, σ_{vr}, may be computed using (5.118) with κ_{er} replaced by σ_{vr} and ξ_e replaced by the Mie backscattering

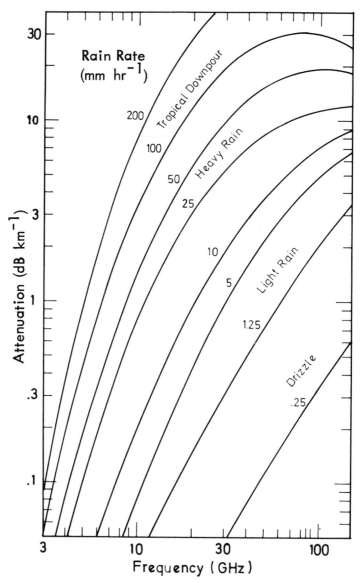

Fig. 5.29 Horizontal-path attenuation at various rain rates (compiled by Schanda, 1976, from data by Haroules and Brown, 1968; Treussart et al., 1970; and de Bettencourt, 1973).

efficiency ξ_b, as defined by (5.77). The practice adopted in the literature, however, has been to model σ_{vr} using the form obtained when the Rayleigh approximation is valid. The Rayleigh volume backscattering coefficient is given by the same expression developed earlier for clouds, namely (5.112):

$$\sigma_{vr} = 10^{-10} \frac{\pi^5}{\lambda_0^4} |K_w|^2 Z, \tag{5.121}$$

where σ_{vr} (m^{-1}) is the backscattering cross-section per unit volume, λ_0 (cm) is the wavelength, $|K_w|$ is a function of the refractive index of water and is given by (5.73), and Z (mm^6 m^{-3}) is the reflectivity factor defined by (5.110). For rain, (5.121) is adequate for frequencies below about 10 GHz. The relationship between Z and the rain rate R_r depends on the drop-size distribution. A widely used expression developed by Marshall and Palmer (1948) is given by

$$Z = 200 R_r^{1.6}, \qquad f < 10 \text{ GHz}, \tag{5.122}$$

where Z is in mm^6 per m^3 and R_r is in mm hr^{-1}.

At frequencies above 10 GHz, the practice has been to continue to use the form of (5.121) by empirically determining an effective (or equivalent) reflectivity factor Z_e that fits the form of (5.121).

Figure 5.30 shows Z_e as a function of rain-rate R_r for various wavelengths λ_0. These relationships were determined by first computing σ_{vr} at 0°C using Mie scattering and the Marshall-Palmer (1948) drop-size distribution, and then calculating Z_e from the expression

$$Z_e = \frac{\lambda_0^4 \sigma_{vr} \times 10^{10}}{\pi^5 |K_w|^2}. \tag{5.123}$$

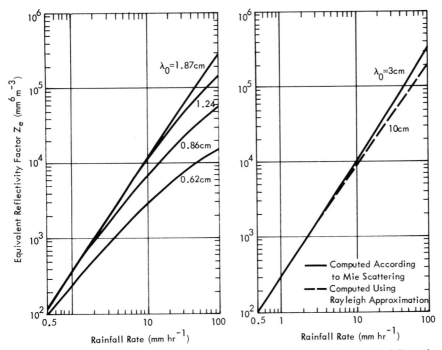

Fig. 5.30 Relationships between equivalent radar reflectivity factor Z_e and rainfall rate for 0°C; Marshall-Palmer drop-size distribution assumed (Wexler and Atlas, 1963).

The dashed curve in Fig. 5.30 was computed using a modified form of (5.122). A thorough review of rain backscatter is available in Battan (1973).

5-13 EXTINCTION AND BACKSCATTERING BY SNOW

5-13.1 Volume Extinction Coefficient

For N_v snow particles per unit volume, the extinction coefficient is given by

$$\kappa_{es} = 4.34 \times 10^3 \left[\sum_{i=1}^{N_v} Q_s(r_i) + \sum_{i=1}^{N_v} Q_a(r_i) \right], \tag{5.124}$$

where κ_{es} is in dB km^{-1}, and $Q_s(r_i)$ and $Q_a(r_i)$ are, respectively, the scattering and absorption cross-sections in m^2 of the ith particle with equivalent radius r_i, defined as the radius of a spherical particle with the same mass as the actual snowflake ($r_s^3 = r_i^3/\rho_s$, where r_s is the radius of the snowflake and ρ_s is its density). In the Rayleigh region, Q_s and Q_a are given by (5.75) and (5.76), respectively, which leads to

$$\kappa_{es} = 4.34 \times 10^{-4} \left[\frac{2 \times 10^{-3} \pi^5}{3\lambda_0^4 \rho_s^2} |K_{ds}|^2 \sum_{i=1}^{N_v} d_i^6 \right.$$

$$\left. + \frac{\pi^2}{\rho_s \lambda_0} \mathrm{Im}\{-K_{ds}\} \sum_{i=1}^{N_v} d_i^3 \right], \tag{5.125}$$

where $d_i = 2r_i$ is the drop diameter in mm, λ_0 is the wavelength in cm, and K_{ds} is related to the refractive index of dry snow through (5.83).

It was shown in Section 5-9.3 that for dry snow $|K_{ds}/\rho_s| \simeq 1.1|K_i/\rho_i| \simeq 0.5$, where the subscript i refers to ice. Now let us consider $\mathrm{Im}\{-K_{ds}\}$. Starting with the expression

$$K_{ds} = \frac{\varepsilon_{ds} - 1}{\varepsilon_{ds} + 2} = \frac{(\varepsilon'_{ds} - 1) - j\varepsilon''_{ds}}{(\varepsilon'_{ds} + 2) - j\varepsilon''_{ds}} \tag{5.126}$$

and using the fact that $\varepsilon''_{ds}/\varepsilon'_{ds} \ll 1$, it can be shown easily that

$$\mathrm{Im}\{-K_{ds}\} \simeq \frac{3\varepsilon''_{ds}}{(\varepsilon'_{ds} + 2)^2}, \tag{5.127}$$

and a similar expression may be obtained for ice,

$$\mathrm{Im}\{-K_i\} \simeq \frac{3\varepsilon''_i}{(\varepsilon'_i + 2)^2}. \tag{5.128}$$

The imaginary part of the relative dielectric constant of dry snow is modeled in terms of the real part ε'_{ds} and of the dielectric constant of ice in the form (from Appendix E of Volume III).

$$\varepsilon''_{ds} = \frac{\varepsilon''_i \rho_i}{\rho_s} \left(\frac{\varepsilon'_{ds} - 1}{\varepsilon'_i - 1} \right)^2.$$

After inserting the above expression in (5.127), it can be shown that

$$\frac{\text{Im}\{-K_{ds}\}/\rho_s}{\text{Im}\{-K_i\}/\rho_i} \simeq \frac{|K_{ds}|^2}{\rho_s^2} \frac{\rho_i^2}{|K_i|^2} \simeq (1.1)^2 = 1.21. \tag{5.129}$$

The quantity Σd_i^6 in (5.125) is recognized as the reflectivity factor Z, which in turn is related to the precipitation rate R_r through (5.135(c)). Also, for a constant snow terminal velocity v_s, the quantity Σd_i^3 is proportional to R_r through (5.120). Incorporating all the above factors, and taking $v_s = 1$ m s^{-1} (which is typical for snow), (5.125) simplifies to

$$\kappa_{es} = 2.22 \times 10^{-2} \frac{R_r^{1.6}}{\lambda_0^4} + 3.0 \, \text{Im}\{-K_i\} \frac{R_r}{\lambda_0} \qquad \text{dB km}^{-1}, \tag{5.130}$$

where R_r is defined as the precipitation rate in millimeters of *melted* water per hour, λ_0 (cm) is the free-space wavelength, and $\text{Im}\{-K_i\}$ is given by (5.128). The above expression may be extended a step further by using (5.128) with $\varepsilon'_i = 3.15$ (see Appendix E of Volume III):

$$\kappa_{es} = 2.22 \times 10^{-2} \frac{R_r^{1.6}}{\lambda_0^4} + 0.34 \varepsilon''_i \frac{R_r}{\lambda_0} \qquad \text{dB km}^{-1}. \tag{5.131}$$

In general, ε''_i varies with frequency and temperature. At $\lambda_0 = 15$ cm, $\varepsilon''_i \simeq 10^{-3}$ at $-1°$C, which results in

$$\kappa_{es} = 4.38 \times 10^{-7} R_r^{1.6} + 2.27 \times 10^{-5} R_r \qquad \text{dB km}^{-1}.$$

For snowfall rates in the range of a few millimeters per hour, the first term (due to scattering) is negligible in comparison with the second term (due to absorption). At $\lambda_0 = 1.5$ cm (which is about the upper limit for the region of validity of the Rayleigh approximation),

$$\kappa_{es} = 4.38 \times 10^{-3} R_r^{1.6} + 2.27 \times 10^{-3} R_r,$$

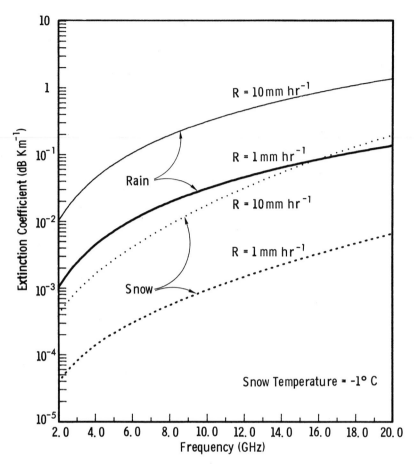

Fig. 5.31 Extinction coefficient of rain as a function of frequency, based on a summary of experimental data (adapted from Barton, 1974).

where $\varepsilon_i'' \simeq 1 \times 10^{-2}$ (for $\lambda_0 = 1.5$ cm and $T = -1°C$) has been used. We note that at the shorter wavelength, the two terms are of comparable magnitude.

The Rayleigh expression given by (5.131) is applicable at frequencies up to about 20 GHz. At higher frequencies, the Mie formulation should be used for computing κ_{es}, following the same basic procedure outlined earlier for rain. Figure 5.31 shows the variation of κ_e as a function of frequency for rain and snow. For the same precipitation rate R_r, the extinction coefficient of dry snow is about 20 to 50 times smaller than that of rain. However, the extinction coefficient of melting snow has been observed to be substantially larger than that of rain (Atlas, 1964). The regions in the atmosphere where snow melting occurs are referred to as "bright bands" due to their high reflectivities on radar images. They usually occur at altitudes just below the 0°C isotherm.

5-13.2 Volume Backscattering Coefficient

The volume backscattering coefficient of dry snow is given by the same basic expression given earlier for rain, namely (5.121). Thus,

$$\sigma_{vs} = 10^{-10} \frac{\pi^5}{\lambda_0^4} |K_{ds}|^2 Z_s. \tag{5.132}$$

Following the same approach employed in the previous section wherein the snowflake of diameter d_s is replaced by an ice particle of diameter d_i containing the same mass, we have

$$Z_s = \sum_{i=1}^{N_v} d_s^6 = \frac{1}{\rho_s^2} \sum_{i=1}^{N_v} d_i^6 = \frac{1}{\rho_s^2} Z_i. \tag{5.133}$$

Inserting (5.133) into (5.132) and using (5.84), we have

$$\sigma_{vs} \simeq 10^{-10} \frac{\pi^5}{4\lambda_0^4} Z_i, \tag{5.134}$$

where the factor $\frac{1}{4}$ comes about from $|K_{ds}|^2/\rho_s^2 \simeq \frac{1}{4}$. According to Atlas et al. (1953), experimental observations suggest that

$$Z_i = 500 R_r^{1.6} \qquad \text{for single crystals} \tag{5.135a}$$

and

$$Z_i = 2000 R_r^2 \qquad \text{for aggregate snowflakes}, \tag{5.135b}$$

where R_r is in millimeters of water per hour. It is suggested further that an average expression characterizing all types of snow is

$$Z_i = 1000 R_r^{1.6}. \tag{5.135c}$$

For water the factor $|K_w|^2$ is approximately 0.9, which is about four times larger than the corresponding factor for snow. On the other hand, the coefficient of $R_r^{1.6}$ in (5.135c) is five times larger than the corresponding coefficient for rain as given in (5.122). Hence, the two factors approximately cancel out, and therefore, the volume backscattering coefficient of dry snow is approximately equal to that of rain for the same precipitation rate. It should be noted, however, that the range of snow precipitation rates is several times lower than that for rain because snowflakes fall at a much lower velocity than raindrops do. As was mentioned earlier, *melted* snow has volume-backscattering-coefficient values exceeding those for rain of the same precipitation rate.

5-14 RADAR EQUATION FOR METEOROLOGY

For a short-pulse radar, the received power due to backscattering from volume-distributed incoherent scatterers is given by

$$P_r = \frac{P_t G_0^2 \lambda_0^2}{(4\pi)^3 R^4} \sigma e^{-2\tau}, \tag{5.136}$$

where P_t = peak transmitted power, W,
        G_0 = antenna gain along the beam axis (dimensionless),
        R = range to scattering volume, m,
        λ_0 = wavelength, m,
        τ = total path attenuation, Np,
        σ = radar cross-section of scattering volume.

The attenuation τ is the sum of the attenuation (extinction) coefficients due to atmospheric gases, clouds, and precipitation (rain or snow), integrated along the path between the radar and the scattering volume at range R:

$$\tau = \int_0^R (\kappa_g + \kappa_{ec} + \kappa_{ep}) \, dr, \qquad \text{Np}, \tag{5.137}$$

where κ_{ep} is equal to κ_{er} for rain or equal to κ_{es} for snow, whichever is present. The radar cross-section σ is equal to the backscattering cross-section per unit volume, σ_v, integrated over the volume contributing to the received power P_r. For a narrow-beam antenna with half-power beamwidths β_θ and β_ϕ, the contributing volume at a range R is

$$V = \pi \left(\frac{R\beta_\theta}{2} \right) \left(\frac{R\beta_\phi}{2} \right) \left(\frac{c\tau_p}{2} \right), \tag{5.138}$$

where c is the velocity of light and τ_p is the pulse length, assumed sufficiently short for R to be considered constant over the depth range $c\tau_p/2$ of the scattering volume. If σ_v is approximately uniform over V, then

$$\sigma = \sigma_v V, \qquad \text{m}^2, \tag{5.139}$$

and P_r becomes

$$P_r = \left[\frac{P_t G_0^2 \lambda_0^2 \beta_\theta \beta_\phi c \tau_p e^{-2\tau}}{32(4\pi R)^2} \right] \sigma_v. \tag{5.140}$$

Expressions for σ_v of clouds, rain, and snow are given in Sections 5.11, 5.12, and 5.13, respectively.

5-15 EMISSION BY CLOUDS AND RAIN

Downward emission by atmospheric gases was discussed in Section 5-6.2. For moderate cloud cover and rain-rate conditions, the atmosphere may be considered a nonscattering medium in the centimeter and part of the millimeter wavelength regions. In this case, the apparent temperature expression given by (5.49) may be used:

$$T_{DN}(\theta) = \sec\theta \int_0^\infty \kappa_a(z')T(z')e^{-\tau(0,\,z')\sec\theta}\,dz', \qquad (5.141)$$

where T_{DN} represents the downwelling atmospheric radiation at angle θ from the vertical, $T(z')$ is the thermometric temperature of the atmosphere at height z', and $\tau(0, z')$ is the zenith optical thickness of the layer between the surface and height z',

$$\tau(0, z') = \int_0^{z'} \kappa_a(z)\,dz, \qquad \text{Np}.$$

The quantity $\kappa_a(z)$ is the total absorption coefficient at height z (km) consisting of contributions due to atmospheric gases, clouds (if present), and precipitation (if present). It is given by

$$\kappa_a(z) = \kappa_g(z) + \kappa_{ec}(z) + \kappa_{ep}(z), \qquad \text{Np km}^{-1}, \qquad (5.142)$$

where the subscripts g, c, and p refer to gases, clouds, and precipitation, respectively. In the Rayleigh region, the extinction coefficients κ_{ec} and κ_{ep} are due primarily to absorption. The expression for κ_g is given by (5.43) in dB km^{-1}; therefore, it should be divided by the factor 4.34 to convert it to Np km^{-1} before using it in (5.142). For clouds, the Rayleigh approximation for computing the volume extinction absorption coefficient κ_{ec} (as given by (5.104)) is valid up to about 50 GHz (Section 5-11.2), and for fair-weather clouds it is applicable throughout the microwave region.

Because raindrops are larger than water drops in clouds, ignoring scattering effects of rain in favor of absorption is valid only over a limited range of rain-rate and frequency combinations. Figure 5.32 shows the scattering albedo $a = Q_s/Q_e$ for a raindrop as a function of $\chi = \pi d/\lambda_0$, where d is the drop diameter. Recall that Q_s is the scattering cross-section and $Q_e = Q_s + Q_a$ is the extinction cross-section. If $a \leqslant 0.2$ is used as the criterion for neglecting scattering losses, the corresponding value of χ is approximately 0.45 (from Fig. 5.32). At a given wavelength of interest, this value of χ can be translated to rainfall rate R_r through a curve similar to that shown in Fig. 5.33. At 35 GHz ($\lambda_0 = 8.6$ mm), for example, $\chi \leqslant 0.45$ is equivalent to $d \leqslant 1.3$ mm, which corresponds to $R_r \leqslant 6$ mm hr^{-1}. Since this result is based on the maximum

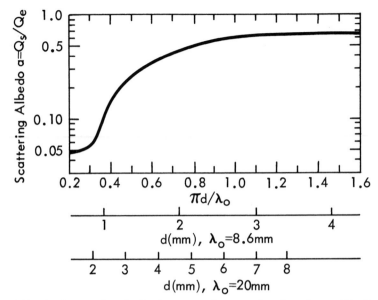

Fig. 5.32 Single-scattering albedo of a water sphere as a function of $\chi = \pi d/\lambda_0$ (from Wulfsberg and Altshuler, © 1972 IEEE).

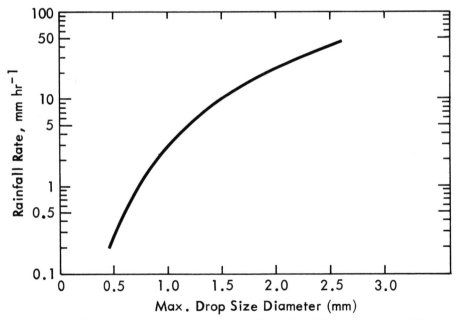

Fig. 5.33 Rain rate versus maximum drop-size at Hilo, Hawaii (from Blanchard and Spencer, 1957).

drop size, which represents a small percentage of the total drop-size distribution, the effects of scattering by raindrops remain negligible for somewhat higher precipitation rates, or equivalently, at higher frequencies for the same rainfall rate.

If the antenna main beam is not pointing at the sun, the contributions of extraterrestrial radiation sources can be neglected above 10 GHz, in which case the sky radiometric temperature $T_{SKY}(\theta)$, as defined by (5.51), reduces to $T_{DN}(\theta)$:

$$T_{SKY}(\theta) = T_{DN}(\theta).$$

Weger (1960) computed $T_{SKY}(\theta)$ at several wavelengths for each of three atmospheric conditions, which he describes as follows:

Case 1: Clear sky with sea-level water-vapor content $\rho_0 = 7.5 \text{ gm}^{-3}$ and temperature 290 K.

Case 2: Uniform moderate cloud cover between 900 and 1800 m with condensed-water content 0.3 gm^{-3}, superimposed on Case 1.

Case 3: Uniform moderate rain between 0 and 900 m with a precipitation rate of 4 mm hr^{-1}, superimposed on Case 2.

The results of Weger's computations are shown in Figs. 5.34 to 5.36 for Cases 1 to 3, respectively. For the clear-sky case, T_{SKY} at $\lambda_0 = 1.25$ cm is larger in magnitude than at 0.86 cm because the former is close to the 22-GHz water-vapor absorption line while the latter is in the 35-GHz atmospheric window (see Fig. 5.5). Similarly, the $\lambda_0 = 0.43$-cm curve is higher than the $\lambda_0 = 0.30$-cm curve because of the proximity of 0.43-cm wavelength to the oxygen absorption complex centered at 60 GHz ($\lambda_0 = 0.5$ cm). As the weather conditions become progressively worse (Cases 2 and 3), the monotonic increase of cloud and rain attenuation (and therefore emission) with frequency causes T_{SKY} at $\lambda_0 = 0.86$ cm to exceed that at $\lambda_0 = 1.25$ cm for Case 3 (Fig. 5.36). Also, the $\lambda_0 = 0.3$-cm and $\lambda_0 = 0.43$-cm curves in Fig. 5.36 are much closer to one another than for Cases 1 and 2.

The radiation received by an upward-looking radiometer is due to emission from, primarily, the lower two to three kilometers of the atmosphere. In this region, the thermometric temperature decreases linearly with a lapse rate of about 6.5 K per kilometer. Thus, on a percentage basis, the change in $T(z)$ is small in the lower few kilometers, and therefore $T(z)$ may be considered a constant equal to T_m, a mean or effective physical temperature. In the presence of precipitation, the attenuation due to rain overshadows the contributions due to clouds and atmospheric gases (at frequencies below 18 GHz or in one of the atmospheric windows), and therefore $\kappa_a(z)$ may be considered a constant over the vertical extent of the rain. These two approximations lead to

$$T_{SKY}(\theta) = T_{DN}(\theta) = \sec\theta \, T_m \int_0^{z_1} \kappa_a e^{-\kappa_a z' \sec\theta} \, dz', \qquad (5.143)$$

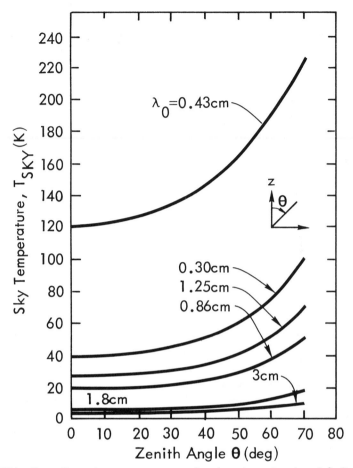

Fig. 5.34 Sky radiometric temperatures as a function of wavelength and θ. Case 1. Conditions: Clear sky (water-vapor content at sea level 7.5 $\mathrm{g\,m^{-3}}$); sea-level temperature 290 K (Weger, 1960).

where z_1 is the vertical extent of the rain. The above expression integrates to

$$T_{SKY}(\theta)=T_m\left(1-\frac{1}{L_a}\right), \tag{5.144}$$

where L_a is the atmospheric (primarily rain) loss factor defined by

$$L_a=e^{\kappa_a z_1 \sec\theta}. \tag{5.145}$$

By estimating T_m from radiosonde data (or through measurements of T_{SKY} under clear-sky conditions (Wulfsberg and Altshuler, 1972)), a measurement of T_{SKY} for rain can provide an estimate of the loss factor L_a.

Another approach used for measuring L_a is one that makes use of the sun as a transmission source. If the antenna is made to point at the sun, T_{SKY}

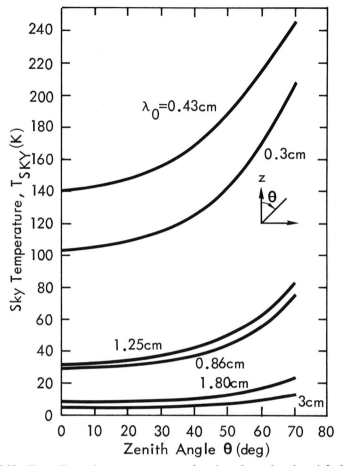

Fig. 5.35 Sky radiometric temperatures as a function of wavelength and θ. Case 2. Conditions: Moderate cloud cover ($m_v = 0.3 \ \mathrm{g\,m^{-3}}$) between 900 and 1800 m; sea-level temperature 290 K (Weger, 1960).

becomes

$$T_{SKY}(\theta) = \frac{\overline{T}_{SUN}}{L_a} + T_{DN}(\theta), \tag{5.146}$$

where $\overline{T}_{SUN}$ is the "effective" radiometric temperature of the sun. It is an "effective" temperature in the sense that

$$\overline{T}_{SUN} = \begin{cases} T_{SUN} & \text{if } \Omega_s > \Omega_p, & (5.147a) \\[2mm] T_{SUN}\dfrac{\Omega_s}{\Omega_p} & \text{if } \Omega_s < \Omega_p, & (5.147b) \end{cases}$$

where T_{SUN} is the true radiometric (blackbody) temperature of the sun, Ω_s is

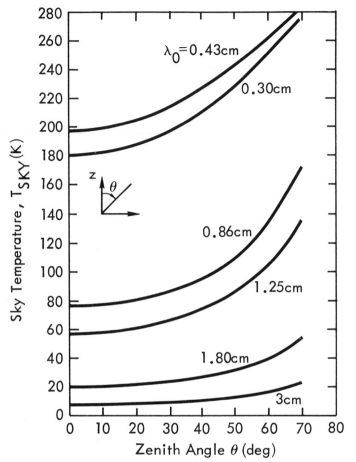

Fig. 5.36 Sky radiometric temperatures as a function of wavelength and θ. Case 3. Conditions: moderate rain ($R_r = 4$ mm hr^{-1}) between 0 and 900 m; moderate cloud cover ($m_v = 0.3$ g m^{-3}) between 900 and 1800 m; sea-level temperature 290 K (Weger, 1960).

the solid angle subtended by the solar disc, and Ω_p is the antenna-pattern solid angle (or approximately, the main-beam solid angle).

When pointed at the sun, a radiometer measures $T_{SKY}(\theta)$ as given by (5.146), and when pointed away from the sun but at approximately the same atmospheric mass, the radiometer measures $T_{DN}(\theta)$. The difference, which is equal to $\bar{T}_{SUN}/L_a$, may be used to determine L_a (assuming $\bar{T}_{SUN}$ is known from measurements made under clear-sky conditions.

Figures 5.37 and 5.38 compare values of L_a(dB) ($= 10 \log L_a$) calculated from measurements of T_{SKY} according to (5.144), plotted along the vertical axis, against values (horizontal axis) calculated using the sun as a source, as discussed above. At both frequencies, the agreement between the two methods is quite good. For values of L_a(dB) > 10 dB, however, the authors note that substantial variability between the two methods is observed. Similar remarks

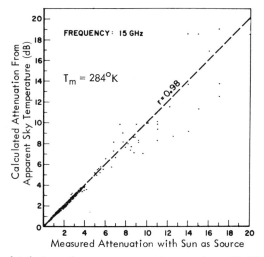

Fig. 5.37 Calculated attenuation versus measured attenuation at 15 GHz (from Wulfsberg and Altshuler, © 1972 IEEE).

have been made by Wilson (1969) in connection with atmospheric-loss measurements made by the sun tracker of Bell Laboratories.

Measurements of the downwelling atmospheric temperature also may be used for estimating the total integrated water vapor and cloud liquid in a vertical column of the atmosphere. Guiraud et al. (1979) discuss the results of such a technique using a dual-frequency microwave radiometer operating at 20.6 GHz, in close proximity to the 22.23-GHz water-vapor absorption line, and at 31.6 GHz in the transmission window above the water-vapor line.

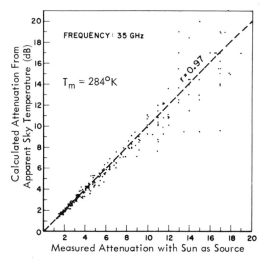

Fig. 5.38 Calculated attenuation versus measured attenuation at 35 GHz (from Wulfsberg and Altshuler, © 1972 IEEE).

PROBLEMS

5.1. For the earth's atmosphere, the total air mass contained in a semiinfinite vertical column of 1-m^2 cross-sectional area is 1.034×10^4 kg. How does this value compare with the value obtained on the basis of the density profile defined by:

(a) Equation (5.2)?
(b) Equation (5.3)?

5.2. For the water-vapor density profile given by (5.7), what percentage of the total mass of water M_v is contained within the lowermost layer of the atmosphere, if its vertical thickness is equal to

(a) one scale height?
(b) two scale heights?

5.3. The text gives two expressions for the water-vapor absorption coefficient: (5.22), which is applicable for $f \leqslant 100$ GHz, and (5.30), which is applicable throughout the microwave region. Compare the two expressions by computing each of them at 100 GHz for sea-level conditions ($T = 300$ K, $P = 1013$ mbar, and $\rho_0 = 7.5$ g m^{-3}).

5.4. Compute the oxygen absorption coefficient at 45 GHz using (5.33), and compare with the value obtained using (5.40). Assume sea-level conditions ($T = 300$ K and $P = 1013$ mbar).

5.5. Compute the zenith sky temperature at 35 GHz for the 1962 U.S. Standard Atmosphere, assuming a water-vapor scale height of 2 km and surface values $T_0 = 300$ K, $P_0 = 1013$ mbar, and $\rho_0 = 7.5$ g m^{-3}.

5.6. Compute the Mie extinction, scattering, absorption, and backscattering efficiencies of a spherical particle whose index of refraction is $n = 1.3 - j0.5$ and whose circumference is $\lambda/2$. Limit the computation to the first few significant terms.

5.7. Repeat Problem 5.6 using the Rayleigh approximations. Compare the results.

5.8. Consider a cumulus congestus cloud described by the drop-size distribution function given by (5.89) and the parameters listed in Table 5.5. Compute the radius r that is exceeded by only one percent of the total number of drops. Compare this value of r with the mode radius r_c.

5.9. The cloud attenuation coefficient given by (5.102) was derived by summing the absorption cross-sections of N_v particles per unit volume (Equation (5.98)). Show that the same result is obtained if the integral form given by (5.97) is used.

5.10. Consider a horizontally polarized 35-GHz satellite-borne radiometer observing the ocean surface. Compute and plot the apparent temperature as a function of the angle of incidence between 0° (nadir) and 70°, assuming a flat-surface model and a water physical temperature of 300

K, for each of the following conditions:

(a) A lossless atmosphere.
(b) An atmosphere containing a 2-km-thick water cloud with a water content of 1 gm^{-3} (again ignoring the influence of atmospheric gases). The cloud may be considered to have a constant temperature of 273 K.
(c) An atmosphere containing a 2-km-thick precipitating cloud with a rainfall rate of 10 $mm\,hr^{-1}$ (again ignoring the influence of atmospheric gases). The rain volume may be considered to have a constant temperature of 280 K.

Note: At 35 GHz, the relative dielectric constant of water is approximately $\varepsilon = 20 - j\,30$.

5.11. Show that for spherical raindrops, the rainfall rate is given by (5.120).

References

Artman, J. O., and J. P. Gordon (1954), Absorption of Microwaves by Oxygen in the Millimeter Wavelength Region, *Phys. Rev.*, 96, pp. 1237–1245.

Atlas, D., M. Kerker, and W. Hitschfeld (1953), Scattering and Attenuation by Non-Spherical Atmospheric Particles, *J. Atmos. Terr. Phys.*, 3, p. 108.

Atlas, D. (1964), Advances in Radar Meteorology, in *Advances in Geophysics*, 10, H. E. Landsberg and J. Van Miegham, eds., Academic Press, New York, pp. 318–483.

Atlas, D., R. M. Cunningham, R. J. Donaldson, Jr. G. Kantor, and P. Newman (1965), Some Aspects of Electromagnetic Wave Propagation, in *Handbook of Geophysics and Space Environment*, S. L. Valley, ed., Office of Aerospace Research, USAF, Cambridge Res. Labs., Chapter 9.

Barrett, A. H., and V. K. Chung (1962), A Method for the Determination of High-Altitude Water Vapor Abundance from Ground-Based Microwave Observations, *J. Geophys. Res.*, 67, pp. 4259–4266.

Barton, David K., ed. (1974), *Radars. Vol. 2—The Radar Equation*, Artech House Inc., pp. 219–220.

Battan, L. J. (1973), *Radar Observations of the Atmosphere.* The University of Chicago Press, Chicago.

Becker, G. E., and S. H. Autler (1946), Water Vapor Absorption of Electromagnetic Radiation in the Centimeter Wave-Length Range, *Phys. Rev.*, 70, pp. 300–307.

Benoit, A. (1968), Signal Attenuation Due to Neutral Oxygen and Water Vapor, Rain and Clouds, *Microwave J.*, 11, pp. 73–80.

Best, A. C. (1950), The Size Distribution of Raindrops, *Quart. J. Roy. Meteor. Soc.*, 76, pp. 16–36.

Blanchard, D., and T. Spencer (1957), Raindrop Measurements During Project Shower, *Tellus*, 4, pp. 541–552.

Carter, C. J., R. L. Mitchell, and E. E. Reber (1968), Oxygen Absorption Measurements in the Lower Atmosphere, *J. Geophys. Res.*, 73, pp. 3113–3120.

Chu, T. S., and D. C. Hogg (1968), Effects of precipitation on Propagation at 0.63, 3.5, and 10.6 Microns, *Bell Sys. Tech. J.*, 47, pp. 723–759.

Cole, A. E., A. Court, and A. J. Kantor (1965), Model Atmospheres, in *Handbook of Geophysics and Space Environment*, S. L. Valley, ed., Office of Aerospace Research, USAF, Cambridge Res. Labs., Chapter 2.

Crane, R. K. (1971), Propagation Phenomena Affecting Satellite Communication Systems Operating in the Centimeter and Millimeter Wavelength Bands, *Proc. IEEE*, 59, pp. 173–188.

Crane, R. K. (1981), Fundamental Limitations Caused by RF Propagation, *Proc. IEEE*, 69, pp. 196–209.

de Bettencourt, J. T. (1973), Statistics of Terrestrial Millimeter-Wave Rainfall Attenuation, Preprint, *Symposium Inter Union Commun. Radio Meteorology*, Nice, France.

de Bettencourt, J. T. (1974), Statistics of Millimeter-Wave Rainfall Attenuation, *Journal de Recherches Atmospheriques*, 8, pp. 89–119.

Deirmendjian, D. (1969), *Electromagnetic Scattering on Spherical Polydispersions*, American Elsevier Publishing Co., Inc., New York.

Dryagin, Yu. A., A. G. Kislyakov, L. M. Kukin, A. I. Naumov, and L. I. Fedoseev (1966), *Sov. Radiophys.*, 9, p. 1078.

Evans, J. V., J. Ruze, H. G. Weiss, R. H. Kingston, and C. Blake (1968), Radar Astronomy Systems: Equipment, in *Radar Astronomy*, J. V. Evans and T. Hagfors, eds., McGraw-Hill, New York.

Fraser, K. S., N. E. Gaut, E. C. Reifenstein, II, and H. Sievering (1975), Interaction Mechanisms—Within the Atmosphere, in *Manual of Remote Sensing*, I, R. G. Reeves, ed., American Society of Photogrammetry, Falls Church, Virginia, Chapter 5, pp. 207–210.

Gaut, N. E., and E. C. Reifenstein III (1971), Environmental Research and Technology, Inc., Report No. 13, Lexington, Massachusetts.

Goldhirsh, J. (1975), Prediction Methods for Rain Attenuation Statistics at Variable Path Angles and Carrier Frequencies Between 13 and 100 GHz, *IEEE Trans. Ant. Prop.*, AP-30, pp. 706–791.

Gordy, W., and R. L. Cook (1970), *Microwave Molecular Spectra*, John Wiley & Sons, Inc., New York.

Gross, E. P. (1955), Shape of Collision-Broadened Spectral Lines, *Phys. Rev.*, 97, pp. 395–403.

Guiraud, F. O., J. Howard, and D. Hogg (1979), A Dual-Channel Microwave Radiometer for Measurement of Precipitable Water Vapor and Liquid, *IEEE Trans. Geos. Elec.*, GE-17, pp. 129–142.

Gunn, K. L. S., and T. W. R. East (1954), The Microwave Properties of Precipitation Particles, *Quart. J. Royal Meteorol. Soc.*, 80, pp. 522–545.

Haddock, F. T. (1948), Scattering and Attenuation of Microwave Radiation Through Rain, Naval. Res. Lab., Washington (unpublished manuscript).

Hall, J. T. (1967), Attenuation of Millimeter Wavelength Radiation by Gaseous Water, *Appl. Opt.*, 6, pp. 1391–1398.

Harden, G. N., J. R. Norbury, and W. J. K. White (1978), Estimation of Attenuation by Rain on Terrestrial Radio Links in the UK at Frequencies from 10 to 100 GHz, *Microwaves, Optics and Acoustics*, 2, pp. 97–104.

Haroules, G. G., and W. E. Brown, III (1968), Radiometric Measurement of Attenuation and Emission by the Earth's Atmosphere at Wavelengths from 4 cm to 8 mm, *IEEE Trans. on Microwave Theory and Techniques*, MTT-16, pp. 611–620.

Haroules, G. G., and W. E. Brown (1969), The Simultaneous Investigation of Attenuation and Emission by the Earth's Atmosphere at Wavelengths from 4 cm to 8 mm, *J. Geophys. Res.*, 74, pp. 4453–4471.

Hering, W. S. (1965), Atmospheric Composition, Section 6.2 in *Handbook of Geophysics and Space Environment*, S. L. Valley, ed., Office of Aerospace Research, USAF, Cambridge Res. Labs.

Hogg, D. C. (1969), Statistics on Attenuation of Microwaves by Intense Rain, *Bell Syst. Tech. J.*, 48, pp. 2949–2962.

Kerr, D. E. (1951), *Propagation of Short Radio Waves*, Dover Publications, Inc., New York, pp. 451–452.

Laws, J. O., and D. A. Parsons (1943), The Relationship of Raindrop Size to Intensity, *Trans. Am. Geophys. Union*, 24th Annual Meeting, pp. 452–460.

Liebe, H. J. (1969), Calculated Tropospheric Dispersion and Absorption Due to the 22-GHz Water Vapor Line, *IEEE Trans. Ant. Prop.*, AP-17, pp. 621–627.

Liebe, H. J., and T. A. Dillon (1969), Accurate Foreign Gas Broadening Parameters of the 22 GHz H_2O Line from Refraction Spectroscopy, *J. Chem. Phys.*, 50, pp. 727–732.

Liebe, H. J., M. C. Thompson, Jr., and T. A. Dillon (1969), Dispersion Studies of the 22 GHz Water Vapor Line Shape, *J. Quant. Spectr. Radiative Transfer*, 9, pp. 31–47.

Liebe, H. J., and W. M. Welch (1973), Molecular Attenuation and Phase Dispersion Between 40 and 140 GHz for Path Models from Different Altitudes, U.S. Commerce Dep., Office of Telecommunications Rep. 73-10.

Lin, S. H. (1975), A Method for Calculating Rain Attenuation Distributions on Microwave Paths, *Bell Syst. Tech. J.*, 54, pp. 1051–1086.

Marshall, J. S., and W. McK. Palmer (1948). The Distribution of Raindrops with Size, *J. Meteorol.*, 5, pp. 165–166.

Marshall, J. S., and K. L. S. Gunn (1952), Measurement of Snow Parameters by Radar, *J. Meteorol.*, 9, p. 322.

McCormick, G. C., and A. Hendry (1975), Principles for the Radar Determination of the Polarization Properties of Precipitation, *Radio Sci.*, 10, pp. 421–434.

McCormick, G. C., and A. Hendry (1979), Techniques for the Determination of the Polarization Properties of Precipitation, *Radio Sci.*, 14, pp. 1027–1040.

Medhurst, R. G. (1965), Rainfall Attenuation of Centimeter Waves: Comparison of Theory and Measurement, *IEEE Trans. Ant. Prop.*, AP-13, pp. 550–564.

Meeks, M. L., and A. E. Lilley (1963), The Microwave Spectrum of Oxygen in the Earth's Atmosphere, *J. Geophys. Res.*, 68, pp. 1683–1703.

Mie, G. (1908), Beitrage zur Optik trüber Medien, speziell Kolloidaler Metaläsungen, *Ann. Physik*, 25, p. 377.

Morrison, J. A., and M. J. Cross (1974), Scattering of a Plane Electromagnetic Wave by Axi-Symmetric Raindrops, *Bell Sys. Tech. J.*, 53, pp. 955–1020.

Oguchi, T. (1964), Attenuation of Electromagnetic Wave Due to Rain with Distorted Raindrops (Pt. II), *J. Radio Res. Lab. (Japan)*, 11, pp. 19–44.

Oguchi, T. (1973), Attenuation and Phase Rotation of Radio Waves Due to Rain: Calculations at 19.3 and 34.8 GHz, *Radio Sci.*, 8, pp. 31–38.

Oguchi, T. (1975), Rain Depolarization Studies at Centimeter and Millimeter Wavelengths: Theory and Measurement, *J. Radio Res. Lab. (Japan)*, 22, pp. 165–211.

Reber, E. E. (1972), Absorption of the 4- to 6-Millimeter Wavelength Band in the Atmosphere, *J. Geophys. Res.*, 77, pp. 3831–3845.

Rosenkranz, P. W. (1975), Shape of the 5 mm Oxygen Band in the Atmosphere, *IEEE Trans. Ant. Prop.*, AP-23, pp. 498–506.

Ryde, J. W., and D. Ryde (1945), *Attenuation of Centimeter Waves by Rain, Hail, Fog, and Clouds*, General Electric Co., Wembly, England.

Schanda, E. (1976), *Remote Sensing for Environmental Sciences*, Springer-Verlag, New York, p. 196.

Semplak, R. A., and R. H. Turrin (1969), Some Measurements of Attenuation by Rainfall at 18.5 GHz, *Bell Syst. Tech. J.*, 48, pp. 1767–1787.

Setzer, David E. (1970), Computed Transmission Through Rain at Microwave and Visible Frequencies, *Bell Syst. Tech. J.*, October.

Skolnik, Merrill I. (1980), *Radar Handbook*, McGraw-Hill, New York, p. 34.

Stratton, J. A. (1941), *Electromagnetic Theory*, McGraw-Hill, New York, pp. 563–573.

Tolbert, D. E., and A. W. Straiton (1963), Synopsis of Attenuation and Emission Investigations of 58 to 62 kMc Frequencies in the Earth's Atmosphere, *Proc. IEEE*, 51, pp. 1754–1760.

Townes, C. H., and A. L. Schawlow (1955), *Microwave Spectroscopy*, McGraw-Hill, New York.

Treussart, H., W. B. Beckwith, S. G. Bigler, K. Otani, V. V. Kostarev, and R. Schwarz (1970), Use of Weather Radar for Aviation, World Meteor. Org., Techn. Note No. 110, Geneva.

Ulaby, F. J., and A. W. Straiton (1970), Atmospheric Absorption of Radio Waves Between 150 and 350 GHz, *IEEE Trans. Ant. Prop.*, AP-18, pp. 479–485.

Valley, S. L., ed. (1965), *Handbook of Geophysics and Space Environment*, Office of Aerospace Research, USAF, Cambridge Res. Labs.

van de Hulst, H. C. (1957), *Light Scattering by Small Particles*, John Wiley and Sons, Inc., New York.

Van Vleck, J. H., and V. F. Weisskopf (1945), On the Shape of Collision-Broadened Lines, *Rev. Mod. Phys.*, 17, pp. 227–236.

Van Vleck, J. H. (1947a), The Absorption of Microwaves by Oxygen, *Phys. Rev.*, 71, pp. 413–424.

Van Vleck, J. H. (1947b), The Absorption of Microwaves by Uncondensed Water Vapor, *Phys. Rev.*, 71, pp. 425–433.

Waters, J. W. (1976), Absorption and Emission of Microwave Radiation by Atmospheric Gases, in *Methods of Experimental Physics*, M. L. Meeks, ed., 12, Part B, Radio Astronomy, Academic Press, Section 2.3.

Weger, E. (1960), Apparent Sky Temperatures in the Microwave Region, *J. Meteorol.*, 17, pp. 159–165.

Welch, W. M. and M. Mizushima (1972), Molecular Parameters of the O_2 Molecule, *Phys. Rev. A*, 5, pp. 2692–2695.

Westwater, E. R., and O. N. Strand (1967), Application of Statistical Estimation Techniques to Passive Probing of the Tropospheric Temperature Structure, ESSA, Boulder, Colo., Tech. Rept. IER-ITSA 37, p. 41.

Wexler, R. (1948), Rain Intensities by Radar, *J. Meteorol.*, 5, p. 171.

Wexler, R., and D. Atlas (1963), Radar Reflectivity and Attenuation of Rain, *J. Appl. Meteorol.*, 2, pp. 276–80.

Wilheit, T. T. (1970), Studies of Microwave Emission and Absorption by Atmospheric Oxygen, Ph.D. Dissertation, Mass. Inst. of Tech., Cambridge, Mass.

Wilheit, T. T., and A. H. Barrett (1970), Microwave Spectrum of Molecular Oxygen, *Phys. Rev. A*, 1, pp. 213–215.

Wilson, R. W. (1969), Sun Tracker Measurements of Attenuation by Rain at 16 and 30 GHz, *Bell Syst. Tech. J.*, 48, pp. 1383–1404.

Wulfsberg, K. N., and E. E. Altshuler (1972), Rain Attenuation at 15 and 35 GHz, *IEEE Trans. Ant. Prop.*, AP-20, pp. 181–187.

Zhevakin, S. A., and A. P. Naumov (1963), On the Absorption Coefficient of Electromagnetic Waves by Water Vapor in the 10 μm to 2 cm Band, *Izv. Vysshikh Uchebn. Zavedenii, Radiofiz.*, 6, pp. 674–695.

Zhevakin, S. A., and A. P. Naumov, (1965), The Coefficient of Absorption of Centimeter and Millimeter Radiowaves in Atmospheric Oxygen, *Radio Eng. Electron. Phys. (USSR)*, 10, pp. 844–852.

Zhevakin, S. A., and A. P. Naumov (1967), Refraction of Millimeter and Submillimeter Radiowaves in the Lower Atmosphere, *Radio Engrg. Electronic Phys. (USSR)* (English transl.), 12, pp. 885–894, 1067–1076.

Radiometer Systems

Radiometers are highly sensitive receivers designed to measure thermal electro-magnetic emission by material media. In Chapter 4, the theory of radiative transfer was used to relate the electromagnetic properties of the scene observed by an antenna to the power delivered by the antenna to the receiver, $P'_A = kT'_A B$. The antenna temperature T'_A incorporates the intensity of radiation incident upon the antenna (weighted by the antenna directional pattern) as well as self-emission by the antenna structure itself. The function of a radiometer is to measure T'_A. However, T'_A represents the average value of a fluctuating noiselike signal. Hence, strictly speaking, a radiometer provides an *estimate* of T'_A; therefore, not only is the radiometer transfer function (relating T'_A to the output voltage V_{out}) of interest, but so is the precision with which T'_A can be estimated. The latter, often referred to as the radiometer sensitivity or radio-metric resolution ΔT, is the key quantity characterizing the performance of a microwave radiometer.

This chapter covers four major topics. The first topic, which is a brief treatment of the methodology used to characterize the noise properties of individual devices and multidevice receiver systems, provides the background for discussing the operation and performance characteristics of the several different types of radiometers considered in Sections 6-7 to 6-14. Receiver noise characterization also is relevant to the detection of radar signals (Chapter 8). The third and fourth topics are radiometer calibration techniques and imaging considerations.

6-1 EQUIVALENT NOISE TEMPERATURE

According to thermodynamics, electrons in a conductor are always in a state of random motion and the kinetic energy of an electron is proportional to T, the temperature of the conductor. These random motions of the electrons produce fluctuations in electric charge, which in turn produce voltage fluctuations. If we were to measure the voltage V_n across a conductor of resistance R through an ideal rectangular filter of bandwidth B, we would observe an output similar

Fawwaz T. Ulaby, Richard K. Moore, and Adrian K. Fung,
Microwave Remote Sensing: Active and Passive,
Vol. I: Microwave Remote Sensing Fundamentals and Radiometry   ISBN 0-201-10759-7

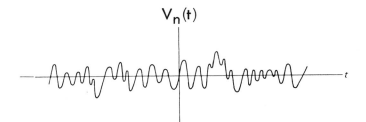

Fig. 6.1 Random variation of noise voltage across a resistor.

to that shown in Fig. 6.1. Sources that emit incoherent energy usually are referred to as noise sources. Hence, the voltage V_n usually is called the noise voltage generated by the resistor. Moreover, since V_n is related to the temperature of the conductor, the noise thus generated is called *thermal* noise. As one might expect, the average, or mean, value of V_n is zero. Its rms value, however, is not zero. Nyquist (1928) showed that

$$V_{rms}^2 = \langle V_n^2(t) \rangle = 4RkTB, \tag{6.1}$$

where k is Boltzmann's constant and B, often called the *noise bandwidth*, is the bandwidth of the rectangular filter.

The thermal noise power delivered by a *noisy* resistor at a temperature T usually is determined by replacing the noisy resistor with an equivalent circuit consisting of a voltage generator V_{rms} in series with a noise-free resistance R and a reactance X as shown in Fig. 6.2. The reactance X accounts for the self-inductance of the resistor and the capacitance between its ends. The power transferred from the equivalent voltage generator to a load Z_L is maximum when Z_L is matched to the generator impedance $Z = R + jX$—that is, when $Z_L = Z^* = R - jX$. Under this condition, the average noise power dissipated in R_L is

$$P_n = \frac{V_{rms}^2}{4R} = kTB. \tag{6.2}$$

We recognize the above result as being identical to the power delivered by a lossless antenna placed inside a chamber of constant temperature T. We may extend the similarity further by stating that the average power delivered by any antenna, lossless or not, to a matched load (Fig. 6.3) is equal to the average power delivered by a resistor to a matched load if the temperature of the resistor is identical to the antenna radiometric temperature T_A'. This equivalence between the antenna and the resistance provides a convenient tool for calibrating microwave receivers, as will be discussed later in Section 6-16.1.

Thermal-noise generation is a universal characteristic of matter at temperatures above absolute zero, but it is not the only source of random-noise generation. Other types of noise include quantum noise, shot noise, and flicker noise. Quantum noise, which arises from the discrete nature of electron energy,

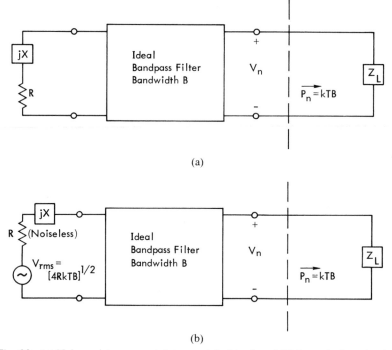

Fig. 6.2 (a) Noisy resistor connected to a matched load, and (b) its equivalent circuit.

is insignificant in comparison with thermal noise unless the frequency is very high or the temperature is very low; that is, quantum noise may be neglected as long as the Rayleigh-Jeans approximation holds (Section 4-3.3). Shot noise arises from the discrete nature of current flow in electronic devices such as diodes and transistors, and flicker noise arises from surface irregularities in cathodes and semiconductors.

According to (6.2), the thermal noise power per unit bandwidth is dependent only on the physical temperature of the resistor and is independent of the operating frequency and of the resistance R. This property of thermal-noise

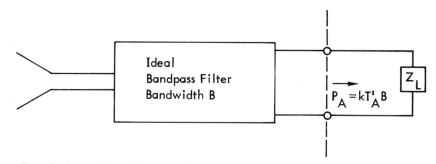

Fig. 6.3 Power delivered to a matched load by an antenna with radiometric antenna temperature T_A' is $P_A' = kT_A'B$.

sources has been extended to define an *equivalent output noise temperature** T_{Eo} for any noise source, regardless of the mechanism responsible for the generated noise. If $P_{no}(f)$ is the output noise power of a nonthermal noise source over a narrow bandwidth Δf centered at f, its equivalent output noise temperature is defined as

$$T_{Eo}(f) = \lim_{\Delta f \to 0} \frac{P_{no}(f)}{k \, \Delta f}. \tag{6.3}$$

In practice, however, most systems and devices are configured so that $P_{no}(f)$ is approximately constant over the operating frequency range (of bandwidth B) so that the output noise may be defined as

$$P_{no} = k T_{Eo} B, \tag{6.4}$$

where T_{Eo} represents an effective value of $T_{Eo}(f)$ over the bandwidth B. The above concept of equivalent noise temperature also has been used to define an *equivalent input noise temperature* T_{Ei} for two-terminal devices, which facilitates the quantification of the overall noise performance of a system consisting of several devices in terms of the T_{Ei}'s of the individual devices, as will be shown in the next section. Note that (6.4) applies *only* for a matched load.

6-2 CHARACTERIZATION OF NOISE

6-2.1 Noise Figure

The *noise figure F* of a linear two-port device (or system) is a measure of the degradation in signal-to-noise ratio between the input and output ports of the device, due to noise addition by the device. For the device shown in Fig. 6.4(a),

$$F = \frac{P_{si}/P_{ni}}{P_{so}/P_{no}}, \tag{6.5}$$

where P_{si} = available input signal power, W,
P_{ni} = available input noise power = $k T_0 B$, W,
P_{so} = available output signal power, W,
P_{no} = available output noise power, W.

F is defined for a specific input noise power, namely that power which would be provided by a resistor matched to the input port of the device and whose temperature is $T_0 = 290$ K. If, over the bandwidth B, the average power gain of

---

*Conforming to the notation adopted in previous chapters, if the first subscript of T is lowercase, then T is a physical (thermometric) temperature, and if it is uppercase, then T is equivalent radiometric or noise temperature.

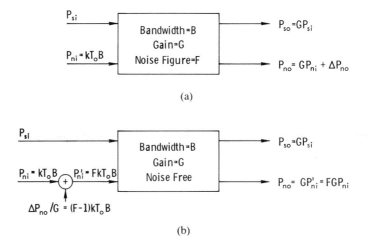

(a)

(b)

Fig. 6.4 A noisy device can be replaced by a noise-free device if the input noise is increased by the noise figure of the device: (a) noisy device; (b) equivalent representation of (a) in terms of a noise-free device.

the device is G, then

$$P_{so} = GP_{si} \tag{6.6}$$

and

$$P_{no} = GP_{ni} + \Delta P_{no}, \tag{6.7}$$

where ΔP_{no} is the noise power generated by the device. Hence,

$$F = \frac{P_{si}}{P_{so}} \cdot \frac{P_{no}}{P_{ni}} = \frac{1}{G} \cdot \frac{GkT_0 B + \Delta P_{no}}{kT_0 B}$$

$$= 1 + \frac{\Delta P_{no}}{GkT_0 B}. \tag{6.8}$$

The noise figure F is always larger than or equal to 1; for an ideal noise-free device ($\Delta P_{no} = 0$), $F = 1$. Occasionally, F is expressed in decibels:

$$F(\text{dB}) = 10 \log F. \tag{6.9}$$

From (6.8), ΔP_{no} is given by

$$\Delta P_{no} = (F - 1)GkT_0 B, \tag{6.10}$$

and therefore the output noise power is, from (6.7), given by

$$P_{no} = GkT_0 B + (F - 1)GkT_0 B$$

$$= FGkT_0 B. \tag{6.11}$$

Thus, the noise performance of the device shown in Fig. 6.4(a) is equivalent to that of an ideal noise-free device with input noise temperature equal to $T_0 + (F-1)T_0 = FT_0$ (Fig. 6.4(b)).

6-2.2 Effective Noise Temperature

For a linear two-port device, the internally generated noise power ΔP_{no} should be independent of both the signal and the noise at the device input. But according to (6.10), ΔP_{no} is a function of T_0, the input noise temperature. This "apparent" dependence on T_0 follows from the form of the definition of the noise figure F. A closer look would show that for a given device, $(F-1)T_0$ is a constant. That is, when the noise figure is used to describe the noise performance of a device (or network) it is necessary to specify the value of T_0 at which F is measured. To avoid confusion, the definition of noise figure has been standardized by choosing $T_0 = 290$ K (room temperature).

The *equivalent input noise temperature* T_{Ei} is an alternative concept for describing the noise performance of a device. Its attractive feature is that it depends only upon the parameters of the device. T_{Ei} is defined on the basis of the equivalence of the two networks shown in Fig. 6.5. If ΔP_{no} is the noise generated by the device with its input connected to a noise-free termination (fictitious resistor at absolute zero temperature), T_{Ei} is defined as the temperature of a thermal resistor that, if placed at the input of an equivalent noise-free device, would produce the same noise power ΔP_{no} at the output terminals of the device. Thus,

$$\Delta P_{no} = G k T_{Ei} B, \tag{6.12}$$

where G is the power gain of the device. *It is important to remember that* [*] $T_{Ei} \triangleq T_E$ *is referred to the input terminals of the device.* The corresponding equivalent (or effective) input noise power, denoted P_E, is $P_E = k T_E B$.

If the actual noise power available at the input to the device, P_{ni}, is characterized by a noise temperature $T_I (= P_{ni}/kB)$, then the total input noise temperature of the equivalent noise-free device is $T_I + T_E$, and the noise power available at the output (Figure 6.5(c)) is

$$P_{no} = G(P_{ni} + P_E) = G k (T_I + T_E) B. \tag{6.13}$$

The effective input noise temperature T_E can be related to the noise figure F by equating (6.10) to (6.12). The result is

$$T_E = (F-1)T_0. \tag{6.14}$$

Although both quantities, F and T_E, describe the same property of a device or

---

[*]Most of the material that follows in this chapter is discussed in terms of the equivalent input noise temperature of devices. Hence, for brevity, the second subscript (i for input) will be dropped, but the subscript o will be retained when referring to output noise temperature.

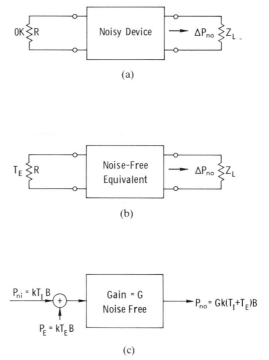

Fig. 6.5 Definition and representation of equivalent input noise temperature T_E: (a) noisy device with input connected to a fictitious resistor at 0-K temperature; (b) equivalent noise-free device with input connected to a fictitious resistor at temperature T_E; (c) device-generated noise referred to its input terminals.

network, F has been used more commonly for describing the noise performance of conventional receivers, whereas T_E has been preferred for low-noise devices and systems.

6-3 NOISE OF A CASCADED SYSTEM

The concepts used to characterize the noise performance of an individual device or system now will be extended to relate the noise behavior of a system consisting of N subsystems to the noisiness of the individual subsystems (or stages). We shall consider first two subsystems in cascade, each with the same noise bandwidth B, but with different equivalent input noise temperatures and available gain (Fig. 6.6). G_1 and T_{E1} are the available gain and equivalent input noise temperature of the first subsystem, and G_2 and T_{E2} are similar quantities for the second subsystem. From the definition of equivalent input noise temperature, each noisy subsystem can be replaced by a noise-free subsystem with an input noise source whose available power is $P_{E1} = kT_{E1}B$ for subsystem 1 and $P_{E2} = kT_{E2}B$ for subsystem 2, as shown in Fig. 6.6(b). The total available

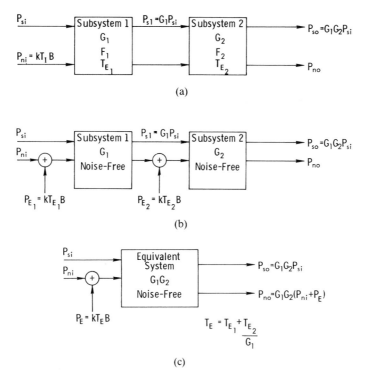

Fig. 6.6 Effective input noise temperature of two systems in cascade: (a) two noisy subsystems in cascade; (b) equivalent representation of (a) in terms of noise-free subsystems; (c) equivalent single-system representation of (b).

noise power at the output of the cascade is

$$P_{no} = G_1 G_2 P_{ni} + G_1 G_2 P_{E1} + G_2 P_{E2}$$
$$= G_1 G_2 k \left(T_I + T_{E1} + \frac{T_{E2}}{G_1} \right) B, \qquad (6.15)$$

where T_I is the input noise temperature. For the equivalent system shown in Fig. 6.6(c),

$$P_{no} = G_1 G_2 (P_{ni} + P_E)$$
$$= G_1 G_2 k (T_I + T_E) B, \qquad (6.16)$$

where T_E is the equivalent input temperature of the overall system. Comparing (6.15) with (6.16), we see that the equivalent input noise temperature T_E of the cascade is given by

$$T_E = T_{E1} + \frac{T_{E2}}{G_1}. \qquad (6.17)$$

From (6.14), the overall noise figure of the cascade is

$$F = 1 + \frac{T_E}{T_0}$$

$$= 1 + \frac{T_{E1}}{T_0} + \frac{T_{E2}}{G_1 T_0}$$

$$= 1 + (F_1 - 1) + \frac{F_2 - 1}{G_1}$$

$$= F_1 + \frac{F_2 - 1}{G_1}, \tag{6.18}$$

where F_1 and F_2 are the noise figures of subsystems 1 and 2, respectively.

The above results may be generalized into a system consisting of N subsystems,

$$T_E = T_{E1} + \frac{T_{E2}}{G_1} + \frac{T_{E3}}{G_1 G_2} + \cdots + \frac{T_{EN}}{G_1 G_2 \cdots G_{N-1}} \tag{6.19a}$$

and

$$F = F_1 + \frac{F_2 - 1}{G_1} + \frac{F_3 - 1}{G_1 G_2} + \cdots + \frac{F_N - 1}{G_1 G_2 \cdots G_{N-1}}. \tag{6.19b}$$

6-4 NOISE CHARACTERIZATION OF AN ATTENUATOR

Consider an attenuator of physical (ambient) temperature T_p and loss factor L. The attenuator is shown in Fig. 6.7 with matched impedances (maintained at the same temperature T_p) on both sides. The loss factor L is the inverse of power gain G,

$$L = \frac{1}{G} = \frac{P_i}{P_o}, \tag{6.20}$$

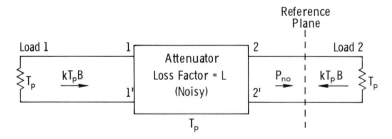

Fig. 6.7   Noise generated in an attenuator of loss L and physical temperature T_p.

where P_i and P_o are, respectively, the attenuator input and output power. Since the network is in thermodynamic equilibrium, the flow of power into load 2 (crossing the reference plane from the left) should be equal to the flow of power from load 2 (crossing the reference plane from the right). The former is designated P_{no} and the latter is equal to kT_pB. Hence,

$$P_{no} = kT_pB \tag{6.21}$$

where P_{no} is the available power at terminals 2–2' of the attenuator. P_{no} consists of the noise power flowing into terminals 1–1' (due to load 1) towards terminals 2–2', attenuated by the loss factor L as it passes through the attenuator, plus noise generated internally by the attenuator and denoted ΔP_{no}:

$$P_{no} = \frac{1}{L}kT_pB + \Delta P_{no}. \tag{6.22}$$

Equating (6.21) to (6.22) gives

$$\Delta P_{no} = \left(1 - \frac{1}{L}\right)kT_pB. \tag{6.23}$$

This internally generated noise power at the attenuator output (terminals 2–2') is equal to the noise power that would appear at the output of an equivalent noise-free attenuator with an input noise power P_E given by

$$P_E = L\Delta P_{no} = (L-1)kT_pB, \tag{6.24}$$

which is equivalent to an effective input noise temperature T_E given by

$$T_E = (L-1)T_p \tag{6.25a}$$

and $\quad T_{E0} = \frac{T_E}{L} = \left(1 - \frac{1}{L}\right)T_p. \tag{6.25b}$

From (6.14), the noise figure of an attenuator is

$$F = 1 + (L-1)\frac{T_p}{T_0} \tag{6.26}$$

which reduces to $F = L$ for $T_p = T_0$.

The variation of T_{E0} with L(dB) $(= 10\log L)$ is shown in Fig. 6.8 for $T_p = T_0 = 290$ K. It is noted that the magnitude of L may have a significant effect on the performance of a system. Consider for example a transmission line of loss L connecting an antenna to a low-noise receiver with equivalent input noise temperature T_{REC}, as shown in Fig. 6.9. The overall noise performance of the transmission-line and receiver combination can be characterized by the effective input noise temperature T'_{REC} at the antenna terminals

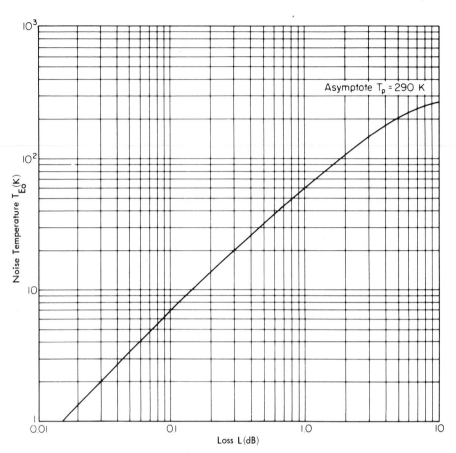

Fig. 6.8 Output noise generated by a matched attenuator.

(thereby treating the transmission line and receiver as noise-free). For a two-stage system, T'_{REC} is given by

$$T'_{REC} = T_{E1} + \frac{T_{E2}}{G_1}. \qquad (6.27)$$

In this case, T_{E1} is the equivalent input noise temperature of the transmission

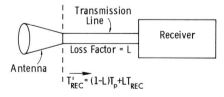

Fig. 6.9 T'_{REC} is the equivalent input noise temperature of an equivalent noise-free transmission line and receiver combination. T_{REC} is the receiver input noise temperature, and T_p is the physical temperature of the transmission line.

line (given by 6.25(a)), $T_{E2} = T_{REC}$, and $G_1 = 1/L$. Hence,

$$T'_{REC} = (L-1)T_p + LT_{REC}. \tag{6.28}$$

If the low-noise receiver is characterized by $T_{REC} = 50$ K and if $T_p = 290$ K and $L = 0.5$ dB, $T'_{REC} = 91.5$ K. Thus, even a loss factor as low as 0.5 dB can degrade the noise performance of the overall receiver system by approximately a factor of 2 (below a receiver connected to the antenna directly). Had the receiver been of the conventional type, with a typical noise temperature $T_{REC} = 1000$ K, the noise added by the transmission line would have been of minor significance, since in this case $T'_{REC} = 1155$ K, an increase of only 11.5 percent.

6-5 EQUIVALENT NOISE TEMPERATURE OF A SUPERHETERODYNE RECEIVER

Consider the *single-sideband** superheterodyne receiver shown in Fig. 6.10(a). The available input noise power P_{ni} is the noise delivered by the antenna via a transmission line, and P_{no} is the noise power available at the output. We wish to replace the noisy receiver with an equivalent noise-free receiver as shown in Figure 6.10(b) by referring the internally generated receiver noise to its input terminals. Specifically, we wish to relate its equivalent input noise temperature T_{REC} to the parameters characterizing its individual subsystems through the use of the results obtained previously for the cascaded system.

The superheterodyne receiver is characterized by the following parameters:

G_{RF} = radio-frequency (RF) amplifier power gain,
F_{RF} = RF amplifier noise figure,
T_{RF} = RF amplifier equivalent input noise temperature $= (F_{RF} - 1)T_0$,
G_M = mixer-preamplifier RF-to-IF power gain,
F_M = mixer-preamplifier noise figure,
T_M = mixer-preamplifier equivalent input noise temperature $= (F_M - 1)T_0$,
G_{IF} = intermediate-frequency (IF) amplifier power gain,
F_{IF} = IF amplifier noise figure,
T_{IF} = IF amplifier equivalent input noise temperature $= (F_{IF} - 1)T_0$,
$T_0 = 290$ K.

The noise parameters of the stages following the IF amplifier were not included in the above list because, as we will see below, the noise performance of the receiver is governed primarily by the stages at its front end. Applying (6.19a), we have

$$T_{REC} = T_{RF} + \frac{T_M}{G_{RF}} + \frac{T_{IF}}{G_{RF}G_M} + \cdots. \tag{6.29}$$

*See Problem 6.3.

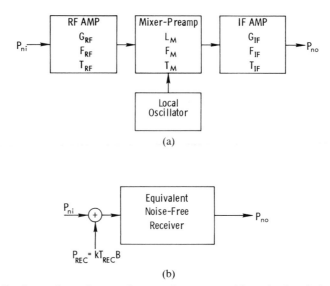

(a)

(b)

Fig. 6.10 A superheterodyne receiver may be represented by noise-free devices if its internally generated noise is properly represented by an input noise temperature T_{REC}: (a) front-end elements; (b) equivalent representation.

For a typical receiver operating at a center frequency of 1.5 GHz, $F_{RF} = 2.3$ dB, $G_{RF} = 30$ dB, $G_M = 23$ dB, $F_M = 7.5$ dB, $G_{IF} = 30$ dB, and $F_{IF} = 1.2$ dB. Hence,

$$T_{RF} = (F_{RF} - 1)T_0 = (1.7 - 1)290 = 203 \text{ K},$$

$$T_M = (F_M - 1)T_0 = (5.62 - 1)290 = 1340 \text{ K},$$

$$T_{IF} = (F_{IF} - 1)T_0 = (1.32 - 1)290 = 92 \text{ K},$$

where the noise figures have been converted from dB to natural numbers. Employing the above noise temperatures in (6.29), we have

$$T_{REC} = 203 + \frac{1340}{1000} + \frac{92}{1000 \times 200} + \cdots$$

$$= 203 + 1.34 + 4.6 \times 10^{-4} + \cdots$$

$$\simeq 204.34 \text{ K}.$$

For all practical purposes, the receiver equivalent input noise temperature is equal to the equivalent input noise temperature of the first stage, the RF amplifier. Thus, with regard to noise performance, the first stage of a receiver is the most critical, if its gain is much larger than 1.

6-6 EQUIVALENT-SYSTEM NOISE POWER AT THE ANTENNA TERMINALS

Now we shall consider the total-system equivalent input noise power P_{SYS} referred to the antenna terminals of Fig. 6.11. P_{SYS} consists of P'_A, the noise power delivered by the antenna, and P'_{REC}, the equivalent input noise power of the transmission-line–receiver combination. For an antenna with a radiation efficiency η_l and physical temperature T_p, the antenna noise temperature T'_A is given by (4.61),

$$T'_A = \eta_l T_A + (1 - \eta_l)T_p,\qquad(4.61)$$

where T_A is the antenna radiation temperature of the scene observed by a lossless antenna (see (4.53)). The antenna noise power is

$$\begin{aligned}P'_A &= k T'_A B\\ &= k\left[\eta_l T_A + (1-\eta_l)T_p\right]B,\end{aligned}\qquad(6.30)$$

where B, the bandwidth, usually is the effective bandwidth of the IF amplifier. The equivalent input noise temperature of the transmission-line–receiver combination (referred to the input terminals of the transmission line) is given by (6.28). Hence,

$$\begin{aligned}P'_{REC} &= k T'_{REC} B\\ &= k\left[(L-1)T_p + LT_{REC}\right]B,\end{aligned}\qquad(6.31)$$

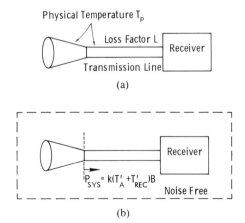

Physical Temperature T_p

Loss Factor L

Receiver

Transmission Line

(a)

Receiver

$P_{SYS} = k(T'_A + T'_{REC})B$

Noise Free

(b)

Fig. 6.11 Equivalent input system noise power incorporates noise generated by the receiver, transmission line, antenna self-emission and emission by the scene observed by the antenna: (a) "Noisy" antenna of radiation efficiency η_l connected to a receiver via a transmission line; (b) equivalent noise-free configuration with equivalent input system noise power P_{SYS}.

and therefore,

$$P_{SYS} = P_A' + P_{REC}'$$

$$= k\{\eta_l T_A + (1-\eta_l)T_p + (L-1)T_p + LT_{REC}\}B. \qquad (6.32)$$

Setting $P_{SYS} = kT_{SYS}B$, where T_{SYS} is defined as the system input noise temperature, the following expression is obtained from (6.32):

$$T_{SYS} = \eta_l T_A + (1-\eta_l)T_p + (L-1)T_p + LT_{REC}. \qquad (6.33)$$

For a radiometer receiver, P_{SYS} represents the "signal" at the input terminals of an equivalent noise-free receiving system (transmission line and receiver). That is, the receiver output voltage is proportional to P_{SYS}. By comparing the output voltage due to P_{SYS} with the output voltage due to a matched load (in place of the antenna) of known physical temperature, a radiometer receiver provides an estimate of T_A, the antenna temperature of the scene under observation (provided T_p and η_l are known). Details of the technique and the precision associated with the estimate of T_A are given in future sections.

In the case of a radar receiver, P_{SYS} represents the effective noise power at the input to the receiving system, while the input signal is the received power P_r given by the radar equation (Chapter 7). The input signal-to-noise ratio, with the noise added by the receiving system taken into account, is $S_n = P_r/P_{SYS}$. This ratio is used to establish the transmitter power and antenna parameters required for a given performance specification. If, through the application of signal-processing techniques, the signal-to-noise ratio at the receiver output is better than the input ratio, then the effective input signal-to-noise ratio is S_n multiplied by the improvement factor. Considerations of radar-system design and performance are given in Volume II.

6-7 RADIOMETER OPERATION

The function of a radiometer is to measure the antenna radiometric temperature T_A', which represents the radiation power delivered by the antenna to the receiver. The measurement process is characterized by two important attributes: (1) accuracy and (2) precision.

6-7.1 Measurement Accuracy

Conceptually, the transfer function of the radiometer receiver is established by measuring the output voltage as a function of the noise temperature of a noise source connected to the receiver input terminals in place of the antenna. Alternatively, calibration is achieved through the use of a switch placed at a point as close to the antenna as possible. The scheme is shown in Fig. 6.12(a). Also, if the radiometer employs square-law detection, which most radiometers do, its output voltage is linearly related to the noise temperature of the input

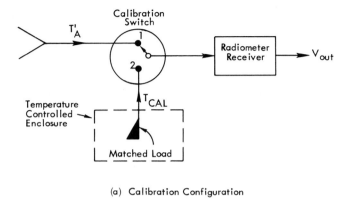

(a) Calibration Configuration

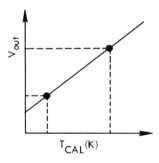

(b) Calibration Line

Fig. 6.12 Calibration of a microwave radiometer: (a) configuration; (b) calibration line.

source. Therefore, it is sufficient to measure the output voltage corresponding to each of two input noise temperatures to establish the calibration line (Fig. 6.12(b)). This calibration line then is used for converting the output voltage measured by the receiver (when connected to the antenna) to antenna temperature values. Assuming that the calibration measurements are made with a high degree of measurement precision, the absolute accuracy of T_A' then is dictated by the accuracy with which the absolute values of the calibration noise temperatures are known. If a passive device, such as a matched load (resistor), is used as a calibration source, its noise temperature accuracy may be maintained within 1 K or better by controlling the temperature of its environment. In practice, however, other sources of error also contribute to the absolute measurement accuracy of T_A', as discussed in Section 6-16.

6-7.2 Measurement Precision

In radiometric terminology, the *radiometric sensitivity* (or *radiometric resolution*) ΔT is defined as the smallest change in T_A' that can be detected by the radiometer output. A more formal definition, in the statistical sense, is given below.

Consider the total-power radiometer system shown in Fig. 6.13(a). The antenna is connected to a superheterodyne receiver of bandwidth B and total power gain G, followed by a detector and a low-pass filter. The power delivered by the antenna usually is broadband noise extending over a wider bandwidth than the receiver bandwidth B. The function of the RF amplifier is to filter the input signal by amplifying the frequency components contained in the bandwidth B centered at the RF frequency of interest, f_{RF}. The mixer and IF amplifier translate the RF band of signals of bandwidth B to the same bandwidth at the IF and provide further amplification. In practice, the RF amplifier usually has a wider bandwidth than that of the IF amplifier, and therefore the predetection bandwidth B is effectively determined by the IF amplifier bandpass characteristics. Such a system consisting of RF-to-IF translation of a single band of width B is called a *single-sideband* receiver (see Problem 6.3).

Without an RF amplifier (or with a very wideband amplifier), the IF signal band contains signals from two RF bands centered at frequencies f_1 and f_2, where

$$f_1 = f_{LO} - f_{IF},$$
$$f_2 = f_{LO} + f_{IF}.$$

Because the input signal at each RF frequency, f_1 and f_2, is of bandwidth B, the total input power for such a *double-sideband* receiver is twice the input power received by a single-sideband receiver, since in the latter, one of two RF bands is rejected by the RF amplifier. Although the signal power is larger by a factor of 2 (assuming that the antenna temperature T_A' is about the same at f_1 and f_2), the absence of a low-noise RF amplifier usually results in an increase in receiver noise temperature by a much larger factor (see Fig. 6.26). Furthermore, if the total available frequency band is fixed, the single-sideband receiver can be designed to use the entire bandwidth, while in the double-sideband receiver, part of the available bandwidth is not used. This consideration is particularly pertinent in microwave radiometry. To avoid the threat of interference from radio transmitters, radiometric observations usually are made in the "protected" frequency bands allocated for radio-astronomy observations (Table 1.3). As will be shown later, the radiometric measurement sensitivity (resolution) improves with increasing bandwidth B. Hence, to take full advantage of the relatively narrow width of a protected band, single-sideband receivers are preferred.

A representation equivalent to Fig. 6.13(a) is shown in Fig. 6.13(b), in which the antenna is replaced by a noise source with output power $P_A' = kT_A'B$ and the receiver (including transmission line) is replaced by a combination of a noise-free receiver and an input noise source with output power given by $P_{REC}' = kT_{REC}'B$, where T_{REC}' is the equivalent input noise temperature of the transmission-line–receiver combination. The total system input noise power is

$$P_{SYS} = P_A' + P_{REC}'$$
$$= kT_{SYS}B, \qquad\qquad (6.34)$$

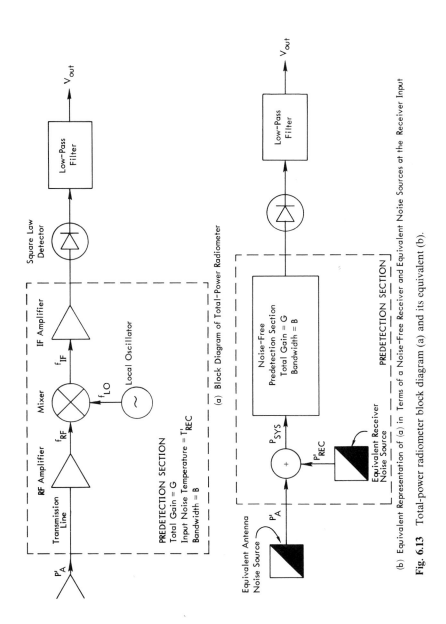

(a) Block Diagram of Total-Power Radiometer

(b) Equivalent Representation of (a) in Terms of a Noise-Free Receiver and Equivalent Noise Sources at the Receiver Input

Fig. 6.13 Total-power radiometer block diagram (a) and its equivalent (b).

where

$$T_{SYS} = T'_A + T'_{REC}. \tag{6.35}$$

The IF amplifier (average) output power P_{IF} is given by

$$P_{IF} = GkT_{SYS}B. \tag{6.36}$$

Figure 6.14 illustrates the voltage waveforms and corresponding power spectra at several points between the RF input and the final output. Since the input power consists of thermal noise, the instantaneous IF voltage is described by a Gaussian probability distribution with zero mean, and, as shown in Section 7-2.3, its envelope is Rayleigh distributed. Thus,

$$p(V_e) = \begin{cases} \dfrac{V_e}{\sigma^2} e^{-V_e^2/2\sigma^2}, & V_e \geq 0, \\ 0, & V_e \leq 0, \end{cases} \tag{6.37}$$

where σ is the standard deviation of the Gaussian distribution. The mean value

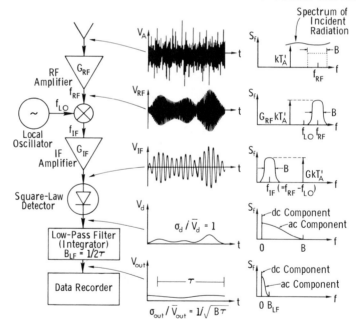

G = Power gain of predetection section (between RF amplifier input and IF amplifier output).

S_f = Power spectral density, W Hz^{-1}

Fig. 6.14 Total-power radiometer with a superheterodyne receiver. The signal voltage and corresponding spectrum are shown at various stages.

of V_e^2 can be easily shown to be given by

$$\overline{V_e^2} = 2\sigma^2. \qquad (6.38)$$

Without loss of generality, we assume that the IF power is developed across a 1-ohm resistor, which leads to

$$P_{IF} = \overline{V_e^2} = 2\sigma^2. \qquad (6.39)$$

The output of the square-law detector, V_d, is related to its input, V_e, via the relation

$$V_d = C_d V_e^2, \qquad (6.40)$$

where C_d is the square-law detector power-sensitivity constant (volts per watt). The average value of V_d is given by

$$\begin{aligned} \overline{V_d} &= C_d \overline{V_e^2} = 2C_d\sigma^2 = C_d P_{IF} \\ &= C_d G k B T_{SYS} \end{aligned} \qquad (6.41)$$

and represents the average value of the input noise power, P_{SYS} (except for multiplicative constants).

Using (6.40), the Rayleigh distribution given by (6.37) may be converted to a distribution for V_d from

$$p(V_d)dV_d = p(V_e)dV_e,$$

which leads to the exponential distribution

$$p(V_d) = \frac{1}{\overline{V_d}} e^{-V_d/\overline{V_d}}, \qquad (6.42)$$

whose mean value is given by (6.41). The variance of V_d is σ_d and is obtained through

$$\sigma_d^2 = \overline{V_d^2} - \overline{V_d}^2, \qquad (6.43)$$

which can be shown to lead to

$$\sigma_d^2 = \overline{V_d}^2, \qquad (6.44)$$

or

$$\frac{\sigma_d}{\overline{V_d}} = 1. \qquad (6.45)$$

In terms of the input power P_{SYS}, $\overline{V}_d$ (the dc value of V_d) represents its average value and σ_d (the rms value of the ac component) represents the statistical uncertainty associated with the measurement of P_{SYS} (through $\overline{V}_d$). Certainly, such a high level of uncertainty as given by (6.45) is not an acceptable result. The solution to this problem is to filter out the high-frequency fluctuations of the detected voltage, which is equivalent to averaging V_d over some interval of time τ. This is precisely the function of the low-pass filter (integrator) shown in Fig. 6.14.

The voltage V_{out} at the output of the low-pass filter consists of a dc component $\overline{V}_{out}$ and an ac component V_{ac}:

$$V_{out}(t) = \overline{V}_{out} + V_{ac}(t). \tag{6.46}$$

According to the results of Section 7-2.4, integrating a random signal of bandwidth B over a time τ leads to a reduction of its variance (normalized to the square of its mean value) by the factor $N = B\tau$. That is, the ratio $\sigma_{out}^2 / \overline{V}_{out}^2$ at the low-pass filter output (where σ_{out} is the standard deviation of V_{out}) is related to $\sigma_d^2 / \overline{V}_d^2$ at the filter input by

$$\frac{\sigma_{out}^2}{\overline{V}_{out}^2} = \frac{\sigma_d^2}{\overline{V}_d^2} \cdot \frac{1}{B\tau}. \tag{6.47}$$

Using (6.45), we have

$$\frac{\sigma_{out}}{\overline{V}_{out}} = \frac{1}{\sqrt{B\tau}}. \tag{6.48}$$

The dc output voltage $\overline{V}_{out}$ is directly related to the average input power P_{SYS} (and therefore to the radiometric temperature T_{SYS}) through

$$\begin{aligned}
\overline{V}_{out} &= g_{LF}\overline{V}_d \\
&= g_{LF}C_d G k T_{SYS} B \\
&= G_S T_{SYS},
\end{aligned} \tag{6.49}$$

where g_{LF} is the voltage gain of the low-pass filter, and G_S, termed the *system gain factor*, is an abbreviation for

$$G_S = g_{LF}C_d G k B. \tag{6.50}$$

Assuming that all the system parameters in (6.49) are constant, (6.48) is equivalent to

$$\frac{\Delta T_{SYS}}{T_{SYS}} = \frac{1}{\sqrt{B\tau}}, \tag{6.51}$$

where ΔT_{SYS} is the standard deviation associated with the measured (estimated) value of T_{SYS}.

From an observation standpoint, ΔT_{SYS} may be viewed as the minimum change in T_{SYS} that is necessary to produce a detectable change at the radiometer output, where detectable change is defined as a change in the dc level of the output voltage equal to the standard deviation of the ac component. Recalling that $T_{SYS} = T'_A + T'_{REC}$ and that T'_{REC} (the receiver input noise temperature) is independent of the radiation incident upon the antenna, (6.51) may be rewritten as

$$\Delta T \triangleq \Delta T_{SYS} = \frac{T_{SYS}}{\sqrt{B\tau}} = \frac{T'_A + T'_{REC}}{\sqrt{B\tau}}, \tag{6.52}$$

where ΔT is regarded as the minimum detectable change in the radiometric antenna temperature T'_A of the observed scene. The above equation defines the radiometric sensitivity (or resolution) of an *ideal* total-power radiometer with no gain fluctuations. As will be discussed in the next section, this assumption is not always valid. To emphasize the importance of this assumption, ΔT will be denoted ΔT_{IDEAL}, and (6.52) rewritten in the form

$$\Delta T_{IDEAL} = \frac{T_{SYS}}{\sqrt{B\tau}}. \tag{6.53}$$

In the above derivation, the low-pass filter was characterized as having an integration time τ. We shall now relate τ to the filter power transfer function $G_{LF}(f)$.

The effective bandwidth B_{LF} of a low-pass filter is defined as the bandwidth of an equivalent ideal filter with a rectangular passband extending from zero to B_{LF} hertz and of constant gain equal to the maximum gain G_{max} of the actual filter. In practice, $G_{max} = G_{LF}(0)$. Thus,

$$B_{LF} = \frac{\int_0^\infty G_{LF}(f)\,df}{G_{LF}(0)}. \tag{6.54}$$

An *ideal integrator* of integration time τ relates the output voltage V_{out} to the input voltage V_d through

$$V_{out}(t) = \frac{1}{\tau} \int_{t-\tau}^t V_d(t')\,dt'. \tag{6.55}$$

If we define the ideal integrator (low-pass filter) by the rectangular time function

$$h(\tau - t') = \begin{cases} 1/\tau & \text{for } t-\tau < t' < t, \\ 0 & \text{otherwise,} \end{cases} \tag{6.56}$$

then (6.55) may be rewritten as

$$V_{out}(t) = \int_{-\infty}^{\infty} h(\tau - t') V_d(t') \, dt',$$

(6.57)

which we recognize as a convolution integral. Since convolution in the time domain corresponds to multiplication in the frequency domain, the power-frequency transfer function of an ideal integrator is the square of the magnitude of the Fourier transform of $h(\tau - t')$:

$$G_I(f) = |\mathcal{F}\{h(\tau - t')\}|^2.$$

(6.58)

The Fourier transform of a rectangular function is a sinc function, thereby leading to the result

$$G_I(f) = \frac{\sin^2(\pi f \tau)}{(\pi f \tau)^2}.$$

(6.59)

The equivalent bandwidth B_{LF} of an ideal integrator may now be obtained by inserting (6.59) into (6.54) and performing the integration. The result is

$$B_{LF} = \frac{1}{2\tau}.$$

(6.60)

The above result now may be used to define the equivalent ideal integration time of any low-pass filter as

$$\tau = \frac{G_{LF}(0)}{2 \int_0^{\infty} G_{LF}(f) \, df}.$$

(6.61)

It is interesting to note that an ideal integrator is not the same as an ideal low-pass filter; an ideal integrator is described by a rectangular function in the time domain, while an ideal filter is characterized by a rectangular passband in the frequency domain. In terms of smoothing (filtering) out ac fluctuations, however, the two are equivalent if the integration time of the ideal integrator is equal to the reciprocal of twice the bandwidth of the ideal filter.

One of the main objectives of this section has been to derive the radiometer sensitivity equation given by (6.53). The treatment was based on Gaussian noise statistics and essentially consisted of tracking the dc and ac components of the noise voltage from the IF amplifier output to the low-pass filter output. An alternate, equivalent approach would be to perform the tracking in the frequency domain, as shown by Tiuri (1964) and by Evans and McLeish (1977). Tiuri's derivation conveniently leads to the following definition for the equivalent predetection bandwidth B of a nonrectangular power-transfer function $G(f)$:

$$B = \frac{\left[\int_0^\infty G(f)\,df\right]^2}{\int_0^\infty G^2(f)\,df}. \tag{6.62}$$

Figure 6.14 shows the power spectra at different stages in the radiometer receiver, adapted in part from Tiuri (1964), to whom the reader is referred for details.

6-8 EFFECTS OF RECEIVER GAIN VARIATIONS

As we stated earlier, the expression for ΔT given by (6.52) accounts only for the measurement uncertainty due to noise fluctuations and does not incorporate receiver gain fluctuations. For convenience, (6.52) is repeated below in the form

$$\Delta T_N = \frac{T_{SYS}}{\sqrt{B\tau}}, \tag{6.63a}$$

where the subscript N denotes *noise*-caused uncertainty.

The output voltage of the total-power radiometer is directly proportional to several system factors (see (6.49)) that were assumed to be constant in the derivation leading to (6.52). In practice, this is a fair assumption for the postdetection stages, but may not be valid for the predetection power gain G. Gain variations in the predetection section arise primarily from the RF amplifier and secondarily from the mixer and IF amplifier.

Since V_{out} is linearly related to the product $G_S T_{SYS}$, an increase in G_S by ΔG_S will be misinterpreted by the output as an increase in T_{SYS} by $\Delta T_{SYS} = T_{SYS}(\Delta G_S / G_S)$. Long-term (slow) variations of G_S, with periods of the order of minutes, may be factored out approximately by calibrating the radiometer output voltage against known input noise sources as frequently as is practicable. However, calibration does not eliminate short-term (fast) gain variations that occur over intervals smaller than the period between successive calibrations. Statistically, the rms uncertainty in T_A' due to system gain variations may be defined as

$$\Delta T_G = T_{SYS}\left(\frac{\Delta G_S}{G_S}\right), \tag{6.63b}$$

where G_S is the average system power gain and ΔG_S is the effective value (rms) of the detected power gain variation (ac component).

Since the noise uncertainty ΔT_N and the gain uncertainty ΔT_G are caused by unrelated mechanisms, they may be considered statistically independent, in which case the total rms uncertainty is given by

$$\Delta T = \left[(\Delta T_N)^2 + (\Delta T_G)^2 \right]^{1/2}$$

$$= T_{SYS} \left[\frac{1}{B\tau} + \left(\frac{\Delta G_S}{G_S} \right)^2 \right]^{1/2}. \tag{6.64}$$

The above expression defines the radiometer sensitivity of the total-power radiometer, incorporating the effects of both noise and gain variations.

To gain an appreciation for the relative significance of the two sources of measurement uncertainty, let us consider the following example. A total-power radiometer operating at a center frequency of 1.4 GHz is characterized by the following parameters: $T'_{REC} = 600$ K, $B = 100$ MHz, $\tau = 0.01$ s, and $\Delta G_S / G_S = 10^{-2}$. For an antenna temperature T'_A in the neighborhood of 300 K, the above values lead to the following conclusions:

$$\Delta T_N = 0.9 \text{ K},$$
$$\Delta T_G = 9 \text{ K},$$
$$\Delta T = 9.05 \text{ K}.$$

That is, the radiometer sensitivity is governed effectively by gain variations. The desired sensitivity in remote-sensing observations usually is of the order of 1 K or less. To reduce ΔT of the above radiometer to 1 K, the product $T_{SYS}(\Delta G_S / G_S)$ has to be reduced by a factor of 20. Since $T_{SYS} = T'_{REC} + T'_A$, the smallest possible value it can have is $T_{SYS} = T'_A$, which corresponds to an ideal noise-free receiver. T'_A may vary between a few kelvins and 330 K for natural (terrestrial) scenes. Hence, even with a noise-free receiver, the desired resolution of 1 K cannot be achieved without improving the gain variation factor $(\Delta G_S / G_S)$. Typically, the gain variation factor for low-noise microwave amplifiers is between 10^{-2} and 10^{-3}; therefore they would not be readily suitable for use in total-power radiometers. Gain variations may be reduced by an order of magnitude or better by controlling the sources that cause these variations, namely, power-supply voltages and environmental temperature variations. This may provide an acceptable solution for a total-power radiometer operating in the centimeter wavelength range, but at millimeter wavelengths it is difficult to construct highly stable receivers with $\Delta G_S / G_S \leqslant 10^{-4}$.

One possible solution to the gain variations problem is to use a receiver with no RF amplifier. In this case, the receiver noise temperature T'_{REC} may be as large as 3000 K or more, but without the RF amplifier, values of $\Delta G_S / G_S$ as low as 10^{-4} to 10^{-5} are achievable (Hersman and Poe, 1981), and therefore the product $T_{SYS}(\Delta G_S / G_S)$ may be reduced to about 0.1 K. Other approaches are discussed in the following sections.

6-9 DICKE RADIOMETER

Although a limited number of studies have been conducted to evaluate the nature of system-gain fluctuations (Steinberg, 1952; Colvin, 1961; Yaroshenko, 1964; Hersman and Poe, 1981), it is generally observed that: (1) the power spectral density of G_S (fluctuation spectrum) decreases with increasing frequency as $1/f$ or faster, (2) the bulk of the fluctuation spectrum lies at frequencies below 1 Hz, and (3) practically no fluctuations with frequencies above 1 kHz exist. Through the example cited in the previous section, it was concluded that gain variations are often the limiting factor to achieving high radiometric resolutions (small values of ΔT). In 1946, the gain-variation problem was alleviated by Dicke (1946) through the use of modulation techniques for reducing the effects of gain fluctuations in a radiometer.

A block diagram of the Dicke radiometer is shown in Fig. 6.15. It is basically a total-power radiometer with two additional features: (1) a switch, which has become known as a "Dicke" switch, connected at the receiver input (at a point as close to the antenna as possible) and used to *modulate* the receiver input signal, and (2) a *synchronous demodulator* (also called synchronous detector) placed in between the square-law detector and the low-pass filter (integrator). The predetection section consists of the RF amplifier, mixer, and IF amplifier and is characterized by a predetection power gain G and bandwidth B.

The modulation consists of periodically switching the receiver input between the antenna and a constant (reference) noise source (Figure 6.15) at a switching rate higher than the highest significant spectral component in the gain variation spectrum. That is, the switching rate f_s is chosen so that over a period of one switching cycle (typically between 1 and 20 ms) the system gain G_S essentially is constant, and therefore *identical* for the half-cycle during which the receiver is connected to the antenna and the half-cycle during which the receiver is connected to the reference source. For square-wave modulation, the detected dc outputs corresponding to the antenna and comparison-source powers are, respectively,

$$\bar{V}_{d\,ANT} = C_d G k B (T_A' + T_{REC}') \qquad \text{for} \quad 0 \leqslant t \leqslant \tau_s/2, \qquad (6.65a)$$

$$\bar{V}_{d\,REF} = C_d G k B (T_{REF} + T_{REC}') \qquad \text{for} \quad \tau_s/2 \leqslant t \leqslant \tau_s, \qquad (6.65b)$$

where T_{REF} is the reference-source noise temperature and τ_s ($=1/f_s$) is the period of one switching cycle. The receiver noise temperature T_{REC}' includes noise contributions from the input switch, which typically are between 7 and 75 K (Section 6-15.1).

Superimposed on the dc voltages are ac components due to noise and gain fluctuations. The synchronous demodulator (Figure 6.15) consists of a switch that operates in synchronism with the input Dicke switch, followed by two unity-gain amplifiers (in parallel), with opposite polarity, one to receive

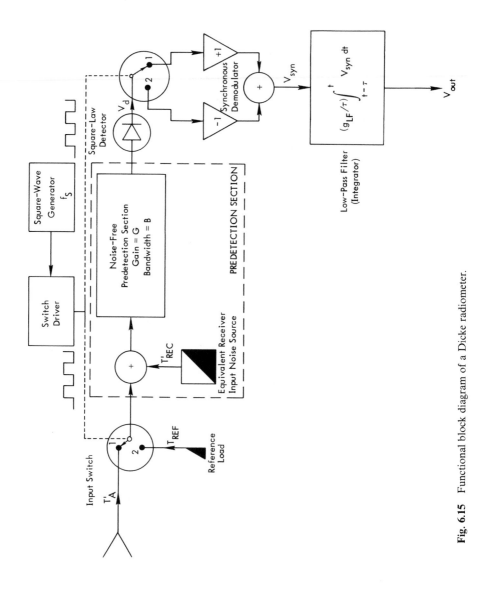

Fig. 6.15 Functional block diagram of a Dicke radiometer.

$V_{dANT}(t)$ and the other to receive $V_{dREF}(t)$. The unity-gain amplifier outputs are then summed and fed into the low-pass filter (integrator). Accordingly, the dc output of the synchronous demodulator is

$$\bar{V}_{syn} = \tfrac{1}{2}\left(\bar{V}_{dANT} - \bar{V}_{dREF}\right)$$
$$= \tfrac{1}{2}C_d Gk B\left(T'_A - T_{REF}\right). \tag{6.66}$$

With an integration time τ, the output of the low-pass filter is effectively equal to

$$V_{out}(t) = \frac{g_{LF}}{\tau}\left[\int_0^{\tau/2} V_{dANT}(t)\,dt - \int_{\tau/2}^{\tau} V_{dREF}(t)\,dt\right]. \tag{6.67}$$

With most of the ac fluctuations removed by the integration, the output voltage consists of a dc component, $\bar{V}_{out}$, and a relatively very small ac component with rms value σ_{out}. From (6.66), $\bar{V}_{out}$ is given by

$$\bar{V}_{out} = \tfrac{1}{2}g_{LF}C_d Gk B\left(T'_A - T_{REF}\right)$$
$$= \tfrac{1}{2}G_S\left(T'_A - T_{REF}\right). \tag{6.68}$$

In addition to filtering out most of the fluctuating component of $V_{syn}(t)$, the low-pass filter also filters out the ac components at f_s and its higher harmonics (due to the square-wave modulation). That is, the switching rate f_s must be much larger than the low-pass filter bandwidth B_{LF}. The relationship between f_s and B_{LF} also may be considered from the viewpoint of the sampling theorem. B_{LF} represents the range of frequencies of the fluctuating component of the input signal that is retained in the output voltage, and f_s represents the frequency at which the input signal is sampled. To satisfy the sampling theorem, $f_s \geqslant 2B_{LF}$.

According to (6.68), the dc output voltage is proportional to the difference between T'_A and T_{REF}, and is independent of the receiver noise temperature T'_{REC}.

Next, we shall derive an expression for the radiometric resolution ΔT of the Dicke radiometer. We start by rewriting (6.68) in the following form:

$$\bar{V}_{out} = \tfrac{1}{2}G_S\left[\left(T'_A + T'_{REC}\right) - \left(T_{REF} + T'_{REC}\right)\right]. \tag{6.69}$$

The ac component of $V_{out}(t)$ consists of three contributions:

1. Gain variations, which from (6.66) lead to a gain uncertainty

$$\Delta T_G = \left(T'_A - T_{REF}\right)\left(\Delta G_S / G_S\right). \tag{6.70}$$

2. Noise variations of $T'_A + T'_{REC}$, which upon integration for a period $\tau/2$ (antenna is observed during only half of the integration time τ) lead to a

noise uncertainty (see (6.63a))

$$\Delta T_{NANT} = \frac{T_A' + T_{REC}'}{\sqrt{B\tau/2}} = \frac{\sqrt{2}\,(T_A' + T_{REC}')}{\sqrt{B\tau}}. \tag{6.71}$$

3. Noise variations of $(T_{REF} + T_{REC}')$, which, similarly, lead to

$$\Delta T_{NREF} = \frac{\sqrt{2}\,(T_{REF} + T_{REC}')}{\sqrt{B\tau}}. \tag{6.72}$$

Assuming that the above three uncertainties are statistically independent, the total radiometric resolution is given by

$$\Delta T = \left[(\Delta T_G)^2 + (\Delta T_{NANT})^2 + (\Delta T_{NREF})^2\right]^{1/2}, \tag{6.73}$$

which reduces to

$$\Delta T = \left[\frac{2(T_A' + T_{REC}')^2 + 2(T_{REF} + T_{REC}')^2}{B\tau} + \left(\frac{\Delta G_S}{G_S}\right)^2 (T_A' - T_{REF})^2\right]^{1/2}. \tag{6.74}$$

For reasons that will become obvious later, the above expression will be referred to as the radiometric resolution (sensitivity) of the *unbalanced* Dicke radiometer. Examples of satellite Dicke radiometers operating in the unbalanced mode are the 19.35-GHz Nimbus 5 and the 37-GHz Nimbus 6 electrically scanning microwave radiometer (ESMR) systems; parameters of the Nimbus 5 ESMR are summarized in Table 6.1.

Before we proceed further, let us compare ΔT of the unbalanced Dicke radiometer with that of the total-power radiometer considered earlier. For $B = 100$ MHz, $\tau = 1$ s, $T_{REC}' = 700$ K, and $\Delta G_S/G_S = 10^{-2}$, Eq. (6.64) gives the values

$$\Delta T(\text{Total Power}) \simeq \begin{cases} 7 \text{ K} & \text{for} \quad T_A' = 0 \text{ K}, \\ 10 \text{ K} & \text{for} \quad T_A' = 300 \text{ K}. \end{cases}$$

If we choose the reference noise temperature $T_{REF} = 300$ K, (6.74) gives

$$\Delta T(\text{unbalanced Dicke}) \simeq \begin{cases} 3 \text{ K} & \text{for} \quad T_A' = 0 \text{ K}, \\ 0.2 \text{ K} & \text{for} \quad T_A' = 300 \text{ K}. \end{cases}$$

Overall, the radiometric resolution of the unbalanced Dicke radiometer is superior to that of the total-power radiometer. Of particular significance, however, is the condition $T_A' = T_{REF}$, because when this condition is met, the

TABLE 6.1
Nimbus 5 Electrically Scanning Microwave Radiometer
(ESMR) Flight Model Parameters[a]

Antenna:	
Antenna type	Phased array
Aperture size	83.3 cm × 85.5 cm
Half-power beamwidth	1.4° × 1.4° (at nadir)
Beam efficiency	90–92.7%
Beam scan angle	±50°
Antenna loss	1.7 dB
Polarization	Horizontal
Radiometer:	
Center frequency	19.35 GHz
Predetection bandwidth	200 MHz
Mixer noise figure	6.5 dB
ΔT_{min}[b]	1.5 K
Absolute accuracy	2 K
Dynamic range	50–330 K
Calibration	
(a) Reference load	338 K
(b) Ambient load	Local ambient
(c) Sky horn antenna	3 K

[a] From *Nimbus 5 User's Guide* (NASA, 1972).
[b] For 47-ms integration time.

second term inside the square brackets of (6.74) goes to zero, thereby eliminating the effects of gain variations altogether. When $T_A' = T_{REF}$, the radiometer is said to be *balanced*, in which case (6.74) reduces to

$$\Delta T = \frac{2(T_A' + T_{REC}')}{\sqrt{B\tau}} \quad \text{(balanced Dicke radiometer)}$$

$$= 2\,\Delta T_{IDEAL}, \tag{6.75}$$

or twice the theoretical sensitivity of an ideal total-power radiometer (free of gain variations). The factor of 2 comes about from the fact that T_A' is observed for only half the time.

Techniques used for continuously maintaining the Dicke radiometer in a balanced state are discussed in the next section.

Sometimes, practical considerations dictate that the square wave at the output of the square-law detector be amplified prior to feeding it into the synchronous demodulator. A video amplifier is used for this purpose. To preserve the square-wave shape of the detected signal, the video amplifier must be capable of providing equal amplification to all of the major harmonics of the square-wave signal, which means that the bandpass of the video amplifier should extend from below f_s to at least $5f_s$, and preferably to as high as $10f_s$. A square wave consists of only odd harmonics, with the amplitude of the first harmonic equal to $4/\pi$ times the amplitude of the square wave, and the amplitude of the nth harmonic equal to $1/n$ times the amplitude of the first harmonic. This places an additional requirement on the necessary dynamic range of the video amplifier and makes it vulnerable to noise saturation. To avoid this problem, some Dicke radiometers employ a narrow-bandpass amplifier tuned to f_s, but whose bandwidth exceeds the bandwidth of the low-pass filter, B_{LF}. With only the first harmonic of the square wave reaching the synchronous demodulator, the dc output of the synchronous demodulator is smaller than when the full square wave is used, which leads to a reduction in radiometric sensitivity (larger ΔT) by a factor of $(\pi\sqrt{2}/4)=1.11$, or approximately 11 percent (Tiuri, 1964). The simplification in system design and specification brought about by the sinusoidal demodulation, with a relatively small cost in terms of loss in radiometric sensitivity, has made the square-wave-modulated, sine-wave-demodulated Dicke radiometer a popular choice. The merits of other modulation and demodulation waveforms have been considered also (Colvin, 1961; McGillem and Seling, 1963) but in terms of the radiometric sensitivity ΔT, using square-wave modulation and demodulation gives the best results.

6-10 BALANCING TECHNIQUES

A Dicke radiometer is said to be *balanced* if

$$\overline{V}_{dANT} - \overline{V}_{dREF} = 0, \tag{6.76}$$

where $\overline{V}_{dANT}$ is the dc component of the detected voltage during the half cycle that the receiver input switch is connected to the antenna, and a similar definition applies to $\overline{V}_{dREF}$. In the balanced condition, $\overline{V}_{syn}=0$ and consequently $\overline{V}_{out}=0$. With reference to (6.65), the balanced condition may be realized by either: (1) adjusting T_{REF} to equal T_A' (or vice versa) prior to the input switch, or (2) controlling the predetection gain of $\overline{V}_{dANT}$ and $\overline{V}_{dREF}$ separately, in such a manner that the two voltages are made equal. Some examples of feedback configurations, proposed to realize automatically balanced operations in a Dicke radiometer, are discussed next.

6-10.1 Reference-Channel Control Method

Figure 6.16 is a block diagram of a null-balancing Dicke radiometer employing the reference-channel method (Machin et al., 1952). A feedback loop is used to control the magnitude of T_{REF} so that it continuously balances the antenna temperature T_A'. This is realized by feeding the integrator output into a control circuit that applies the necessary voltage (or current) to an electronically controlled variable attenuator to maintain a null at the integrator output. In this case, the control voltage V_c becomes the output voltage to be recorded,

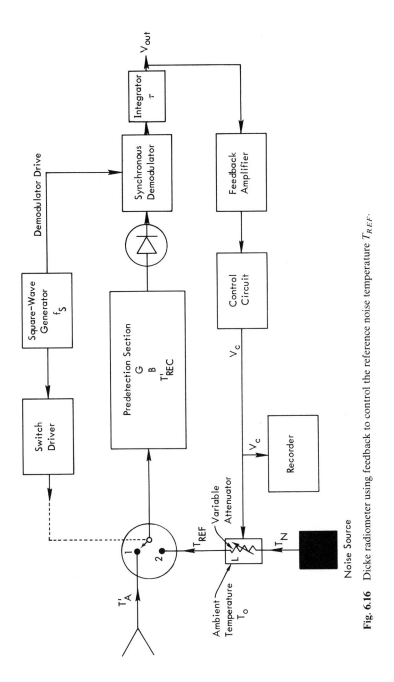

Fig. 6.16 Dicke radiometer using feedback to control the reference noise temperature T_{REF}.

since it is related to T_{REF}, which, in the balanced condition, is equal to T'_A. The radiometer is calibrated by measuring V_c as a function of the noise temperature T_{CAL} of a calibration noise source put in place of the antenna (or through the use of a calibration switch as shown in Fig. 6.12). In general, the calibration curve may be nonlinear, thereby necessitating that V_c be measured over a wide range of values of T_{CAL}.

Returning to Fig. 6.16, the reference noise temperature T_{REF} is in part due to the noise generated by the noise source and in part due to self-emission by the attenuator,

$$T_{REF} = \frac{T_N}{L} + \left(1 - \frac{1}{L}\right)T_0, \tag{6.77}$$

where T_N is the noise temperature of the source, L is the loss factor of the attenuator, and T_0 is its physical temperature. As a function of L, the limiting values of T_{REF} are $T_{REF} = T_N$ for $L = 1$ (no attenuation) and $T_{REF} = T_0$ for L very large. Conceptually, T_N and T_0 can be specified so that the range between them covers the range of values over which T'_A is expected to vary. In practice, however, this specification cannot be realized with passive noise sources unless cryogenic cooling is used (the use of active "cold" sources is discussed below). To illustrate with an example, consider a radiometer system specified to operate over the range 50 K $\leqslant T'_A \leqslant$ 300 K. The upper limit of T'_A can be accommodated easily by maintaining the environmental temperature of the front end of the radiometer, including the attenuator, at $T_0 = 300$ K, which for L very large, gives $T_{REF} = T'_A = 300$ K. To accommodate the lower limit of T'_A, T_N has to be assigned a value of 50 K (or lower). If a matched load is used as the noise source, it has to be physically cooled to the desired noise temperature. Moreover, for real, variable attenuators, the loss factor L cannot be reduced all the way to unity, and therefore the temperature of the matched load has to be lower than 50 K in order to compensate for the noise power generated by the attenuator. Cryogenic techniques sometimes are used in ground-based radiometer systems to reduce the receiver noise temperature and certainly may be used to cool the matched load of the radiometer system under discussion. However, in airborne and spaceborne operations, cryogenic cooling usually is avoided because of the large amounts of power required to maintain the cryogenic fluids at the desired temperature.

Traditionally, active noise sources have been used to provide noise temperatures in excess of their ambient temperatures, thereby relying on cryogenically-cooled matched loads for low noise-temperature sources. Recent advances in FET technology, however, have led to the development of an active circuit that behaves like a noise source with an output noise temperature that is much smaller than its ambient temperature; Frater and Williams (1981) have developed the theory for such a "cold" FET device, which they call a COLDFET, and have demonstrated that a noise temperature as low as 50 K can be achieved at 1.4 GHz. Future developments will undoubtedly extend the use of the COLDFET to higher microwave frequencies.

If, instead of controlling the input noise temperature of the reference channel to equal the noise temperature of the antenna channel, the reverse is done, the cryogenic refrigeration problem associated with the use of passive devices can be alleviated. This approach is discussed next.

6-10.2 Antenna-Channel Noise-Injection Method

The configuration shown in Fig. 6.17 was proposed by Goggins (1967) to achieve null balancing through the use of noise injection into the line connecting the antenna to the input switch. The front end of the radiometer—including the reference load, the variable attenuator, and the directional coupler (as well as other RF devices)—is enclosed in a constant-temperature chamber at a temperature T_0 slightly higher than the highest specified value for T_A' (for reasons that will become obvious later). In other words, when the input switch is connected to terminal 2 (Fig. 6.17), the input noise temperature is $T_{REF} = T_0$ = constant. To balance the reference load, a sufficient amount of noise power is injected into the antenna port through a directional coupler so that the input noise temperature T_A'' appearing at the input switch (terminal 1 in Fig. 6.17) is equal to T_{REF},

$$T_A'' = T_{REF} = T_0. \tag{6.78}$$

The amount of injected power is controlled by the variable attenuator, which itself is controlled by a feedback network. The noise temperature T_A'' is related to the antenna noise temperature T_A' through

$$T_A'' = \left(1 - \frac{1}{F_c}\right)T_A' + \frac{T_N'}{F_c}, \tag{6.79}$$

where F_c ($\geqslant 1$) is the coupling factor of the directional coupler. T_N' is the noise temperature of the injected noise at the input to the directional coupler and is given by

$$T_N' = \frac{T_N}{L} + \left(1 - \frac{1}{L}\right)T_0. \tag{6.80}$$

Combining the above three expressions leads to

$$L = \frac{T_N - T_0}{(F_c - 1)(T_0 - T_A')}. \tag{6.81}$$

The radiometer output indicator is the attenuator control voltage V_c. If V_c is scaled and linearized so that $V_c = 1/L$, then (6.81) becomes a linear relationship between V_c and T_A':

$$V_c = \frac{F_c - 1}{T_N - T_0}(T_0 - T_A'). \tag{6.82}$$

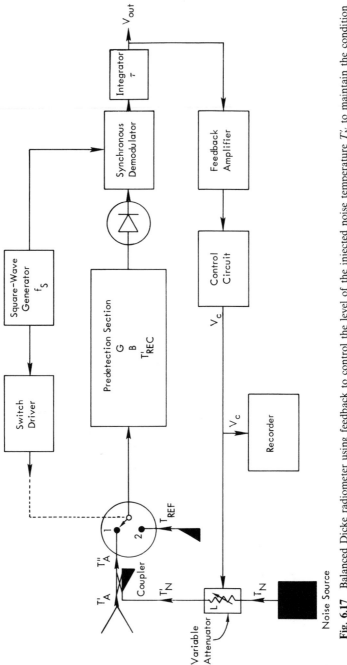

Fig. 6.17 Balanced Dicke radiometer using feedback to control the level of the injected noise temperature T'_N to maintain the condition $T''_A = T_{REF}$.

Suppose that the radiometer is specified to operate over the range $50\ \text{K} \leqslant T_A' \leqslant 300\ \text{K}$. Let us choose $T_0 = 310\ \text{K}$, and let us use a 20-dB directional coupler ($F_c = 100$) and an avalanche noise diode having an output power noise temperature T_N of 50,000 K. From (6.81), L has to vary between 1.9 ($\simeq 2.9$ dB) and 50 ($\simeq 17$ dB) to cover the specified temperature range. This dynamic range of 14.1 dB can easily be accommodated by a *PIN* diode attenuator, which is a current-driven device capable of more than 40 dB in linear dynamic range. The minimum loss factor (usually called insertion loss) of a *PIN* diode typically is about 2 dB. Thus, the values chosen for T_0, F_c, and T_N result in a range of values for L that is compatible with the capabilities of a *PIN* diode. Had we chosen T_0 to be exactly equal to $T_A'(\text{max}) = 300\ \text{K}$ rather than 310 K, L would have had to have been infinite to produce null balancing.

Since the noise temperature seen by the input switch is always equal to T_0, the sensitivity is given by (6.75) with $T_A' = T_0$,

$$\Delta T = \frac{2(T_0 + T_{REC}')}{\sqrt{B\tau}}. \tag{6.83}$$

6-10.3 Pulsed Noise-Injection Method

Diode attenuators are most stable in their extreme ON and OFF states. When operated in only one or the other of these two states (by controlling the magnitude and polarity of the bias voltage), a *PIN* diode attenuator becomes an ON/OFF switch; in the ON position it causes minimum attenuation ($\simeq 2.0$ dB), and in the OFF position it causes maximum attenuation (typically 60 dB). Use is made of this diode property in the configuration shown in Fig. 6.18 (Hardy et al., 1974), which basically is the same as that shown in Fig. 6.17 except that now the injected noise is generated in the form of narrow rectangular pulses rather than continuously. The feedback control circuit drives a voltage-controlled oscillator (VCO), which in turn drives a pulse generator. The output of the pulse generator consists of narrow rectangular pulses, each of length τ_p, with a repetition period $\tau_R = 1/f_R$, where f_R is the pulse repetition frequency (Fig. 6.19). When the diode switch is in the OFF position (no pulse), we have maximum attenuation which, in effect, masks the noise generated by the noise diode. The resultant value of T_N' is designated T_{OFF}', and when the *PIN* diode is switched by a pulse to its ON position, we have minimum attenuation, or a large value of T_N' which we shall designate T_{ON}'. Thus, over a repetition period τ_R

$$T_N' = \begin{cases} T_{ON}' & \text{for} \quad 0 \leqslant t \leqslant \tau_p, \\ T_{OFF}' & \text{for} \quad \tau_p \leqslant t \leqslant \tau_R. \end{cases} \tag{6.84}$$

The pulse repetition frequency f_R should be much higher than f_s, the square-wave modulation frequency of the input switch, so that many pulses are

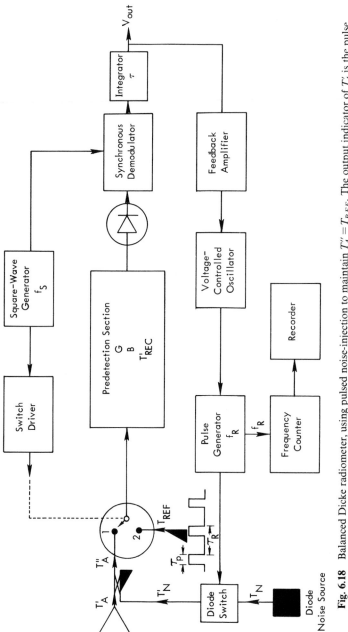

Fig. 6.18 Balanced Dicke radiometer, using pulsed noise-injection to maintain $T_A'' = T_{REF}$. The output indicator of T_A is the pulse repetition frequency f_R.

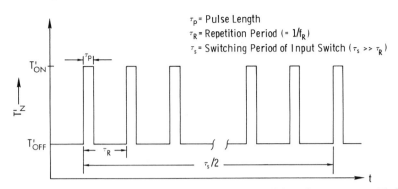

Fig. 6.19 Timing diagram showing the ON and OFF states of the noise temperature T_N' that is injected through the directional coupler of Fig. 6.18.

generated during the period $\tau_s/2$. The average value of T_N' is

$$\overline{T}_N' = \tau_p f_R T_{ON}' + (1 - \tau_p f_R) T_{OFF}', \qquad (6.85)$$

where $\tau_p f_R$ is the total time, during one second, that the diode switch is ON.

If τ_p is kept constant, f_R can be controlled by the feedback loop to provide the necessary value of $\overline{T}_N'$ to inject into the antenna port (via the directional coupler) so that a null condition always is maintained at the integrator output. The radiometer output indicator is a frequency counter that measures f_R, which is linearly related to T_A' by

$$f_R = \frac{(F_c T_0 - T_{OFF}') - (F_c - 1) T_A'}{\tau_p (T_{ON}' - T_{OFF}')} \qquad (6.86)$$

through the use of (6.78), (6.79), and (6.85). If during its OFF position, the attenuator loss factor is high enough to reduce the noise-diode contribution to a negligible value, then T_{OFF}' becomes approximately equal to T_0, and (6.86) reduces to

$$f_R = \frac{(F_c - 1)(T_0 - T_A')}{\tau_p (T_{ON}' - T_0)}. \qquad (6.87)$$

Since T_0 is known, it is sufficient to measure f_R at one value of a known noise temperature of a calibration source in order to determine the value of the quantity multiplying $T_0 - T_A'$ in (6.87). The radiometric sensitivity of this type of radiometer is given by (6.83).

The parameters of a 2.65-GHz pulsed noise-injection Dicke radiometer are listed in Table 6.2. The system was developed as a satellite prototype sensor for measuring the surface temperature of the ocean (Hardy et al., 1974).

TABLE 6.2
2.65-GHz Satellite Prototype Ocean-Temperature Sensing Radiometer
Using Pulsed Noise-Injection Scheme[a]

Antenna:	
Antenna type	Multimode Pyramidal horn
Aperture size	35.6 cm × 35.6 cm
Beam efficiency	98%
Polarization	Circular
Radiometer:	
Center Frequency	2.65 GHz
Predetection bandwidth	100 MHz
Receiver noise temperature	60 K
Switching frequency	50 Hz
Diode excess noise	36 dB
Pulse width	40 μs
Pulse-generator frequency range	0–12 kHz
ΔT_{min} for 1-s integration time	0.15 K

[a] From Hardy et al. (1974).

6-10.4 Gain-Modulation Method

The balanced condition was realized in the methods considered thus far by adjusting the noise temperature of the reference channel to equal the noise temperature of the antenna channel, or vice versa, at the input switch. Another way to effect balance is by modulating the gain of the IF output voltage prior to the square-law detector. In the configuration shown in Fig. 6.20 (Orhaug and Waltman, 1962), the modulation consists of switching the IF output between a constant attenuator and a variable attenuator for the alternate half cycles of the input switch. The attenuator switch is driven by the switch-driver in synchronism with the input switch. The function of the feedback loop is to control the variable attenuator so that its output voltage (corresponding to the reference channel) is equal to the output voltage of the fixed attenuator (corresponding to the antenna channel). That is, if the loss factor of the variable attenuator, L_v, is adjusted to maintain the condition

$$\frac{1}{L_0}(T_A' + T_{REC}') = \frac{1}{L_v}(T_{REF} + T_{REC}'), \qquad (6.88)$$

then the dc value of the output voltage will be zero. The system is calibrated by relating the control voltage V_c to the noise temperature of a calibration noise source replacing the antenna. If the voltage V_c is scaled and linearized so that $V_c = 1/L_v$, then V_c becomes linearly related to T_A':

$$V_c = \frac{1}{L_0(T_{REF} + T_{REC}')}(T_A' + T_{REC}'). \qquad (6.89)$$

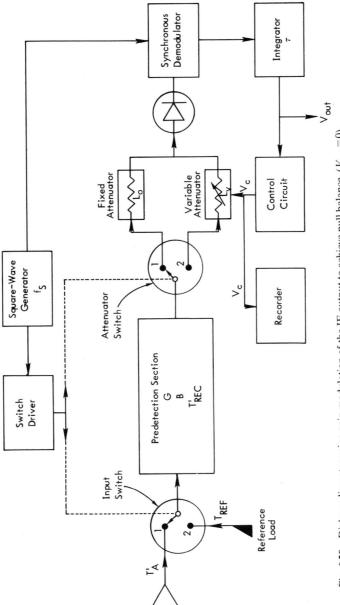

Fig. 6.20 Dicke radiometer using gain modulation of the IF output to achieve null balance ($V_{out} = 0$).

Conceptually, the gain modulation may be applied before or after the mixer, but in practice it is easier to control the loss factor (or gain) of a device operating in the IF frequency range than to control a microwave device.

One drawback of the gain-modulation technique is that slow variations in the receiver noise temperature T'_{REC} (between calibrations) result in a measurement error of the absolute value of T'_A. This is due to the dependence of V_c on T'_{REC}. In contrast, the techniques employing temperature control to balance the radiometer are insensitive to drifts in T'_{REC}. Another limitation of the gain-modulation technique pertains to the amplitude of the gain modulation, L_v/L_0. If this factor is large, the gain modulation is liable to produce excessive output fluctuations. Thus, for low-noise receivers (relatively small T'_{REC}), the gain-modulation method is useful over a narrow range of the difference $T'_{REC} - T'_A$.

6-11 AUTOMATIC-GAIN-CONTROL (AGC) TECHNIQUES

Automatic gain control (AGC) is a feedback technique used for stabilizing the gain of receiver systems. In continuous AGC, the output voltage of the receiver is compared with a reference voltage on a continuous basis, and the difference between the two voltages is used to adjust the gain of the receiver so that the output voltage is maintained at a constant level. Continuous AGC is inapplicable to radiometer receivers because the AGC action removes all variations, including those due to the signal (T'_A) that the radiometer is intended to measure. To eliminate the dependence of the AGC voltage on the antenna temperature, Seling (1964) introduced the *sampled*-AGC technique in which the detector output voltage is monitored by the AGC feedback circuit during only the half cycles (of the square-wave Dicke switching period) for which the Dicke switch is connected to the (constant-temperature) reference load. Successful operation of the sampled-AGC technique depends upon meeting certain constraints that dictate the choice of the AGC bandwidth, as discussed by Seling (1964).

The sampled-AGC technique shares a drawback with the gain-modulated radiometer (Section 6-10.4) in that slow variations in the receiver noise temperature (between calibrations) are compensated for as if they were gain variations, thereby introducing a bias error in the measurement accuracy of T'_A.

The sampled-AGC approach was extended by Hach (1966, 1968), who developed the *two-reference-temperature AGC radiometer* shown in Fig. 6.21. This radiometer has several attractive features: (1) insensitivity to system gain variations, (2) insensitivity to receiver noise-temperature variations, and (3) the ability to provide continuous calibration. Hach's concept was adopted by General Electric (1973) in the construction of the radiometer section of the RADSCAT system that was flown aboard the Skylab satellite in 1973. A list of the RADSCAT radiometer parameters is given in Table 6.3.

The discussion that follows is based on the papers by Hach (1966, 1968), to which the reader is referred for details. Other than differences in notation,

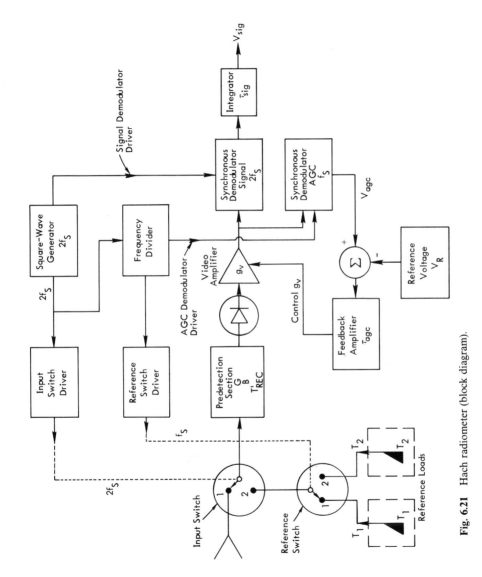

Fig. 6.21 Hach radiometer (block diagram).

TABLE 6.3
Radiometer Section of Skylab's RADSCAT [a]

Antenna:	
Antenna type	Parabolic reflector
Reflector diameter	114 cm
Half-power beamwidth	1.5°
Beam efficiency	90%
Antenna loss	0.3 dB
Polarization	Horizontal and vertical
Radiometer:	
Center frequency	13.9 GHz
Predetection half-power bandwidth	210 MHz
Receiver noise temperature	1195 K
Comparison temperatures	318 and 393 K
Switching frequency	996 Hz
Video amplifier gain	42 ± 4 dB
AGC integration time-constant	0.9 s
ΔT_{min} for integration time:	
32 ms	1.15 K
128 ms	0.6 K
256 ms	0.425 K

[a] General Electric Space Systems Division (1973).

the only notable difference is that we shall assume the switches to have such a short switching time constant, compared to the switching periods, that switching between ports may be assumed to be essentially instantaneous. Hach's treatment is more general in that it takes into account the effects of the nonzero switching time constant on the radiometer signals, although the final results are the same as those obtained assuming zero switching time constant.

The two-reference-temperature radiometer shown in Fig. 6.21 uses two RF switches: an input switch which connects the receiver to either the antenna port or to the reference port, and a reference switch which connects the input switch to one or the other of two reference noise sources (loads) with constant noise temperatures T_1 and T_2. The switching frequency of the input switch is $2f_s$, and it is exactly twice the switching frequency of the reference switch. Both switching waveforms are generated by the same square-wave generator of frequency $2f_s$, with the addition of a frequency divider prior to the reference-switch driver.

With reference to the switching sequences shown in Fig. 6.22(a) and (b), the output voltage of the square-law detector (Fig. 6.22(c)) is given by

$$
V_d(t) = C_d G k B \begin{cases} (T_A' + T_{REC}') & \text{for} \quad 0 \leqslant t \leqslant \frac{1}{4}\tau_s, \\ (T_2 + T_{REC}') & \text{for} \quad \frac{1}{4}\tau_s \leqslant t \leqslant \frac{1}{2}\tau_s, \\ (T_A' + T_{REC}') & \text{for} \quad \frac{1}{2}\tau_s \leqslant t \leqslant \frac{3}{4}\tau_s, \\ (T_1 + T_{REC}') & \text{for} \quad \frac{3}{4}\tau_s \leqslant t \leqslant \tau_s, \end{cases} \tag{6.90}
$$

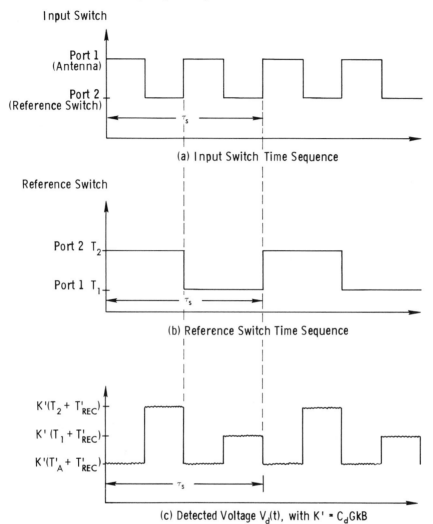

Fig. 6.22 Switching sequences of (a) input switch, (b) reference switch, and (c) square-law-detector output of Hach radiometer.

where τ_s ($=1/f_s$) is the period of one switching cycle of the reference switch. The components due to noise and gain fluctuations have been ignored, since they will effectively be filtered out by the signal or AGC integrators.

The square-law detector is followed by an ac-coupled video amplifier with controllable voltage gain g_v and a rectangular passband that should extend from about $0.01f_s$ to $10f_s$ (Hach, 1968) in order to preserve the relative phase between the fundamental wave at f_s and the first harmonic at $2f_s$. The output voltage of the ac-coupled video amplifier is

$$V_v(t)=g_v\left[V_d(t)-\bar{V}_d\right]. \tag{6.91}$$

$\overline{V}_d$, the dc value of $V_d(t)$, is equal to one-quarter the sum of the four components given in (6.90), or

$$\overline{V}_d = K_0(2T_A' + T_1 + T_2 + 4T_{REC}'),\tag{6.92}$$

where

$$K_0 \triangleq C_d G k B / 4.\tag{6.93}$$

Inserting (6.90) and (6.92) into (6.91) leads to

$$V_v(t) = K_0 g_v \begin{cases} (2T_A' - T_1 - T_2) & \text{for } 0 \leqslant t \leqslant \tfrac{1}{4}\tau_s, \\ (3T_2 - T_1 - 2T_A') & \text{for } \tfrac{1}{4}\tau_s \leqslant t \leqslant \tfrac{1}{2}\tau_s, \\ (2T_A' - T_1 - T_2) & \text{for } \tfrac{1}{2}\tau_s \leqslant t \leqslant \tfrac{3}{4}\tau_s, \\ (3T_1 - T_2 - 2T_A') & \text{for } \tfrac{3}{4}\tau_s \leqslant t \leqslant \tau_s. \end{cases}\tag{6.94}$$

$V_v(t)$ serves as the input waveform to each of two synchronous demodulators (detectors): the AGC demodulator and the signal demodulator. The AGC synchronous demodulator is followed by a low-pass filter (integrator) with integration time τ_{agc} (the reference voltage V_R of Fig. 6.21 may be ignored for the time being), and similarly, the signal demodulator is followed by a filter with integration time τ_{sig}. The integrators are, of course, used to filter out the noise and system-gain fluctuations, and therefore their bandwidths are of prime importance to the radiometric sensitivity ΔT, as discussed later. The total voltage gain of the AGC synchronous demodulator-integrator is designated g_{agc}, and g_{sig} is defined similarly for the signal branch.

The AGC demodulator-integrator branch demodulates $V_v(t)$ at the reference frequency f_s. The average value of its output voltage is

$$\overline{V}_{agc} = \frac{g_{agc}}{\tau_s} \left[\int_0^{\tau_s/2} V_v(t)\,dt - \int_{\tau_s/2}^{\tau} V_v(t)\,dt \right],\tag{6.95}$$

which, upon inserting (6.94), leads to

$$\overline{V}_{agc} = K_0 g_v g_{agc}(T_2 - T_1).\tag{6.96}$$

The signal demodulator-integrator branch performs a similar function, except that its reference frequency is $2f_s$. Hence, its output voltage is given by

$$\overline{V}_{sig} = \frac{g_{sig}}{\tau_s} \left[\int_0^{\frac{1}{4}\tau_s} V_v(t)\,dt - \int_{\frac{1}{4}\tau_s}^{\frac{1}{2}\tau_s} V_v(t)\,dt + \int_{\frac{1}{2}\tau_s}^{\frac{3}{4}\tau_s} V_v(t)\,dt - \int_{\frac{3}{4}\tau_s}^{\tau_s} V_v(t)\,dt \right],\tag{6.97}$$

which yields

$$\overline{V}_{sig} = K_0 g_v g_{sig} (2T_A' - T_1 - T_2). \tag{6.98}$$

Before we proceed further, it is worth noting the following observations:

1. Both output voltages, $\overline{V}_{agc}$ and $\overline{V}_{sig}$, are independent of the receiver noise temperature T_{REC}'. This is due to the ac coupling of the video amplifier.
2. Both output voltages are directly proportional to the factor $K_0 g_v$ $(=C_d G k B g_v / 4)$, which contains all the RF parameters that give rise to the system gain. Hence, the ratio V_{sig}/V_{agc} is independent of system gain variations.

The two-reference-temperature Dicke radiometer may be operated in either of two modes. The first mode consists of measuring $\overline{V}_{sig}$ and $\overline{V}_{agc}$ separately and then forming the ratio

$$\frac{\overline{V}_{sig}}{\overline{V}_{agc}} = \frac{g_{sig}}{g_{agc}} \frac{2T_A' - T_1 - T_2}{T_2 - T_1}, \tag{6.99}$$

from which T_A' can be determined. The measurement accuracy of T_A' depends on the stability of the reference temperatures T_1 and T_2, which, in practice, can be maintained constant to within a fraction of a kelvin. Since g_{sig} and g_{agc} are low-frequency parameters, they can be maintained at essentially constant levels. In this first mode, the gain of the video amplifier is kept constant also.

The second mode of operation uses the AGC output voltage $\overline{V}_{agc}$ to drive a feedback loop. Since $\overline{V}_{agc}$ is independent of T_A' and T_{REC}', and since T_1 and T_2 are maintained constant, changes in $\overline{V}_{agc}$ are due to variations in the receiver parameters. Such changes can be compensated for by controlling the video-amplifier gain with a feedback loop. After experimentally measuring $\overline{V}_{agc}$ without feedback, the measured value (call it V_R) then is used to set the voltage level of a reference dc voltage source.

With $\overline{V}_{agc}$ maintained equal to V_R by the feedback loop, the ratio of (6.98) to (6.96) yields

$$\overline{V}_{sig} = \frac{V_R g_{sig}}{g_{agc}} \left(\frac{2T_A' - T_1 - T_2}{T_2 - T_1} \right), \tag{6.100}$$

from which the following expression for T_A' is obtained:

$$T_A' = \frac{1}{2} \left[\overline{V}_{sig} \left(\frac{g_{agc}}{V_R g_{sig}} \right) (T_2 - T_1) + (T_2 + T_1) \right]. \tag{6.101}$$

The radiometric sensitivity ΔT is given by (Hach, 1968)

$$\Delta T = \frac{1}{\sqrt{B\tau_{sig}}} \left\{ \left[1 + \left(\frac{1}{1 + \tau_{agc}/\tau_{sig}} \right) \left(\frac{T_2 + T_1 - 2T_A'}{T_2 - T_1} \right)^2 \right] \right.$$

$$\left. \times \left[(T_2 + T_{REC}')^2 + (T_1 + T_{REC}')^2 + 2(T_A' + T_{REC}')^2 \right] \right\}^{1/2}$$

(6.102)

where τ_{agc} and τ_{sig} are the integration times (not time constants) of the AGC and signal channels, respectively. For comparison purposes, the ratio of ΔT as given by (6.102) to ΔT of the balanced Dicke radiometer (Eq. (6.75)) is shown in Fig. 6.23 as a function of T_A' for several values of the ratio τ_{agc}/τ_{sig}. The values used for T_2, T_1, and T_{REC}' are 393, 318, and 1200 K, respectively (see Table 6.3).

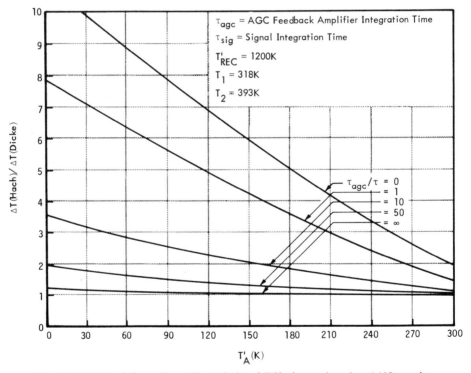

Fig. 6.23 Ratio of the radiometric resolution ΔT(Hach) as given by (6.102) to the radiometric resolution of the balanced Dicke radiometer, ΔT(Dicke), as given by (6.75), plotted as a function of T_A' for several values of τ_{agc}/τ_{sig}. Both types of radiometers are assumed to have the same bandwidth B and signal integration time τ_{sig} (or τ in (6.75)). The values used for T_1, T_2, and T_{REC}' are from Table 6.3.

6-12 NOISE-ADDING RADIOMETER

The noise-adding radiometer (Ohm and Snell, 1963; Batelaan et al., 1974) removes the effects of gain variations, but without the use of a Dicke switch. Square-wave noise is coupled into the receiver input from a noise diode driven by a constant-rate square-wave generator, as shown in Fig. 6.24. The output voltage of the square-law detector is synchronously detected (demodulated) at the same rate, and a voltage ratio Y is formed, whose average value is given by

$$\bar{Y} = \frac{\bar{V}_1}{\bar{V}_2 - \bar{V}_1} = \frac{T'_A + T'_{REC}}{T''_N}, \tag{6.103}$$

where $\bar{V}_1, \bar{V}_2 =$ average square-law detector output voltage corresponding to the half cycle (of the switching period) during which the noise diode is OFF and ON, respectively,

$T''_N =$ added noise to receiver input during the diode ON half cycle.

The ratio meter is followed by a low-pass filter to reduce noise fluctuations. For a unity-gain low-pass filter, we have

$$\bar{V}_{out} = \bar{Y} = (T'_A + T'_{REC})/T''_N. \tag{6.104}$$

The measurement accuracy of T'_A is independent of system gain variations, but it is linked directly to the stability of the receiver noise temperature T'_{REC} and to the excess noise temperature T''_N.

The theoretical sensitivity of the noise-adding radiometer is given by (Batelaan et al., 1974)

$$\Delta T = \frac{2(T'_A + T'_{REC})}{\sqrt{B\tau}} \left[1 + \frac{(T'_A + T'_{REC})}{T''_N} \right]. \tag{6.105}$$

The quantity multiplying the square bracket is recognized as twice the radiometric sensitivity of the ideal radiometer. Hence,

$$\Delta T(\text{noise-adding}) = 2\Delta T_{IDEAL} \left[1 + \frac{T_{SYS}}{T''_N} \right].$$

The absence of an input switch is an attractive feature of the noise-adding radiometer, particularly in low-noise receivers. A Dicke switch usually adds about 7–75 K to the receiver noise temperature T'_{REC}. In star-tracking and astronomical research, the brightness temperature of some targets may be only a few kelvins, which necessitates the use of low-noise receivers with noise temperatures of the order of a few tens of kelvins in order to achieve radiometric sensitivities of the order of 0.01–0.1 K. For such cases, the absence of an input switch becomes a significant factor.

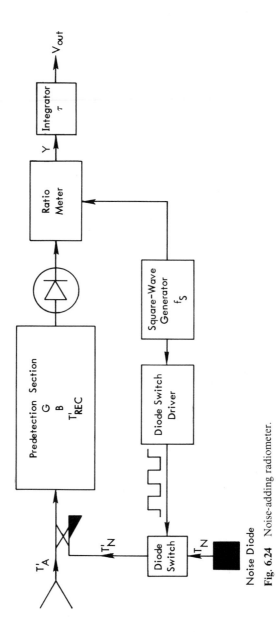

Fig. 6.24 Noise-adding radiometer.

6-13 OTHER TYPES OF RADIOMETERS

The radiometric techniques considered in the previous sections are those commonly used in microwave remote sensing. Other types of receivers also have been reported in the literature, primarily for use in radio astronomy. Among these are the interferometer receiver (Wesseling, 1967; Clark, 1968), the correlation receiver (Blum, 1959; Batchelor et al., 1968), and the Graham receiver (Graham, 1958), as well as receiver configurations that are hybrids of two or more techniques.

Most radiometer receivers use wide bandwidths and long integration times to achieve good radiometric resolutions. In some cases, however, the information being sought is contained in the spectral and/or temporal variation of the incoming radiation. Measurements of the emission spectra of spectral lines often require receiver systems with spectral resolutions of the order of 1–100 kHz. Such measurements usually are made using tunable spectrometers, multichannel spectrometers, or autocorrelation spectrometers (Price, 1976). Good temporal resolution is essential in observations of solar events, some of which are only a few milliseconds long, and in radio observations of pulsars. The emission from a pulsar consists of narrow pulses that occur at a regular interval, typically between 0.5 and 1.5 s (Manchester, 1973). The pulse width usually is of the order of 5 percent of the pulse repetition period, and the pulse substructure sometimes may be as short as 8 μs (Hankins, 1972). Techniques developed for observations of pulsars with high temporal and spectral resolutions are described by Huguenin (1976).

6-14 SUMMARY OF RADIOMETER PROPERTIES

For easy reference, Table 6.4 provides a summary of the input-output relationship and of the radiometric sensitivity for most of the receiver configurations discussed in the previous sections. The output indication I_{out} is related linearly to the antenna radiometric temperature T_A' through

$$I_{out} = a(T_A' + b), \qquad (6.106)$$

where a and b are constants and I_{out} is either V_{out} (integrator output voltage), V_c (control voltage), or f_R (pulse-repetition frequency).

Since, in general, the radiometric sensitivity ΔT is a function of T_A', Table 7.4 considers ΔT for each of two values of T_A', namely, $T_A' = 0$ K and $T_A' = T_0$, where T_0 ($\simeq 310$ K) is the environmental temperature of the radiometer front end. In both cases, ΔT is normalized to ΔT_{IDEAL}, the sensitivity of the ideal total-power radiometer, which is given by (6.53),

$$\Delta T_{IDEAL} = \frac{T_A' + T_{REC}'}{\sqrt{B\tau}}. \qquad (6.53)$$

TABLE 6.4
Summary of System Transfer Functions and Sensitivities of Different Types of Radiometers[a]

Radiometer type	Output indicator I_{out}	a	b	$\Delta T/\Delta T_{IDEAL}$ for $T'_A = 0$ K	$\Delta T/\Delta T_{IDEAL}$ for $T'_A = T_0$	Relevant expressions
Ideal (Fig. 6.13)	V_{out}	G_S	T'_{REC}	1	1	(6.49), (6.53)
Total power (Fig. 6.13)	V_{out}	G_S	T'_{REC}	$\left[1 + B\tau\left(\dfrac{\Delta G_S}{G_S}\right)^2\right]^{1/2}$	$\left[1 + B\tau\left(\dfrac{\Delta G_S}{G_S}\right)^2\right]^{1/2}$	(6.49), (6.64)
Dicke (unbalanced) (Fig. 6.15)	V_{out}	$G_S/2$	$-T_0$	$\sqrt{2}\left[\left(\dfrac{T_0+T'_{REC}}{T'_{REC}}\right)^2 + 1 + \dfrac{B\tau}{2}\left(\dfrac{\Delta G_S}{G_S}\right)^2\left(\dfrac{T_0}{T'_{REC}}\right)^2\right]^{1/2}$	2	(6.68), (6.74)
Balanced Dicke, with noise injection (Fig. 6.17)	V_c	$-\left(\dfrac{F_c-1}{T_N-T_0}\right)$	$-T_0$	$2\left(\dfrac{T_0}{T'_{REC}}+1\right)$	2	(6.82), (6.83)

Balanced Dicke, with pulsed noise injection (Fig. 6.18)	f_R	$-\dfrac{(F_c-1)}{\tau_p(T_{0N}-T_0)}$	$-T_0$	$2\left(\dfrac{T_0}{T_{REC}}+1\right)$	2	(6.87), (6.83)
Hach (Fig. 6.21)	V_{sig}	$\dfrac{2V_R g_{sig}}{g_{agc}(T_2-T_1)}$	$\dfrac{-T_2-T_1}{2}$	See (6.102) and Fig. 6.23	See (6.102) and Fig. 6.23	(6.100), (6.102)
Noise adding (Fig. 6.24)	V_{out}	$\dfrac{1}{T''_N}$	T'_{REC}	$2\left(\dfrac{T_{REC}}{T''_N}+1\right)$	$2\left(\dfrac{T_0+T'_{REC}}{T''_N}+1\right)$	(6.104), (6.105)

[a]The radiometer output indication I_{out} is related to the input antenna temperature T'_A by $I_{out}=a(T'_A+b)$, and the sensitivity ΔT is defined relative to ΔT_{IDEAL} of the ideal radiometer (given by (6.53)).

$T'_{REC}=$ system
$G_S=$ system gain factor, defined by (6.50),
$T_{REC}=$ receiver input noise temperature referred to the antenna terminals (includes transmission line and switch losses),
$T_{REF}=T_0$ for Dicke receivers,
$T_0=$ Environmental temperature of radiometer front end (≈ 310 K).

6-15 PRACTICAL CONSIDERATIONS

Radiometer performance is measured in terms of measurement accuracy and precision, both of which are determined (in practice) by the RF portion of the radiometer. Although some mention of practical details was made occasionally in the preceding sections, most systems and devices were described in terms of their intended (ideal) functions, with little or no description of their operational characteristics. This section is intended to provide the reader with an overview of the factors that should be considered in the design of microwave radiometer systems.

Perhaps the single most important parameter that determines the performance (and/or cost) of a microwave radiometer is its frequency. Generally speaking, the noise performance and stability of microwave devices and systems decrease with increasing frequency, as does the number of available types of devices that can perform a certain function. For example, in present-day technology, a 100 K receiver noise temperature is fairly easy to achieve at 1 GHz using an uncooled field-effect-transistor (FET) RF amplifier. At 30 GHz, a 500-K receiver noise temperature is considered state-of-the-art (without cryogenic cooling), and the cost of such a receiver typically is an order of magnitude higher than that of the 1-GHz receiver. These figures soon will be out of date, however, because the field of microwave semiconductor and solid-state devices is moving at a tremendous rate, as illustrated by the example shown in Fig. 6.25. In 1968, solid-state amplifiers were limited to frequencies below 500 MHz and consisted primarily of bipolar transistor amplifiers. Most microwave receivers used traveling-wave-tube (TWT) amplifiers. The rapid development of the FET in the late sixties and early seventies brought about a revolution in microwave amplifiers; solid-state amplifiers began to and have continued to replace TWT amplifiers. In addition to the FET, several semiconductor devices also were developed in this timeperiod, including the tunnel, Gunn, and IMPATT diodes, among others. Kennedy (1978), the author of Fig. 6.25, projects the status of transistor-amplifier performance into the year 2000, at which time it is predicted (according to Fig. 6.25) that a similar performance will be attainable at 100 GHz to that attained at 0.1 GHz in 1968.

6-15.1 Dicke Input Switch

The purpose of the input switch is to switch the receiver periodically between the antenna and the reference load at a high enough rate that the system-gain remains essentially constant over a period of one cycle. In other words, in order to successfully subtract out system-gain variations in the synchronous demodulation, the switching rate f_s should be higher than the highest significant frequency in the system-gain variation spectrum. As was noted earlier, although no detailed studies have been conducted of the variation spectrum, its upper limit usually is assumed to be around 10 Hz. Another constraint on the lower limit of f_s is set by the effective bandwidth of the low-pass filter, B_{LF}. To

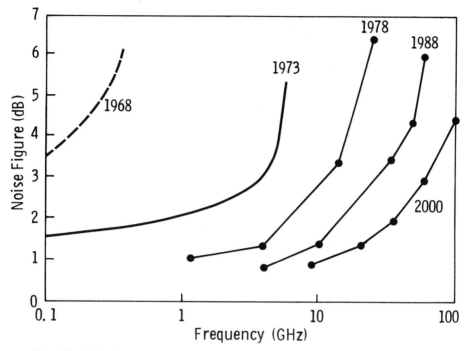

Fig. 6.25 Noise figure of narrow-band transistor amplifiers as a function of frequency and time (Kennedy, 1978).

satisfy the sampling theorem, we must have $f_s > 2B_{LF}$. Integration times τ $(= 1/(2B_{LF}))$ used in ground-based radiometer systems typically are around 1 s, which corresponds to $B_{LF} = 0.5$ Hz, or $f_s > 1$ Hz. However, airborne and spaceborne imaging systems often use integration times as short as 30 ms, which means that $f_s > 2B_{LF} = 1/\tau \approx 33$ Hz.

The upper limit of f_s usually is governed by the switching time τ_{sw}. To avoid the effects of switching time on the square-wave shape of the radiometer signal, it usually is recommended that

$$\frac{2\tau_{sw}}{\tau_s} < 10^{-2}, \tag{6.107}$$

where τ_s is the switching period. Electronically controlled microwave switches generally are one of two types: (1) semiconductor diode switches and (2) ferrite circulators (Table 6.5). The most commonly used diode switch is the *PIN* single-pole double-throw (SPDT) switch, whose switching-time is typically between 10 and 200 ns. Ferrite circulators are slower switching devices, with τ_{sw}-values in the 1–10-μs range. For $\tau_{sw} = 10$ μs, (6.107) is equivalent to $f_s < 500$ Hz. Most Dicke radiometers are operated at switching frequencies in the 10–1000-Hz range.

TABLE 6.5
Typical 1980 Properties of Dicke Input Switches[a]

		Frequency (GHz)			
		1	10	30	100
Isolation (dB):	PIN	70	65	30	15
	Ferrite[b]	20	20	18	18
Insertion loss (dB):	PIN	0.5	1.1	1.9	3.8
	Ferrite	0.1	0.3	0.8	1.5
Switching time:	PIN	10–200 ns			
	Ferrite	1–10 μs			
Temperature stability:	PIN	Good			
	Ferrite	Performance degrades at high temp.			

[a]PIN=SPDT PIN switch; Ferrite=latching ferrite circulator.
[b]Ferrite values are for $T=25°C$.

The choice between the *PIN* diode switch and the switchable ferrite circulator usually is made on the basis of properties other than switching speed, namely, isolation and insertion loss. The switch isolation is a measure of the amount of power that leaks into the common port from the "unconnected" input port. While the Dicke switch is connected to the antenna, for example, its output (at the receiver input) is equal to

$$T_{OUT} = T'_A + \frac{T_{REF}}{L_{iso}} \qquad (6.108)$$

where L_{iso} is the isolation loss. If $L_{iso}(dB)=20$ dB, it means that 1 percent of T_{REF} is coupled into the receiver during the half cycle that the receiver is connected to the antenna. Similarly, during the following half cycle, 1 percent of T'_A is coupled into the receiver, together with T_{REF}. If T_{REF} is maintained at a constant level, which usually is the case, and T'_A varies, then the amount of energy that leaks through during one half of the cycle is different from what leaks through during the second half, and the difference varies with T'_A. This T'_A-dependent bias may be factored out in the calibration process, depending upon the specific system configuration. From Table 6.5, it is clear that the *PIN* diode switch provides isolation superior to that of the ferrite circulator, except at 100 GHz.

Insertion loss, L_{ins}, is the attenuation suffered by the signal between either of the input ports and the output port of the switch. For a receiver with input noise temperature T_{REC}, the noise temperature referred to one of the input ports of the switch is given by (refer to (6.28))

$$T'_{REC} = (L_{ins}-1)T_p + L_{ins}T_{REC}, \qquad (6.109)$$

where T_p is the physical temperature of the switch. The degradation in system noise performance introduced by the switch should be viewed in terms of the corresponding degradation in the radiometric sensitivity ΔT. For a 1-GHz receiver with $T_{REC} = 300$ K, the PIN diode switch (Table 6.5) results in $T'_{REC} = 389$ K (at a physical temperature $T_p = 300$ K), a degradation of approximately 30 percent in receiver noise temperature. The principal interest in keeping T'_{REC} small is its effect on the radiometric sensitivity ΔT, which for a balanced Dicke radiometer is proportional to $T_{REF} + T'_{REC}$. For $T_{REF} = 300$ K, the degradation in ΔT introduced by the switch is only 15 percent (compared to an ideal lossless switch). If a ferrite circulator with an insertion loss of 0.1 dB were used instead, the increase in ΔT would be only 1 percent.

In general, latching ferrite circulators are preferred to PIN switches unless the system configuration demands greater isolation than can be provided by ferrite devices. Considering the fast rate at which semiconductor devices are developing, it may not be long before PIN or other diodes surpass ferrite circulators with regard to insertion loss.

6-15.2 Receiver Front End

The overall receiver noise temperature is effectively determined by the noise temperature of the first stage at its front end. Most radiometers use superheterodyne receivers with either an RF amplifier or a mixer-preamplifier at the front end. The choice is dictated by the noise figure (or noise temperature) of available devices, which in turn depends on the center frequency and bandwidth of the radiometer. Since cryogenic cooling (which is used to reduce the noise temperature of devices) usually is avoided in airborne and spaceborne remote-sensing operations, we shall limit the present discussion to uncooled devices.

Figure 6.26 shows the noise temperature as a function of frequency for 1980 commercially available parametric amplifiers, FET amplifiers, and mixer-preamplifier assemblies. The values shown are for single-sideband in the case of amplifiers, and for double-sideband for the mixer-preamplifier assemblies. Below 30 GHz, the noise temperatures of gallium arsenide (GaAs) FET amplifiers are lower than those of other uncooled microwave amplifiers except for parameteric amplifiers, which are higher in cost, lower in output power, and larger in size and weight than FET amplifiers. Low-noise FET amplifiers are not yet available commercially above 30 GHz, but if the prediction suggested by Fig. 6.25 is realized, FET amplifiers may become available at higher frequencies by 1985. At the present state of the art (1980), mixer-preamplifier assemblies offer the most practical solution above 30 GHz for receivers built with discrete components. Using hybrid microwave-integrated-circuit (MIC) technology, radiometer receivers have been produced recently with double-sideband noise temperatures as low as 230 K at 35 GHz and 500 K at 94 GHz (Cardiasmenos, 1980). It is projected that MIC design will be used extensively in the future.

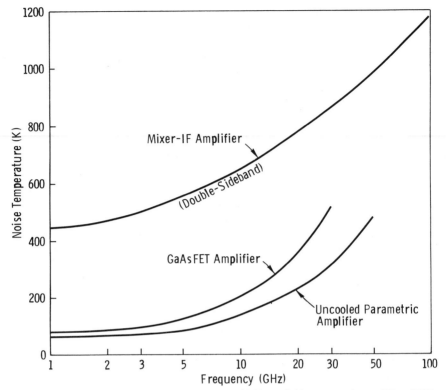

Fig. 6.26 Typical noise performance of commercially available parametric amplifiers, FET amplifiers, and mixer-preamplifier assemblies. Operating bandwidth is typically 10 percent of RF frequency for $f < 20$ GHz, and between 0.1 and 2 GHz for $f > 20$ GHz.

For state-of-the-art reviews, the reader is referred to the paper by Kennedy (1978), which provides a review of the development of microwave semiconductor and solid-state devices; to the paper by Sterzer (1978) on FET devices; and to the papers by Kerr (1975, 1979) on microwave mixers. Mixer design and noise performance at frequencies above 100 GHz are discussed by Held (1979).

6-15.3 Noise Sources and Reference Loads

Basically, there are two types of noise sources available for calibration and balancing and as reference sources: (1) passive sources and (2) active sources.

Passive Noise Sources

Any device or component that delivers noise power at a constant level without the use of external (electric) power may be defined as a passive noise source. The simplest passive noise source is a matched load. When maintained at a constant physical temperature T_p, it delivers an average noise power with an equivalent noise temperature equal to its physical temperature. Matched loads are used as reference loads and usually are maintained at temperatures higher than the highest expected environmental temperature of the radiometer by enclosing them in a temperature-stabilized oven. To avoid temperature mismatches, it is sound engineering practice to include the entire front-end of the radiometer in a common temperature enclosure.

Matched loads also are used for calibration, whereby either the antenna is (physically) replaced by a load, or the radiometer is switched to a load via a calibration switch placed as close to the antenna as possible. Low noise-temperature values are obtained by immersing the load in a low-temperature medium such as liquid nitrogen or liquid helium, whose boiling temperatures are 77.4 and 4.2 K, respectively.

Active Noise Sources

Until the late 1960s, the gas-discharge tube was the most commonly used noise generator at frequencies above 1 GHz. Today, solid-state noise sources, primarily avalanche diodes, are available commercially up to 40 GHz.

The term commonly used to characterize the power delivered by a noise source is the *excess noise ratio*, ENR, which is defined as

$$\text{ENR} = \frac{P_n - P_0}{P_0} = \frac{kB(T_N - T_0)}{kBT_0}$$

$$= \frac{T_N}{T_0} - 1 \tag{6.110}$$

where T_N is the noise temperature of the source, and T_0 is its physical temperature. Often, ENR is expressed in dB,

$$\text{ENR(dB)} = 10 \log \text{ENR}. \tag{6.111}$$

Standard avalanche noise sources are available with excess-noise ratios of 35 dB at frequencies up to 12.4 GHz, and with lower levels at higher frequencies, typically 23 dB up to 40 GHz.

As was discussed earlier toward the end of Section 6-10.1, active noise sources may also be used to provide noise temperatures T_N that are lower than the ambient temperature T_0. Specifically, the COLDFET has been shown to have a noise temperature of 50 K at 1.4 GHz (Frater and Williams, 1981).

6-16 RADIOMETER CALIBRATION TECHNIQUES

Radiometer calibration may be divided into two steps. The first step involves relating the receiver output indication (voltage, count, deflection, etc.) to the noise temperature at the radiometer input. This usually is accomplished by measuring the output indication as a function of the noise temperature T_{CAL} of a calibration source connected to the radiometer input (in place of the antenna). The resultant relationship between the output indicator and T_{CAL} provides the scale factors necessary for relating the output to the antenna temperature T_A' (when the radiometer receiver is connected to the antenna). We shall refer to this first step as *receiver calibration*.

The second step involves relating T_A' to the radiative properties of the scene under observation. T_A' consists of three components: (1) energy received through the antenna mainbeam, which is the quantity of interest; (2) energy received from directions outside the antenna mainbeam (sidelobe contributions); and (3) thermal energy emitted by the antenna structure itself. To evaluate the significance of the latter two components and to factor out (partially) their influence on T_A', it is necessary to know the radiative properties of the antenna with a high degree of accuracy. Standard test procedures have been defined for the measurement of antenna properties (IEEE, 1979), but for one of the properties of interest, namely the radiation efficiency η_l, the standard procedures do not provide (in practice) the level of accuracy that is desired for the application of radiometric corrections. Alternate measurement techniques that have been developed specifically for microwave radiometric applications are discussed in Section 6-16.3 under the heading "Antenna Calibration."

6-16.1 Receiver Calibration

Most radiometer receivers are linear systems in the sense that the output indication I_{out} is directly proportional to the antenna temperature T_A'. With reference to (6.106),

$$I_{out} = a(T_A' + b), \tag{6.106}$$

it is sufficient to measure I_{out} for each of two known values of T_A' to determine the constants a and b. For some radiometer configurations, the constant b is given in terms of known constant temperature(s); $b = -T_{REF} = -T_0$ for the three Dicke radiometer types given in Table 6.4, and $b = (T_2 - T_1)/2$ for the Hach radiometer, which uses two reference noise temperatures. In this case, one calibration measurement to determine the constant a is sufficient. In practice, however, it is advisable to calibrate the radiometer at more than one value of the input noise temperature, and at least one point should be for a c libration noise temperature lower than 100 K.

Figure 6.27 shows a calibration noise source placed at the radiometer input. Corresponding to measurements with calibration noise temperature T_{CAL}^h and T_{CAL}^c (where the superscripts h and c stand for hot and cold, respectively), the radiometer output indicator records values of

$$I_{out}^h = a(T_{CAL}^h + b), \tag{6.112a}$$

$$I_{out}^c = a(T_{CAL}^c + b). \tag{6.112b}$$

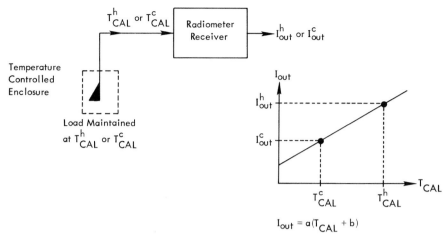

Fig. 6.27 Calibration of a reflection-free radiometer receiver.

The above two equations give the solutions

$$a = \frac{I^h_{out} - I^c_{out}}{T^h_{CAL} - T^c_{CAL}},$$ (6.113a)

$$b = \frac{I^c_{out} T^h_{CAL} - I^h_{out} T^c_{CAL}}{I^h_{out} - I^c_{out}}.$$ (6.113b)

Three types of calibration noise sources have been used. The first type consists of a matched load (resistor) whose temperature may be held at a constant known value. A hot load usually is enclosed in a temperature-controlled oven, and a cold load usually is immersed in a Dewar flask containing a boiling cryogen. Liquid nitrogen (N_2), whose boiling temperature is 77.4 K at sea-level barometric pressure, is used commonly for this purpose.

The second type of calibration source consists of material with known emissivities, such as the highly absorbing, nonreflective materials used in anechoic chambers. These materials can be constructed to have emissivities close to unity, and therefore their brightness temperatures are approximately equal to their physical temperatures. Low brightness-temperature values are obtained by saturating the absorbing material in a boiling cryogen. The calibration procedure consists basically of observing the material with the antenna beam and then relating its emission to the noise temperature at the antenna terminals. The process involves the antenna properties, and therefore we defer discussing the details of the calibration procedure until the next section.

The above two receiver calibration methods usually are used to calibrate a radiometer before and/or after a measurement program only. If the matched-load method were to be used for periodic calibrations during an aircraft measurement mission, it would require the availability of a cryogen for the duration of the flight, and, in spacecraft operations, refrigeration equipment would be needed to maintain the cryogenic fluid at the desired temperature. Radiometers employing balanced Dicke or Hach receiver configurations can be made sufficiently stable that calibration against external sources is needed only occasionally, thereby avoiding the cryogenic refrigeration problem. For example, according to the analysis reported by Blume (1977), the maximum calibration deviation (between calibrations) that was observed among 26 calibration measurements was 1.6 K, and the rms value of the deviation was 0.7 K. The calibration measurements were made over a 3.5-year period for a 2.65-GHz pulsed noise-injection Dicke radiometer (Fig. 6.18).

Satellite-borne radiometer systems use a third type of cold-calibration source, namely, outer space. When the antenna (or an auxiliary antenna) is pointed at cosmic space, it observes a brightness temperature of 2.7 K.

A fourth type of calibration noise source may be added to the above list, namely, the COLDFET circuit mentioned earlier in Section 6-10.1.

6-16.2 Effects of Impedance Mismatches

Throughout the foregoing discussion it was assumed that every RF component and transmission line contained in the radiometer front end was perfectly matched to whatever it was connected to. In other words, no reflections due to impedance mismatches existed. In practice, it may be possible to reduce reflections to small levels through the use of impedance-matching techniques, but they cannot always be eliminated altogether.

The effects of impedance mismatches on the radiometer measurement accuracy may be divided into two groups: (1) mismatches at points beyond the receiver input (Fig. 6.28) and (2) mismatches between the antenna (or calibration source) and the receiver input. For a reflection-free radiometer, the output indication I_{out} is linearly related to the input noise temperature T_{IN}, which represents the net power delivered to the receiver due to noise power supplied by the antenna (or calibration source) and the line in between. That is,

$$I_{out} = a_1 T_{IN} + b_1, \tag{6.114}$$

where a_1 and b_1 are constants. Mismatched components give rise to reflection coefficients that end up modifying the values of a_1 and b_1. As long as the magnitudes and phases of these reflection coefficients remain constant, and as long as the noise temperatures of the components remain constant, the effects of mismatches may be factored out in the calibration process. The reflection coefficients of components are most susceptible to temperature variations. Therefore, not only is it important to maintain the environmental temperature of the radiometer front end at a constant value, but it is equally important that the absolute value of this temperature be the same (as close as possible) during the radiometer operating mode and during the calibration mode. That is, if a_1 and b_1 are maintained constant, I_{out} will be related accurately to T_{IN}.

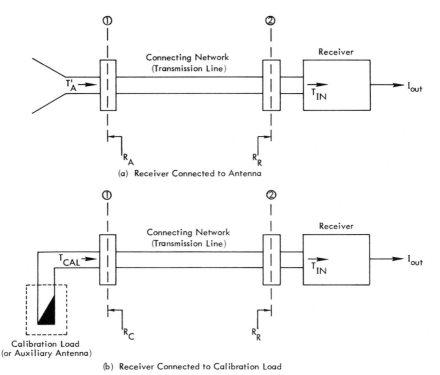

Fig. 6.28 Radiometer receiver connected to (a) antenna and (b) calibration source. The R's are voltage reflection coefficients looking into the indicated ports.

This brings us to the second step, namely, relating T_{IN} to the antenna temperature T'_A or to the noise temperature of the calibration source, T_{CAL}. If the voltage reflection coefficient as seen looking into the antenna, R_A, is equal to the voltage reflection coefficient (in magnitude and phase) as seen looking into the calibration load, R_C, the problem is an easy one. In this case, the calibration constants obtained by calibrating I_{out} against T_{CAL} will be the same as the constants in the relation between I_{out} and T'_A, assuming that the same line used to connect the antenna to the radiometer also is used during calibration. In the general case, however, $R_A \neq R_C$, which means that the relationship between I_{out} and T_{CAL} will not be exactly the same as the relationship between I_{out} and T'_A; therefore, if the calibration equation is used (without corrections) to predict T'_A-values, the predicted values may be in error. The magnitude of the error varies from values of the order of 1 K if $|R_C| < 0.05$ and $|R_A| < 0.05$ to much larger values if the magnitudes of R_C and R_A are larger and very different.

The effect of impedance mismatches may be accounted for by using the following procedure:

1. Develop a relationship between T_{IN} and T_{CAL} (Fig. 6.28) that incorporates reflections. The method is described below and results in a linear form

$$T_{IN} = a_2 T_{CAL} + b_2, \qquad (6.115a)$$

where a_2 and b_2 are constants that are given in terms of measurable quantities.

2. Develop a similar relationship between T_{IN} and T_A':

$$T_{IN} = a_3 T_A' + b_3. \tag{6.115b}$$

3. Measure I_{out}^h and I_{out}^c corresponding to two known calibration temperatures T_{CAL}^h and T_{CAL}^c, respectively.

4. Using (6.115a), calculate T_{IN}^h and T_{IN}^c, and employ the form of (6.114) to determine the constants a_1 and b_1.

5. With a_1 and b_1 known, use (6.114) and (6.115b) to relate T_A' to I_{out}:

$$T_A' = \frac{I_{out} - a_1 b_3 - b_1}{a_1 a_3}. \tag{6.115c}$$

Steps (1) and (2), which are the keys to the above procedure, basically are the same; each involves the development of a relationship between the noise temperature of a noise generator (antenna or calibration source) and T_{IN}. Figure 6.29 shows a noise generator, with output noise temperature T_G, connected to the radiometer input via a lossy two-port network S. The network S may be a transmission line, a calibration switch, or any passive, linear, time-invariant network. It is characterized by a scattering matrix S given by

$$S = \begin{bmatrix} S_{11} & S_{12} \\ S_{21} & S_{22} \end{bmatrix},$$

where the scattering coefficients S_{11} and S_{22} are related to the reflection properties of the network, and S_{12} and S_{21} are related to its transmission properties. Standard techniques for measuring the elements of S are described in Helszajn (1978). The network S is assumed to have a physical temperature T_0, and the voltage reflection coefficients as seen looking into the radiometer and into the generator are respectively R_R and R_G.

The effect of mismatches on receiver calibration has been treated by Wells et al. (1964), Miller et al. (1967), and Otoshi (1968), among others. Manipulation of Otoshi's expressions to suit the configuration shown in Fig. 6.29 can be shown to lead to the expression below for the noise temperature T_{IN} of the net power delivered to the receiver:

$$T_{IN} = \alpha_m \Upsilon T_G + \alpha_m (1 - \Upsilon) T_0 + (1 - \alpha_m) T_R, \tag{6.116}$$

where $\alpha_m \Upsilon T_G$ = net delivered noise temperature from generator,

$\alpha_m (1 - \Upsilon) T_0$ = net delivered noise temperature generated by lossy network S due to self-emission,

$(1 - \alpha_m) T_R$ = net delivered noise temperature generated by the receiver and then reflected back towards the receiver.

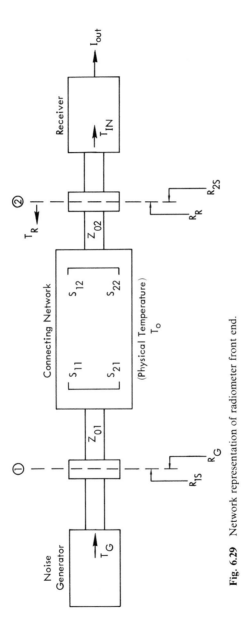

Fig. 6.29 Network representation of radiometer front end.

T_R is the noise temperature generated by the receiver in the direction of the generator, and it is not necessarily equal to the receiver input noise temperature T'_{REC}. Rather, T_R is the noise temperature of the power that would be absorbed by a matched load placed at the radiometer input. In practice, T_R can be either measured (by comparing the receiver output I_{out}, when a matched load is placed at the radiometer input, with the output when a short circuit is placed at the input) or estimated. The quantities α_m and Υ are known as the mismatch loss factor and the transmission factor, respectively, and are given by the expressions

$$\alpha_m = \frac{\left(1-|R_{2S}|^2\right)\left(1-|R_R|^2\right)}{|1-R_{2S}R_R|^2}, \tag{6.117}$$

$$\Upsilon = \frac{1}{L_S}\left[\frac{\left(1-|R_G|^2\right)\left(1-|S_{11}|^2\right)}{|1-S_{11}R_G|^2\left(1-|R_{2S}|^2\right)}\right], \tag{6.118}$$

where

$$R_{2S} = S_{22} + \frac{S_{21}S_{12}R_G}{1-S_{11}R_G}, \tag{6.119}$$

$$L_S = \frac{Z_{02}}{Z_{01}}\frac{\left(1-|S_{11}|^2\right)}{|S_{21}|^2}. \tag{6.120}$$

L_S is the loss factor of network S, and Z_{02} and Z_{01} are the characteristic impedances at ports 2 and 1, respectively. Usually, $Z_{01}=Z_{02}$. To compute α_m and Υ, it is necessary to know the magnitudes and phases of the voltage reflection coefficients R_R and R_G, and of the scattering coefficients of the network S. These quantities can be measured by a network analyzer.

Matched Case

If $Z_{01}=Z_{02}$ and $R_R=R_{2S}=R_G=0$,

$$\alpha_m = 1, \tag{6.121}$$

$$\Upsilon = \frac{1}{L_{S0}} \triangleq |S_{21}|^2, \tag{6.122}$$

where $|S_{21}|^2$ is the power transmission coefficient of the network. That is, L_{S0} is the loss factor under matched conditions, while L_S is the loss factor in the general case. For this matched case, (6.116) becomes

$$T_{IN}(\text{matched}) = \frac{1}{L_{S0}}T_G + \left(1-\frac{1}{L_{S0}}\right)T_0, \tag{6.123}$$

which is the familiar form (given by (6.80)) used for the noise temperature at the output of an attenuator whose input is fed by a matched noise generator.

Transmission-Line Case

If the network S is a uniform transmission line of length l, its scattering coefficients are given by

$$S_{11} = S_{22} = 0, \tag{6.124a}$$

$$S_{12} = S_{21} = e^{-\gamma l}, \tag{6.124b}$$

where $\gamma = \alpha + j\beta$ is the complex propagation factor of the line. Using (6.124), we obtain

$$L_S = e^{2\alpha l}, \tag{6.125}$$

$$\alpha_m = \frac{\left(1 - |R_G|^2 L_S^{-2}\right)\left(1 - |R_R|^2\right)}{|1 - R_R R_G e^{-2\gamma l}|^2}, \tag{6.126}$$

$$\Upsilon = \frac{1}{L_S}\left[\frac{\left(1 - |R_G|^2\right)}{\left(1 - |R_G|^2 L_S^{-2}\right)}\right]. \tag{6.127}$$

Error Bounds

In some cases the magnitudes of R_R and R_G are known, but their phase angles are not. It may be desirable to establish upper and lower bounds for T_{IN} on the basis of the magnitude information only.

The only place where phase angles play a role in the above expressions is in the denominator of α_m. With R_R and R_G defined by

$$R_R \triangleq |R_R| e^{j\phi_R} \tag{6.128a}$$

$$R_G \triangleq |R_G| e^{j\phi_G} \tag{6.128b}$$

we have

$$|1 - R_R R_G e^{-2\gamma l}|^2 = 1 + |R_R|^2 |R_G|^2 L_S^{-2} - 2|R_R||R_G|L_S^{-1} \cos\phi, \tag{6.129}$$

where

$$\phi = 2\beta l - \phi_R - \phi_G. \tag{6.130}$$

The following procedure leads to the determination of the upper and lower bounds, $T_{IN}(\text{max})$ and $T_{IN}(\text{min})$, with ϕ allowed to take any value in the range

$0 \leqslant \phi \leqslant \pi$:

1. Upon substituting (6.129) into (6.126) and then substituting (6.126) and (6.127) into (6.116), we obtain an expression for T_{IN} as a function of ϕ (as the only unknown quantity).
2. The values of ϕ for which T_{IN} is maximum or minimum may then be found by differentiating T_{IN} with respect to ϕ and equating the result to zero.
3. These values of ϕ then are used in the original expression for T_{IN} to determine $T_{IN}(\text{max})$ and $T_{IN}(\text{min})$.

In some cases, the above procedure is unnecessary because the desired values of ϕ for which T_{IN} is maximum or minimum can be deduced from the form of the T_{IN} expression. One such case is when T_R, the receiver noise temperature radiated towards the generator, is equal to T_0, the physical temperature of the transmission line. With $T_R = T_0$, (6.116) simplifies to

$$T_{IN} = T_0 - \alpha_m \Upsilon (T_0 - T_G). \tag{6.131}$$

Since T_G usually is smaller than T_0, $T_{IN} = T_{IN}(\text{max})$ when $\alpha_m = \alpha_m(\text{min})$, and vice versa for $T_{IN}(\text{min})$. With reference to (6.129) and (6.126),

$$\alpha_m(\text{max}) = \alpha_m(\phi = 0), \tag{6.132a}$$

$$\alpha_m(\text{min}) = \alpha_m(\phi = \pi). \tag{6.132b}$$

Comparison of (6.131) with the expression for $T_{IN}(\text{matched})$, given by (6.123), can be shown to lead to the conclusion

$$T_{IN}(\text{matched}) \leqslant T_{IN}(\text{min}) \leqslant T_{IN}(\text{max}),$$

where the equal signs apply when $|R_R| = |R_G| = 0$, or when $T_R = T_G = T_0$. Let us define the mismatch errors

$$\Delta_{min} = T_{IN}(\text{min}) - T_{IN}(\text{matched}) \tag{6.133a}$$

and

$$\Delta_{max} = T_{IN}(\text{max}) - T_{IN}(\text{matched}). \tag{6.133b}$$

If T_{IN} is computed using the expression for $T_{IN}(\text{matched})$, thereby ignoring mismatch errors, the value thus computed will be in error by at least Δ_{min} and by at most Δ_{max}.

To illustrate the significance of mismatch errors that are associated with radiometer calibration, let us consider the following examples.

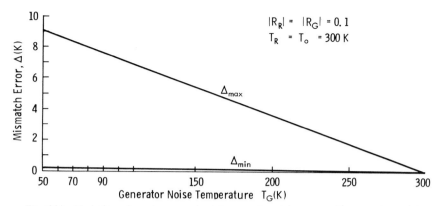

Fig. 6.30 Variation of maximum and minimum mismatch errors with generator noise temperature for $|R_R| = |R_G| = 0.1$.

Example 1:

$$T_R = T_0 = 300 \text{ K},$$
$$|R_R| = |R_G| = 0.1,$$
$$L_S = 1.05 \quad (= 0.21 \text{ dB}).$$

Example 2: Same as Example 1, except $|R_R| = |R_G| = 0.2$.

Figures 6.30 and 6.31 pertain to Examples 1 and 2, respectively. Each figure shows plots of Δ_{min} and Δ_{max} as a function of T_G. As would be expected, the magnitudes of Δ_{min} and Δ_{max} are larger for Example 2 than for Example 1 due to the larger reflection coefficients. Also, for a given T_G, the difference between Δ_{max} and Δ_{min} is larger for Example 2.

When reflections exist, T_{IN} consists of contributions from three sources of noise energy: (1) the generator at the input, (2) the lossy transmission line, and (3) the receiver noise (T_R) emitted in the direction of the generator. If $R_G = 0$, the last term would not contribute to T_{IN}. In the above examples, $T_R = T_0 = 300$ K. When T_G also is equal to 300 K, the entire system becomes thermally balanced, and therefore, insensitive to reflections. This results in T_{IN}(matched) $= T_{IN}$(max)$= T_{IN}$(min)$= 300$ K, or $\Delta_{min} = \Delta_{max} = 0$. The mismatch errors are directly proportional to the difference $T_0 - T_G$, and therefore, they are most important when the generator noise temperature T_G is very different from T_0, as illustrated in Figs. 6.30 and 6.31. This points out an added advantage of radiometer configurations that inject noise into the line connecting the antenna to the receiver (Fig. 6.17) to raise the antenna temperature to the temperature of the reference load, which usually is maintained at the temperature T_0. Thus, use of the noise-injection scheme results in improved measurement precision (by eliminating the effects of system gain fluctuations) as well as improved measurement accuracy. These conclusions hinge on the assumption that $T_R = T_0$. In practice, this is a reasonable assumption because most radiometers employ

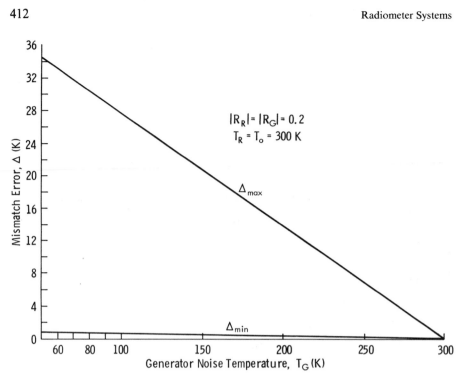

Fig. 6.31 Variation of maximum and minimum mismatch errors with generator noise temperature for $|R_R|=|R_G|=0.2$.

isolators somewhere between the antenna and the receiver. An isolator acts as a low-loss attenuator for propagation in one direction and as a high-loss attenuator for propagation in the opposite direction. When placed with its low-loss propagation direction lying in the direction of the receiver, an isolator attenuates energy emitted by the receiver towards the antenna. Thus, in the direction of the antenna, an isolator exhibits a high loss factor, and therefore emits energy characterized by a noise temperature equal to the isolator's physical temperature, T_0. Hence, when an isolator is used, $T_R = T_0$.

6-16.3 Antenna Calibration

In the preceding material, we discussed calibration methods for transforming the radiometer output indicator to an antenna temperature T'_A, where T'_A represents the noise power delivered by the antenna. Now, we shall discuss a second transformation, namely that between T'_A and $\bar{T}_{ML}$, the main-lobe apparent temperature of the scene observed by the antenna. To that end, use will be made of (4.62):

$$T'_A = \eta_l \eta_M \bar{T}_{ML} + \eta_l (1 - \eta_M) \bar{T}_{SL} + (1 - \eta_l) T_0, \qquad (4.62)$$

where η_l=antenna radiation efficiency
        $=1/L_a$, where L_a=antenna loss factor,
    η_M=antenna main-beam efficiency,
    T_0=physical temperature of the antenna.

$\overline{T}_{ML}$ and $\overline{T}_{SL}$ were defined as the main-lobe and side-lobe contributions, and are given by (4.56) and (4.59), respectively. With T_A' measured by the radiometer, the objective is the estimate $\overline{T}_{ML}$. In the ideal case of a lossless antenna ($\eta_l=1$) with a radiation pattern consisting of only one main lobe ($\eta_M=1$), the above expression reduces to

$$T_A'=\overline{T}_{ML}.$$

In the real case, however, exact determination of $\overline{T}_{ML}$ necessitates that η_l, η_M, and $\overline{T}_{SL}$ be known. Techniques for measuring the antenna parameters η_l and η_M are discussed below, but $\overline{T}_{SL}$ is not a measurable quantity, nor is it a constant, since it depends on the distribution of radiation incident upon the antenna from directions outside the main lobe. As was discussed in Section 4-6.4, the magnitude of the error associated with the estimated value of $\overline{T}_{ML}$ due to the lack of knowledge of $\overline{T}_{SL}$ is a function of η_M only. Therefore, in order to minimize this source of error, whose magnitude is shown in Fig. 4.11 for several values of η_M, it is essential that the radiometer antenna be characterized by a main-beam efficiency that is as close to unity as possible. High main-beam efficiency is achieved by suppressing the side lobes of the radiation pattern, which is accomplished by properly tapering the aperture distribution, as discussed in Chapter 3. A higher main-beam efficiency, however, means a wider main beam, or equivalently, a lower aperture efficiency. The tradeoff between main-beam efficiency η_M and aperture efficiency η_a is shown in Fig. 6.32. For radiometric remote sensing, this is equivalent to a tradeoff between radiometric resolution and angular (or spatial) resolution.

    η_M and η_l were defined in Chapter 3 as

$$\eta_M = \frac{\displaystyle\iint_{main\ lobe} F_n(\theta,\phi)\,d\Omega}{\displaystyle\iint_{4\pi} F_n(\theta,\phi)\,d\Omega}, \tag{6.134}$$

$$\eta_l = \frac{G_0}{D_0} = \frac{4\pi G_0}{\displaystyle\iint_{4\pi} F_n(\theta,\phi)\,d\Omega}, \tag{6.135}$$

where $F_n(\theta,\phi)$=normalized radiation pattern,
        G_0=maximum power gain,
        D_0=maximum directivity.

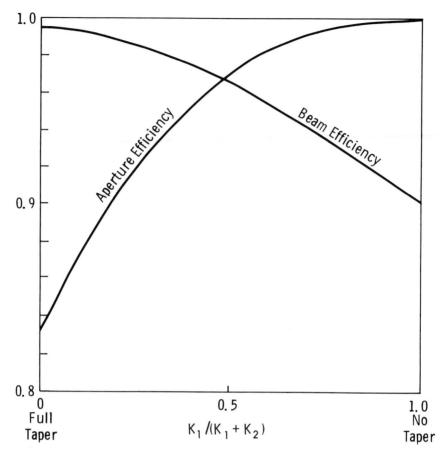

Fig. 6.32 Beam and aperture efficiencies for a one-dimensional aperture as a function of taper (after Nash, © 1964 IEEE). The aperture distribution is $E_a(x_a) = K_1 + K_2(1 - x_1^2)$, where $x_1 = 2x_a/l$ and l is the aperture length.

If the radiation pattern $F_n(\theta, \phi)$ is accurately known for all directions (θ, ϕ) over 4π solid angle, the determination of η_M becomes a straightforward task. Similarly, η_l also can be determined provided G_0 is known. In practice, G_0 is one of the easiest antenna parameters to measure. The problem with the above method is one of accuracy and cost; if the denominator in (6.134) and (6.135) is in error by only 1 percent, it is liable to result in an error of several kelvins in the estimated value of $\bar{T}_{ML}$, and in order to have good accuracy it is necessary to measure the complete two-dimensional variation of $F_n(\theta, \phi)$ with a measurement sensitivity of at least -60 dB relative to the peak value of $F_n(\theta, \phi)$, which is likely to be a costly operation. Alternative, and perhaps more accurate, methods developed for measuring η_l are described next. Once η_l has been determined, η_M can be easily computed from

$$\eta_M = \frac{\eta_l}{4\pi G_0} \iint_{main\ lobe} F_n(\theta, \phi)\, d\Omega. \tag{6.136}$$

As was mentioned earlier, G_0 is an easily measurable quantity, and so is $F_n(\theta, \phi)$ over the narrow angular range covered by the mainlobe. In some cases, it is difficult to define exactly the extent of the main lobe, and so η_M is quoted as the main-beam efficiency for a certain angular range (such as within two half-power beamwidths of the main-beam center) or for a range of $F_n(\theta, \phi)$ relative to the maximum (such as down to the -20-dB level).

6-16.4 Cryoload Technique

The aperture of the antenna shown in Fig. 6.33 is placed directly over a box containing microwave-absorbing material. The porous absorbing material is saturated with liquid nitrogen as described by Hardy (1973). The absorbing material is characterized by a very small reflection coefficient (Fig. 6.34) and therefore acts like a perfect absorber (emitter) with a brightness temperature equal to its physical temperature.

With the antenna aperture viewing an essentially constant brightness temperature distribution T_B, (from all directions), the antenna temperature T_A' measured by a microwave radiometer is given by

$$T_A' = \eta_l T_B + (1 - \eta_l) T_0, \qquad (6.137)$$

where η_l is the radiation efficiency of the antenna and T_0 is its physical

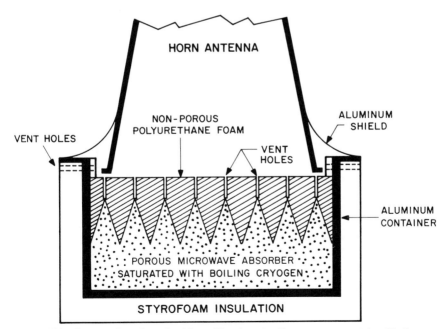

Fig. 6.33 Construction of cryoload for calibration of radiometer antenna (after Hardy et al., © 1974 IEEE).

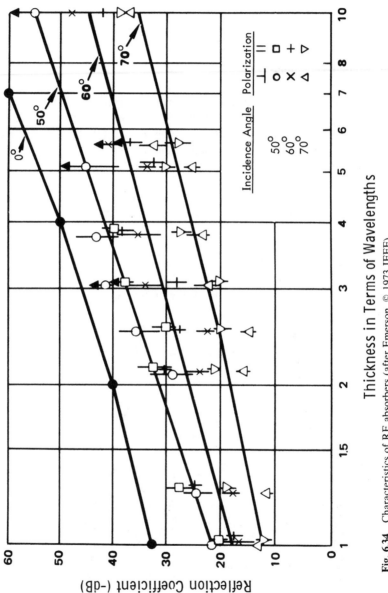

Thickness in Terms of Wavelengths

Fig. 6.34 Characteristics of RF absorbers (after Emerson, © 1973 IEEE).

temperature. Solving for η_l, we have

$$\eta_l = \frac{T_0 - T_A'}{T_0 - T_B},\qquad(6.138)$$

where in this case $T_B = 77.36$ K.

The cryoload calibration technique has several attractive features: it is accurate, repeatable, and relatively inexpensive. According to Hardy et al. (1974), who used the cryoload technique to calibrate a 2.65-GHz radiometer, absolute accuracy of about ± 0.1 percent was achieved, and according to Blume (1977) the calibration repeatability had an rms value of 0.7 K and an average deviation of 0.03 K. A slightly modified version of the above technique also was used to calibrate a small-aperture (10-cm $\times$ 10-cm) horn antenna at 86.1 GHz (Ulich, 1977).

To date, the use of the cyroload calibration technique has been limited to relatively small antenna apertures (of the order of 1 m per side). For large antennas, the *bucket* technique has proved useful.

6-16.5 Bucket Technique

The antenna shown in Fig. 6.35 is placed inside a large metal bucket whose dimensions are sufficiently large that it can be safely assumed that there is no mutual coupling between the antenna and the bucket. The indicated dimensions are those of the New Mexico State University antenna calibration bucket, which was constructed on a mountain to avoid emissions from the surrounding terrain (Carver, 1975). With the antenna main beam pointed in the zenith direction, the antenna temperature T_A' measured by the radiometer is given by

$$T_A' = \eta_l T_A + (1 - \eta_l) T_0,\qquad(6.139)$$

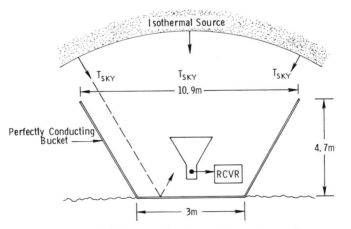

Fig. 6.35 The bucket method for measuring the radiation efficiency of an antenna (after Carver, 1975).

where T_A is the antenna temperature for a lossless antenna and is equal to the integrated brightness temperature of the sky (see (4.53)),

$$T_A = \frac{\iint\limits_{4\pi} T_{SKY}(\theta,\phi) F_n(\theta,\phi)\, d\Omega}{\iint\limits_{4\pi} F_n(\theta,\phi)\, d\Omega} \qquad (6.140)$$

The surface of the perfectly reflecting metal bucket has an emissivity of zero. Hence, the radiation received by the antenna is due entirely to atmospheric emission, the major portion of which is received directly from above and the rest of which is received through the side lobes after being reflected by the bucket walls. Assuming that $T_{SKY}(\theta,\phi)$ is approximately constant over the angular range subtended by the main lobe and the first few significant side lobes, (6.140) reduces to

$$T_A = T_{SKY}(\theta=0°).$$

Using values of meteorological parameters provided by a weather station located next to the bucket, $T_{SKY}(\theta=0°)$ could be calculated using the atmospheric-emission formulas given in Chapter 5. With T_A computed, and T_0 and T_A' measured, η_l is determined from (6.139).

6-17 IMAGING CONSIDERATIONS

According to Slater (1980), "the limit of resolution of an optical system is reached when, according to a given criterion, the system can just separate the elements of a well-defined test object, such as a double star in astronomy, the line of a grating in microscopy, and the bars of a bar target in photography." Several standard methods are used for measuring the resolving power of optical systems (Slater, 1980), but no equivalent methods or standard targets have been adopted for microwave systems.

The most frequently used definition for the spatial resolution of a microwave radiometer is given in terms of the *instantaneous field of view* (IFOV) corresponding to the half-power beamwidths. The IFOV defines the area on the ground covered by the antenna main beam. For the configuration shown in Fig. 6.36, the spatial resolutions Δx and Δy are given by

$$\Delta x = \beta_x h, \qquad (6.141a)$$
$$\Delta y = \beta_y h, \qquad (6.141b)$$

where h is the height of the antenna platform, and β_x and β_y are the half-power beamwidths in the x- and y-directions, respectively. Most microwave radiometric systems use antennas with circularly symmetric patterns, i.e., $\beta_x = \beta_y \triangleq \beta$.

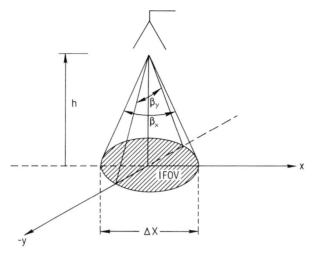

Fig. 6.36 The Instantaneous Field of View (IFOV) for a nadir-pointing antenna with beamwidths β_x and β_y. The antenna platform is at a height h above the ground.

As was discussed in Chapter 3,

$$\beta = k\frac{\lambda}{l}, \qquad \text{radians}, \tag{6.142}$$

where l is the length (and width) of a square aperture or the diameter of a circular aperture, and k is a constant for a given antenna configuration. Usually k is between 0.88 (for a uniformly illuminated aperture) and about 2 (for steeply tapered illuminations) (see Tables 3.1 and 3.2); for calculation purposes, a value of $k = 1.5$ is appropriate for antennas with high main-beam efficiency.

6-17.1 Scanning Configurations

Radiometric imaging of a scene of interest is accomplished by scanning the main beam of the antenna; for a moving platform, scanning in the cross-track dimension is sufficient to produce an image. Both mechanical and electronic (beam-steering) scanning techniques are used in microwave radiometry. In mechanical scanning, the direction of the antenna beam is changed by mechanical rotation or angular movement of the radiating aperture of the antenna system. Examples are shown in Fig. 6.37; they include (a) the simple configuration in which the entire antenna structure is made to scan in angle, (b) a second configuration where scanning is achieved by rotating a reflector (mirror) back and forth while maintaining the antenna in a fixed position, and (c) a parabolic torus configuration consisting of a fixed reflector and a spun feed.

Phased-array antennas are used to steer the direction of the antenna beam electronically, without the involvement of mechanical motion in the scanning

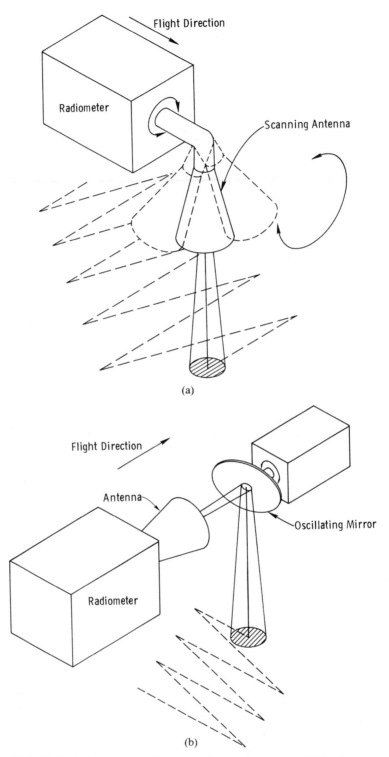

Fig. 6.37 Mechanical scanning configurations: (a) scanning antenna; (b) fixed antenna and oscillating reflector; (c) fixed parabolic reflector and oscillating antenna feed.

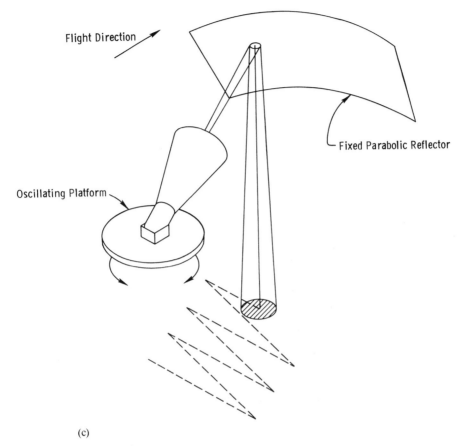

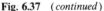

(c)

Fig. 6.37 (*continued*)

process (see Section 3.20). If the antenna is to scan in only one direction, it is sufficient to control the relative phase in one dimension, as illustrated in Fig. 6.38. Another advantage over mechanically scanned antennas is the high-scanning-speed capability of phased arrays. Electronic beam steering has some drawbacks, however: phased arrays are more complex, more expensive, heavier, and lossier than single-antenna structures of comparable size. The higher antenna losses of phased arrays are due to the phase shifters that are used to control the phase of each individual feed line. Usually ferrite or *PIN* diode phase shifters are used.

Among the scanning microwave radiometer systems that have been flown on the Nimbus satellite series, the 19.35-GHz (Nimbus 5) and 37-GHz (Nimbus 6) electrically scanning microwave radiometers (ESMRs) employed phased-array antennas, while the Nimbus 6 scanning microwave spectrometer (SCAMS) and the Nimbus 7 scanning multichannel microwave radiometer (SMMR) employed mechanically scanned antenna configurations.

Figure 6.39 illustrates the two most commonly used viewing configurations. In the first configuration (Fig. 6.39(a)) the antenna beam scans in a

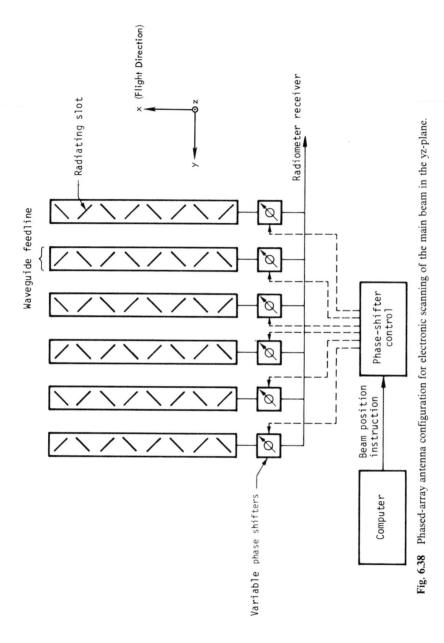

Fig. 6.38   Phased-array antenna configuration for electronic scanning of the main beam in the yz-plane.

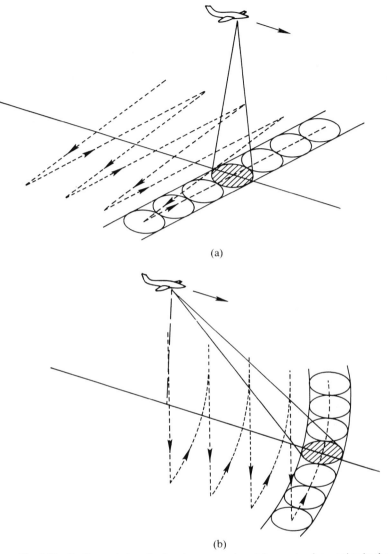

(a)

(b)

Fig. 6.39 Radiometric imaging by zigzag scanning: (a) cross-track scanning in the plane normal to the direction of flight; (b) conical scanning.

plane that is approximately perpendicular to the direction of motion. The angle of incidence varies between $\theta = 0°$ for the nadir beam and $\theta = \theta_s$ at the edge of the scanline. Also, the shape of the IFOV changes from a circle (for a circular antenna pattern) at nadir to an ellipse with its long axis in the y-direction. For some antenna scanning configurations, the direction of the polarization vector also is a function of the beam position within the scanline.

The major advantage of the viewing configuration shown in Fig. 6.39(b) is that the angle of incidence remains approximately constant as the beam scans in azimuth along a conical surface ahead of the radiometer platform. An example of a conical scan system is the 37-GHz ESMR, which scans in azimuth $\pm 35°$ about the forward direction at a constant tilt angle of 45° with respect to the direction of motion. With the earth's curvature taken into account, the angle of incidence at the earth's surface varies between 49.6° for the beam position corresponding to an azimuth angle of zero and 50.8° at the edge of the scanline; in other words, the angle of incidence essentially would be constant across the image generated by such a scanning arrangement.

6-17.2 Radiometer Uncertainty Principle

We pointed out in preceding sections that, for a given integration time τ, there is a tradeoff between spectral resolution (the predetection bandwidth B) and the radiometric resolution ΔT. For most radiometer systems, ΔT may be expressed in the general form

$$\Delta T = \frac{M}{\sqrt{B\tau}}, \tag{6.143}$$

where the radiometer figure of merit M is a constant for a given receiver configuration. For a stationary radiometer (with respect to the scene), there are no fundamental constraints imposed on how long τ may be. The situation is different for a moving platform.

To relate the parameters of a scanning system to τ, consider the simple case shown in Fig. 6.40. The platform is at a height h above the ground and is moving with a speed u in the x-direction. The radiometer antenna scans between $+\theta_s$ ($+y$-direction) and $-\theta_s$ ($-y$-direction) in a direction transverse to the flight direction. The forward motion of the platform provides a line-by-line scanning format. The time it takes to travel through one nadir beamwidth in the longitudinal (forward) direction is given by

$$t_1 = \frac{\Delta x}{u} = \frac{\beta h}{u}. \tag{6.144}$$

Ignoring the reset time involved in steering the beam from the end of one scanline ($\theta = \theta_s$) to start a new scanline, and assuming that one transverse scan is completed per beamwidth of forward motion (i.e., in time t_1), the angular scanning rate is

$$\omega = \frac{2\theta_s}{t_1}, \qquad \text{rad s}^{-1}. \tag{6.145}$$

If we assume further that the antenna beamwidth remains constant as the beam is made to scan between $-\theta_s$ and $+\theta_s$ (which is valid only if the scanning is mechanical or if the effective aperture remains constant), then the time it

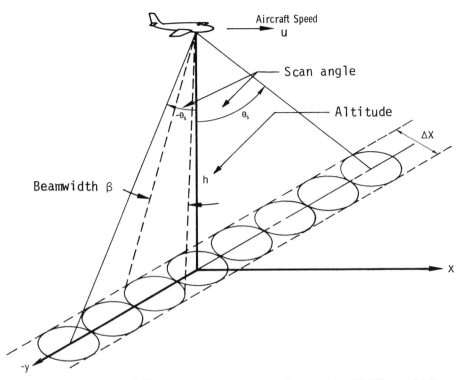

Fig. 6.40 Geometry of airborne scanning microwave radiometer (after McGillem and Seling, © 1963 IEEE).

takes to scan through one beamwidth in the transverse direction is

$$\tau_d = \frac{\beta}{\omega} = \frac{t_1 \beta}{2\theta_s}. \tag{6.146}$$

This time τ_d is called the *dwell time* because it is equal to the time that a point on the ground is observed by the antenna beam. Using (6.144), τ_d can be expressed in terms of the spatial resolution Δx:

$$\tau_d = \frac{(\Delta x)^2}{2u\theta_s h}, \tag{6.147}$$

where θ_s is in radians.

Now let us suppose that the radiometer beam crosses over a sharp boundary (in either direction) between two areas of very different emission characteristics. If the radiometer integration time τ is much smaller than τ_d, it will take the radiometer output approximately τ_d seconds to make the transition between the two levels corresponding to the two dissimilar areas. If, on the other hand, $\tau \gg \tau_d$, it will take the radiometer much longer than τ_d seconds to register the change due to the sharp boundary, which is equivalent to having an

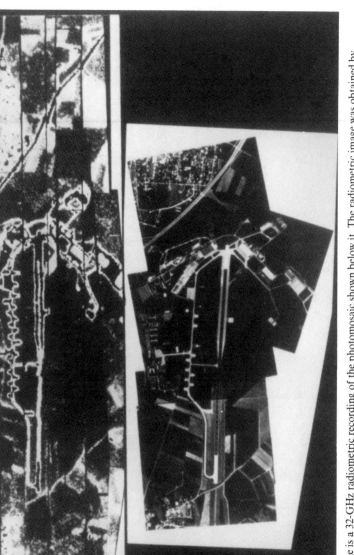

Fig. 6.41 Top image is a 32-GHz radiometric recording of the photomosaic shown below it. The radiometric image was obtained by a low-flying aircraft from a height of 700 m above the ground (photo courtesy of A. Sieber, DFVLR).

effective spatial resolution that is much larger than Δx. Hence, from the standpoint of radiometric resolution it is desirable to have τ as long as possible, and from the standpoint of spatial resolution it is desirable to have $\tau \ll \tau_d$. The optimum choice is dependent upon the nature of the application for which the radiometer is used and on other system parameters. In the general case, however, a compromise solution is to set

$$\tau = \tau_d. \tag{6.148}$$

For $\tau = \tau_d$, inserting (6.147) into (6.143) leads to

$$\Delta T \cdot \Delta x \cdot B^{1/2} = M(2u\theta_s h)^{1/2}. \tag{6.149}$$

The above expression may be termed the *radiometer uncertainty equation*. It states that for given radiometer configuration (i.e., M), flight parameters (h and u), and angular scan range ($2\theta_s$), the product of the radiometric uncertainty ΔT, the spatial uncertainty Δx, and the square root of the spectral uncertainty ($B^{1/2}$) is a constant. Similar expressions may be developed for more complex scanning configurations, but the basic idea remains the same, namely, that the three types of resolutions (uncertainties) are interrelated, and therefore improving one of them is likely to degrade one or both of the other two (unless the flight parameters and/or the scanning configuration is changed).

We close this chapter with an example of a radiometric image consisting of several parallel strips mosaicked together, as shown in the top part of Fig. 6.41. Below the radiometric image is a photograph of the imaged scene, which includes agricultural fields, a residential area, and several streets. The images were recorded by a 32-GHz imaging radiometer flying at a height of 700 m above an area near Oberpfaffenhofen, Federal Republic of Germany.

PROBLEMS

6.1. Consider an antenna connected to a receiver system consisting of a transmission line having a loss factor of 1.5 dB; an RF amplifier with a noise figure of 7 dB and a gain of 20 dB, followed by a mixer-preamplifier with a noise figure of 8 dB and conversion gain of 6 dB; and finally, an IF amplifier with a noise figure of 6 dB and gain of 40 dB. The entire receiver is maintained at an environmental temperature of 290 K.

   (a) Find the overall noise figure and effective noise temperature of the receiver system.
   (b) Find the overall noise figure and effective noise temperature of the receiver system with RF amplifier and transmission line interchanged.

6.2. The receiver of Problem 6.1(a) is connected to an antenna with a radiation efficiency of 0.9. If the calculated antenna temperature of the scene under observation is $T_A = 100$ K, and if the antenna physical temperature is 290 K, what is the system noise temperature at the antenna terminals?

6.3. In a superheterodyne receiver with local oscillator frequency f_{LO} and IF bandwidth B centered at f_{IF}, the IF output spectrum corresponds to two RF spectral bands centered at f_1 and f_2 where

$$f_1 \pm \frac{B}{2} = f_{LO} - f_{IF} \pm \frac{B}{2},$$

$$f_2 \pm \frac{B}{2} = f_{LO} + f_{IF} \pm \frac{B}{2}.$$

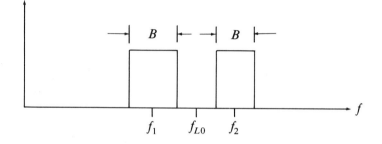

If an RF amplifier is used (ahead of the mixer) whose passband allows only one of the two RF bands to reach the mixer input, the system is referred to as a single-sideband receiver. On the other hand, if the mixer input contains both RF bands (centered at f_1 and f_2), the IF output will include input signals and noise from a total RF bandwidth of $2B$. This latter situation, which is known as double-sideband reception, exists if no RF amplifier (or RF filter) is used or if the RF amplifier passband extends from below $f_1 - B/2$ to above $f_2 + B/2$, thereby amplifying both RF bands.

   If F_{SSB} is the single-sideband noise figure of a mixer-preamplifier assembly, show that for the double-sideband receiver, the double-sideband noise figure F_{DSB} of the mixer-preamplifier is given by

$$F_{DSB} = \tfrac{1}{2}(F_{SSB} + 1)$$

and that the corresponding equivalent noise temperatures are related by

$$T_{DSB} = \tfrac{1}{2}T_{SSB}.$$

6.4. Verify the result given by (6.60).

6.5. The pulsed noise-injection radiometer of Fig. 6.18 drives the *PIN* diode with 40-μs pulses at a pulse repetition frequency f_R. The noise diode has an "excess noise ratio" of 23 dB, and the loss factor of the *PIN* diode is 2 dB in the ON state and 60 dB in the OFF state. The directional coupler has a 20-dB coupling factor ($F_c = 100$), and the entire radiometer is enclosed in a chamber maintained at 320 K. What should the range of f_R be in order to maintain the balanced condition over the range 50 K$\leqslant T_A' \leqslant$300 K?

6.6. A 1-GHz balanced Dicke radiometer with a 100-MHz bandwidth is to be flown on a satellite at an altitude of 600 km and with an average speed of 7.5 km s^{-1}. The radiometer uses a 10-m-diameter antenna, and the receiver is characterized by $T_{REC}' = 1000$ K and $T_{REF} = T_0 = 300$ K. The radiometer integration time is chosen to be equal to 0.1 of the dwell time of the antenna beam for a point on the ground. If the antenna is fixed so that its main beam is always pointed in the nadir direction, what will ΔT be?

6.7. Suppose the antenna of Problem 6.6 is made to scan between $-20°$ and $+20°$ relative to nadir in the plane orthogonal to the flight direction. What is ΔT?

6.8. Verify that (6.95) leads to (6.96) and (6.97) leads to (6.98).

6.9 Repeat the computations leading to Fig. 6.31 for $L_S = 0.5$ dB and $|R_R| = |R_G| = 0.2$.

References

Batchelor, R. A., J. W. Brooks, and B. F. C. Cooper (1968), Eleven-Centimeter Broadband Correlation Radiometers, *IEEE Trans. Antennas and Prop.*, AP-16, pp. 228–234.

Batelaan, Paul E., Richard M. Goldstein, and Charles T. Stelzried (1974), Improved Noise-Adding Radiometer for Microwave Receivers, NASA Tech. Brief 73-10345, Jet Propulsion Laboratory, Pasadena, California.

Blum, E. J. (1959), Sensibilité des Radiotelescopes et Récepteurs à Correlation, *Ann. Astrophys.*, 22, pp. 140–163.

Blume, H. J. C. (1977), Noise Calibration Repeatability of an Airborne Third-Generation Radiometer, *IEEE Trans. Micro. Theory and Tech.*, MTT-25, pp. 852–855.

Cardiasmenos, A. G. (1980), Practical MIC's Ready for Millimeter Receivers, *Micro. Sys. News*, 10, No. 8, pp. 37–51.

Carver, K. R. (1975), Antenna and Radome Loss Measurements for MFMR and PMIS, Phys. Sci. Lab. Tech. Rept. PA00817, New Mexico State University, Las Cruces.

Clark, B. G. (1968), Radio Interferometers of Intermediate Type, *IEEE Trans. Antennas and Prop.*, AP-16, pp. 143–144.

Colvin, R. S. (1961), A Study of Radio Astronomy Receivers, Stanford Elec. Lab., Radio Sci. Lab., Sci. Rept. 18, Stanford, California.

Dicke, R. H. (1946), The Measurement of Thermal Radiation at Microwave Frequencies, *Rev. Sci. Instr.*, 17, pp. 268–275.

Emerson, W. H. (1973), Electromagnetic Wave Absorbers and Anechoic Chambers through the Years, *IEEE Trans. Antennas and Prop.*, AP-21, pp. 484–489.

Evans, G. and C. W. McLeish (1977), *RF Radiometer Handbook*, Artech House, Inc., Dedham, Massachusetts, Appendix A.

Frater, R. H. and D. R. Williams (1981), An Active "Cold" Noise Source, *IEEE Trans. on Micro. Theory and Tech.*, MTT-29, pp. 344–347.

General Electric Space Systems Div. (1973), S-193 Microwave Radiometer/Scatterometer/ Altimeter Calibration Data Report, Flight Hardware, 1A, Valley Forge, Pennsylvania.

Goggins, William B. Jr. (1967), A Microwave Feedback Radiometer, *IEEE Trans. on Aerospace and Elec. Sys.*, AES-3, No. 1, pp. 83–90.

Graham, M. H. (1958), Radiometer Circuits, *Proc. IRE*, 46, pp. 1966.

Hach, Johann-Peter (1966), Proposal for a Continuously Calibrated Radiometer, *IEEE Proceedings Letters*, 54, pp. 2015–2016.

Hach, Johann-Peter (1968), A Very Sensitive Airborne Microwave Radiometer Using Two Reference Temperatures, *IEEE Trans. Micro. Theory and Tech.*, MTT-16, 9, pp. 629–636.

Hankins, T. H. (1972), Short-Timescale Structure in Two Pulsars, *Astrophys. J.*, 177, pp. 211–215.

Hardy, W. N. (1973), Precision Temperature Reference for Microwave Radiometry, *IEEE Trans. Micro. Theory and Tech.*, MTT-21, pp. 149–150.

Hardy, W. N., K. W. Gray, and A. W. Love (1974), An S-Band Radiometer Design with High Absolute Precision, *IEEE Trans. Micro. Theory and Tech.*, MTT-22, pp. 382–390.

Held, D. N. (1979), An Approach to Optimal Mixer Design at Millimeter and Submillimeter Wavelengths, *IEEE MTT-S Int. Micro. Symp. Digest*, pp. 25–27.

Helszajn, J. (1978), *Passive and Active Microwave Circuits*, John Wiley and Sons, New York, Chapter 1.

Hersman, M. S. and G. A. Poe (1981), Sensitivity of the Total Power Radiometer with Periodic Absolute Calibration, *IEEE Trans. Micro. Theory and Tech.*, MTT-29, pp. 32–40.

Huguenin, G. R. (1976), Pulsar Observing Techniques, in *Astrophysics*, 12, Part C., M. L. Meeks, ed., Academic Press, New York, Section 4.5.

IEEE (1979), *Standard Test Procedures for Antennas*, IEEE Press, New York.

Kennedy, W. K. (1978), M. W. Semiconductor Solid State Components, *Microwave J.*, 21, No. 11, pp. 66–69.

Kerr, A. R. (1975), Low-Noise Room-Temperature and Cryogenic Mixers for 80–120 GHz, *IEEE Trans. Micro. Theory and Tech.*, MTT-23, pp. 781–787.

Kerr, A. R. (1979), Noise and Loss in Balanced and Subharmonically Pumped Mixers: Part I—Theory, Part II—Application, *IEEE Trans. Micro. Theory and Tech.*, MTT-27, pp. 938–950.

Machin, K. E., M. Ryle, and D. D. Vonberg (1952), The Design of an Equipment for Measuring Small Radio-Frequency Noise Powers, *Proc. IEE* (London), 99, pp. 127–134.

Manchester, R. N. (1973), The Properties of Pulsars, *Proc. IEEE*, 61, pp. 1205–1211.

McGillem, C. D., and T. V. Seling (1963), Influence of System Parameters on Airborne Microwave Radiometer Design, *IEEE Trans. Military Elec.*, pp. 296–302.

Miller, C. K. S., W. C. Daywitt, and M. G. Arthur (1967), Noise Standards, Measurements, and Receiver Noise Definitions, *Proc. IEEE*, 55, pp. 865–877.

NASA, *Nimbus 5 User's Guide* (1972), The Electrically Scanning Microwave Radiometer (ESMR) Experiment, NASA Goddard Space Flight Center, Greenbelt, Maryland.

NASA, *Nimbus 6 User's Guide* (1975), The Electrically Scanning Microwave Radiometer (ESMR) Experiment, NASA Goddard Space Flight Center, Greenbelt, Maryland.

Nash, R. T. (1964), Beam Efficiency Limitations of Large Antennas, *IEEE Trans. Antennas and Prop.*, AP-12, pp. 918–923.

Nyquist, H. (1928), Thermal Agitation of Electric Charge in Conductors, *Phys. Rev.*, 32, pp. 110–113.

Ohm, E. A., and W. W. Snell (1963), A Radiometer for a Space Communications Receiver, *Bell Sys. Tech. J.*, 42, pp. 2047–2080.

Orhaug, T., and W. Waltman (1962), A Switched Load Radiometer, *Publ. Natl. Radio Astron. Obs.*, 1, pp. 179–204.

Otoshi, T. Y. (1968), The Effect of Mismatched Components on Microwave Noise-Temperature Calibrations, *IEEE Trans. Micro. Theory and Tech.*, MTT-16, pp. 675–686.

Price, R. M. (1976), Radiometers Fundamentals, in *Astrophys.*, *Part B: Radio Telescopes*, M. L. Meeks, ed., Academic Press, New York, Section 3.1.

Seling, Theodore V. (1964), The Application of Automatic Gain Control to Microwave Radiometers, *IEEE Trans. Antennas and Prop.*, AP-12, pp. 636–639.

Slater, P. N. (1980), *Remote Sensing, Optics and Optical Systems*, Addison-Wesley, Reading, Massachusetts, p. 326.

Steinberg, J. L. (1952), Les Récepteurs de Bruits Radioélectriques, *Onde Elec.*, 32, pp. 519–526.

Sterzer, F. (1978), GaAs Field Effect Transistors, *Microwave J.*, 21, No. 11, pp. 73–77.

Tiuri, M. G. (1964), Radio Astronomy Receivers, *IEEE Trans. Antennas & Prop.*, AP-12, pp. 930–938. See also Tiuri, M. E. (1966), Radio-Telescope Receivers, in *Radio Astronomy*, J. D. Kraus, ed., McGraw-Hill Book Company, New York, Chapter 7.

Ulich, B. L. (1977), A Radiometric Antenna Gain Calibration Method, *IEEE Trans. Antennas and Prop.*, AP-21, pp. 484–489.

Wells, J. S., W. C. Daywitt, and C. K. S. Miller (1964), Measurement of Effective Temperatures of Microwave Noise Sources, *IEEE Trans. Instr. and Measurement*, IM-13, pp. 17–28.

Wesseling, K. H. (1967), A Single-Sideband, Double-Sideband Interferometer Receiver for Radio Astronomy, *IEEE Trans. Antennas and Prop.*, AP-15, pp. 332–333.

Yaroshenko, V. (1964), Influence of the Fluctuating Factor of Amplification on the Measurement of Weak Noiselike Signals, *Radiotechnica*, 7, pp. 749–751.

List of Constants

Boltzmann's constant, $k = 1.3805 \times 10^{-23}$ J K^{-1}

$e = 2.71828$

Impedance of free space, $\eta_0 = (\mu_0/\varepsilon_0)^{1/2} = 376.7$ Ω

$\log x \equiv \log_{10} x = 0.4343 \ln x$

$\ln x \equiv \log_e x = 2.3026 \log x$

Permeability of vacuum, $\mu_0 = 4\pi \times 10^{-7}$ henry m^{-1}

Permittivity of vacuum, $\varepsilon_0 = 8.85 \times 10^{-12}$ farad m^{-1}

Planck's constant, $h = 6.6256 \times 10^{-34}$ J s

1 Radian $= 57.296°$

Speed of light in vaccum, $c = 2.997925 \times 10^8$ m s^{-1}

Stefan-Boltzmann constant, $\sigma = 5.6697 \times 10^{-8}$ W m^{-2} K^{-4}

Fawwaz T. Ulaby, Richard K. Moore, and Adrian K. Fung,

Microwave Remote Sensing: Active and Passive,

Vol. I: Microwave Remote Sensing Fundamentals and Radiometry   ISBN 0-201-10759-7

Common Functions and Transforms

B-1 TWO-DIMENSIONAL FOURIER-TRANSFORM PAIR

$$G(f_x, f_y) = \mathcal{F}\{g(x, y)\} = \int_{-\infty}^{\infty} g(x, y) e^{-j2\pi(xf_x + yf_y)} \, dx \, dy, \qquad \text{(B.1)}$$

$$g(x, y) = \mathcal{F}^{-1}\{G(f_x, f_y)\} = \int_{-\infty}^{\infty} G(f_x, f_y) e^{j2\pi(xf_x + yf_y)} \, df_x \, df_y. \qquad \text{(B.2)}$$

B-2 COMMON FUNCTIONS

Sinc function:

$$\text{sinc}(x) = \frac{\sin \pi x}{\pi x}. \qquad \text{(B.3)}$$

Sine Fresnel integral:

$$S(x) = \int_0^x \sin\left(\frac{\pi t^2}{2}\right) dt. \qquad \text{(B.4)}$$

Sine integral:

$$Si(x) = \int_0^x \frac{\sin t}{t} \, dt. \qquad \text{(B.5)}$$

Cosine Fresnel integral:

$$C(x) = \int_0^x \cos\left(\frac{\pi t^2}{2}\right) dt. \qquad \text{(B.6)}$$

Gamma function:

$$\Gamma(n) = \int_0^\infty e^{-x} x^{n-1} \, dx, \qquad n \geqslant 0. \qquad \text{(B.7)}$$

Fawwaz T. Ulaby, Richard K. Moore, and Adrian K. Fung,
Microwave Remote Sensing: Active and Passive,
Vol. I: Microwave Remote Sensing Fundamentals and Radiometry   ISBN 0-201-10759-7

Convolution:

$$y(t)=x_1(t)*x_2(t)=\int_{-\infty}^{\infty}x_1(\tau)x_2(t-\tau)\,d\tau. \tag{B.8}$$

Autocorrelation function:

$$R(\tau)=\lim_{T\to\infty}\frac{1}{2T}\int_{-T}^{T}x(t)x(t+\tau)\,dt. \tag{B.9}$$

B-3 BESSEL-FUNCTION IDENTITIES

$J_n(\cdot)$ is nth-order Bessel function, real argument first kind.

$$J_n(\rho)=\frac{1}{2\pi j^n}\int_{-\pi}^{\pi}e^{j\rho\cos\phi+jn\phi}\,d\phi, \tag{B.10}$$

$$\int_0^x tJ_0(t)\,dt=xJ_1(x), \tag{B.11}$$

$$\int_0^{\infty}x^{n+1}e^{-\alpha x^2}J_n(\beta x)\,dx=\frac{\beta^n}{(2\alpha)^{n+1}}\exp\left(-\frac{\beta^2}{4\alpha}\right),$$

$$\text{Re}\{\alpha\}>0,\quad \text{Re}\{n\}>-1, \quad\text{(B.12)}$$

$$\int_0^{\infty}x^{n+1}e^{-\alpha x}J_n(\beta x)\,dx=\frac{2\alpha(2\beta)^n\Gamma(n+\frac{3}{2})}{\sqrt{\pi}\,(\alpha^2+\beta^2)^{n+3/2}},$$

$$\text{Re}\{n\}>-1,\quad \text{Re}\{\alpha\}>|\text{Im}\{\beta\}|. \quad\text{(B.13)}$$

B-4 PROBABILITY DENSITY FUNCTIONS

Exponential:

$$p(x)=\begin{cases}\dfrac{1}{m}e^{-x/m}, & x\geq0,\\[2mm] 0 & x<0;\end{cases} \tag{B.14}$$

$$\bar{x}=m;\qquad \sigma_x^2=m^2.$$

Gaussian (normal):

$$p(x)=\frac{1}{\sqrt{2\pi}\,\sigma}e^{-(x-m)^2/2\sigma^2},\qquad -\infty\leq x\leq\infty; \tag{B.15}$$

$$\bar{x}=m;\qquad \sigma_x^2=\sigma^2.$$

Lognormal: If $y=e^x$, $y\geq0$, and x is normally distributed according to (B.15) with $\bar{x}=m$ and $\sigma_x=\sigma$,

$$p(y)=\begin{cases}\dfrac{1}{\sqrt{2\pi}\,y\sigma}\exp\left[-\dfrac{(\ln y-m)^2}{2\sigma^2}\right], & y\geqslant 0,\\[4mm] 0, & y<0;\end{cases}$$

(B.16)

$$\bar{y}=\exp\left(m+\frac{\sigma^2}{2}\right);\qquad \sigma_y^2=\bar{y}^2\left[\exp(\sigma^2)-1\right].$$

Rayleigh:

$$p(r)=\begin{cases}\dfrac{re^{-r^2/2\sigma^2}}{\sigma^2}, & r\geqslant 0,\\[4mm] 0, & r<0;\end{cases}$$

(B.17)

$$\bar{r}=\sqrt{\frac{\pi}{2}}\,\sigma;\qquad \sigma_r^2=\left(2-\frac{\pi}{2}\right)\sigma^2.$$

Uniform:

$$p(x)=\begin{cases}\dfrac{1}{b-a}, & a\leqslant x\leqslant b,\\[4mm] 0, & \text{otherwise};\end{cases}$$

(B.18)

$$\bar{x}=\frac{b+a}{2};\qquad \sigma_x^2=\frac{(b-a)^2}{12}.$$

χ^2 (chi-squared) with $2N$ degrees of freedom:

$$p_{2N}(x)=\begin{cases}\dfrac{x^{N-1}}{2^N\sigma^{2N}\Gamma(N)}\exp\left(-\dfrac{x}{2\sigma^2}\right), & x\geqslant 0,\\[4mm] 0, & x<0,\end{cases}$$

(B.19)

where $\Gamma(N)$ is the gamma function, given by (B.7);

$$\bar{x}=2N\sigma^2,\qquad \sigma_x^2=4N\sigma^4,\qquad \bar{x}/\sigma_x=N.$$

For $N=1$, $p_{2N}(x)$ reduces to the exponential PDF, Eq. (B.14).

Useful Reference:

Abramowitz, M. and I. A. Stegun, Eds. (1970), *Handbook of Mathematical Functions*, Dover Publications, Inc., New York.

Appendix C

List of Symbols

Symbol	Units[a]	Name
$\mathbf{A}$	weber m^{-1}	vector potential
A, A_{eff}	m^2	antenna effective area (or effective aperture)
A_p	m^2	physical aperture of antenna
$\mathfrak{a}$	—	absorptivity
a	Hz s^{-1}	chirp rate
a	—	single-scattering albedo
a_B	—	pulse taper factor
a_h, a_v	—	aperture taper factor (horizontal, vertical)
$a(T_i)$	—	voltage amplitude factor for ith target
B	W m^{-2} sr^{-1}	brightness
$B, \Delta f$	Hz	bandwidth
B_D	Hz	Doppler bandwidth
B_{Df}	Hz	Doppler-filter bandwidth
$B(f)$	—	relative spectrum of received signal
$b(t)$	s^{-1}	voltage amplitude factor per unit time
$b(\omega)$	Hz^{-1}	voltage amplitude factor in frequency domain
C_d	V W^{-1}	square-law detector power sensitivity constant
c	m s^{-1}	speed of light (3×10^8 m s^{-1})
$|c(\tau)|^2$	V^{4}S^2	time-domain range-only ambiguity function
D_0	—	antenna maximum directivity
$D(\theta, \phi)$	—	antenna directivity pattern
d	m	antenna diameter
d	m	distance between scatterers
d	m	particle diameter
E	V m^{-1}	electric field strength
$\mathcal{E}$	J	energy
$\mathbf{E(r)}$	V m^{-1}	complex electric field intensity (phasor)
$\mathbf{E(r}, t)$	V m^{-1}	complex electric field intensity in real time
e	—	emissivity
e_c, e_i	—	emissivity (coherent, incoherent)
F	—	noise figure
$F(f, f_{lm})$	Hz^{-1}	line-shape function
$F(\theta, \phi)$	W	antenna radiation pattern (or radiation intensity)
$F_n(\theta, \phi)$	—	normalized antenna radiation pattern (or radiation intensity)
$\mathcal{F}\{g\}$	*	Fourier transform of function g

Fawwaz T. Ulaby, Richard K. Moore, and Adrian K. Fung,
Microwave Remote Sensing: Active and Passive,
Vol. I: Microwave Remote Sensing Fundamentals and Radiometry ISBN 0-201-10759-7

Symbol	Units[a]	Name
$\mathscr{F}^{-1}\{G\}$	*	inverse Fourier transform of function G
f	Hz	frequency
f_c	Hz	carrier frequency
f_D	Hz	Doppler frequency shift
f_{D0}	Hz	maximum Dopper frequency shift
f_F	Hz	fading frequency
f_p	Hz	pusle repetition frequency
$f(\theta, \phi)$	V	directional pattern for electric or magnetic field
G	—	power gain
G_0	—	maximum antenna gain
G_S	VK^{-1}	system gain factor
$G(\theta, \phi)$	—	antenna-gain directional pattern
g	—	voltage gain
$g(\theta, \phi)$	—	normalized antenna gain
H	Am^{-1}	magnetic field strength
$\mathbf{H(r)}$	Am^{-1}	complex magnetic field intensity (phasor)
$\mathbf{H(r}, t)$	Am^{-1}	complex magnetic field intensity in real time
$\mathscr{K}\{q\}$	*	Hankel transform of function q
H	m	antenna height
H, h	m, km	height
h	Js	Planck's constant, 6.6256×10^{-34} Js
$h(\cdot)$	Vm	form factor of radiated electric field
I	A	current
$I_n(\cdot)$	—	Bessel function, first kind, nth order, imaginary argument
I_{out}	*	radiometer output indication
$Im\{\cdot\}$	—	imaginary part of $\{\cdot\}$
J	$Wm^{-2}sr^{-1}$	source function
J_a	$Wm^{-2}sr^{-1}$	absorption source function
J_s	$Wm^{-2}sr^{-1}$	scattering source function
$J_n(\cdot)$	—	Bessel function, first kind, nth order
K	—	function of the index of refraction of a particle
$\mathbf{k}$	m^{-1}	propagation vector
k	m^{-1}	wave number, $2\pi/\lambda$
k	JK^{-1}	Boltzmann's constant, 1.38×10^{-23} JK^{-1}
k_0	m^{-1}	wave number in free space, $2\pi/\lambda_0$
k_r, k_a	—	SAR safety factor (range, azimuth)
$|k(f_D)|^2$	V^4S^4	speed-only ambiguity function
L	m	length of synthetic aperature
L, L_F	—	loss factor
L_{FS}	—	free-space transmission loss
$L_a(\theta; H)$	—	atmospheric loss factor
L_θ	—	total atmospheric loss factor at zenith angle θ
L_p	m	maximum possible length of synthetic aperature
l	m	antenna length
L_{um}	m	maximum length of unfocused synthetic aperature
M	K	radiometer figure of merit
M_v	kgm^{-2}	atmospheric water mass
m	—	surface rms slope, $(\sigma^2|\rho''(0)|)^{1/2}$
m	%	percentage moisture content of leaf by wet weight
m_g	%	percentage moisture content of soil by dry weight

Symbol	Units[a]	Name
m_v	$\mathrm{g\,m^{-3}}$	water content (mass density) of a cloud
m_v	$\mathrm{g\,cm^{-3}}$	moisture content of soil by volume
N	—	normality of a solution
N	—	number of independent samples
N_s	—	number of scan positions, scanning SAR
N_p	—	number of pulses sampled
N_v	$\mathrm{m^{-3}}$	number of particles per unit volume
$\hat{\mathbf{n}}_i$	—	unit vector in the incident direction
$\hat{\mathbf{n}}_s$	—	unit vector in the scattered direction
n	—	refractive index, $(\varepsilon_r)^{1/2}$ (Chapter 5: $n = n_p/n_b$)
n'	—	real part of n
n''	—	imaginary part of n
n_b	—	index of refraction of background medium
n_p	—	index of refraction of particle material
P	W	power
P	mbar	pressure
P_r	W	received power
P_t	W	transmitted power
p	—	polarization configuration
$p(\ )$	*	probability density function, drop-size distribution
$p(t)$	—	normalized pulse shape
Q_a, Q_e, Q_s	$\mathrm{m^2}$	cross-section of a particle (absorption, extinction, scattering)
R	m	range
R	Ω	resistance
R	—	Fresnel reflection coefficient
R_g	m, km	ground swathwidth
R_r	$\mathrm{mm\,hr^{-1}}$	rainfall rate
R_s	m, km	slant swathwidth
$R_s(t)$	W	autocorrelation function for detected voltage
$R_{sf}(t)$	W	autocovariance function for detected voltage
$R_\perp, R_\parallel$	—	Fresnel reflection coefficient for perpendicularly (horizontally), parallel (vertically) polarized wave, respectively
$\mathbf{r}$	m	displacement vector
r	m	particle radius
r_a, r_y	m	spatial resolution (along-track, across-track)
r_{ap}	m	finest possible SAR alongtrack resolution
r_e	m	equivalent square photographic pixel dimension
r_g	—	gray-scale resolution
r_R	m	slant-range resolution
$\mathbf{S}$	—	scattering matrix
$\mathbf{S}_a$	$\mathrm{W\,m^{-2}}$	time-average Poynting vector (real part of $\mathbf{S}_c$)
$\mathbf{S}_c$	$\mathrm{W\,m^{-2}}$	complex Poynting vector
S	0/00	salinity, parts per thousand
S	$\mathrm{W\,m^{-2}}$	power (or flux) density (per unit area)
S_f	$\mathrm{W\,m^{-2}\,Hz^{-1}}$	spectral flux density
S_{lm}	Hz	line strength of the lm spectral line
S_n	—	signal-to-noise ratio
$S(f)$	$\mathrm{W\,Hz^{-1}}$	power spectral density
$Si(\cdot)$	—	sine integral function (see Section B.2 in Appendix B)

Symbol	Units[a]	Name
$\text{sinc}(x)$	(of x^{-1})	$(\sin \pi x)/\pi x$
T	s	time delay, duration, period
T, T_0, T_p	K	physical (thermometric) temperature
T_A	K	antenna radiometric temperature
T_a, T_p	s	time to build synthetic aperture, maximum possible
T_{APP}	K	apparent radiometric temperature
T_B	K	brightness temperature
T_{CAL}	K	calibration noise temperature
T_{COS}	K	cosmic radiometric temperature
T_{DN}	K	downward-emitted atmospheric radiometric temperature
T_E	K	equivalent input noise temperature
T_{EXTRA}	K	extraterrestrial radiometric temperature
T_{GAL}	K	galactic radiometric temperature
$\overline{T}_{ML}$	K	main-lobe apparent temperature
T_N	K	noise temperature of a noise source
T_P	s	interpulse period
T_R	s	repetition period
T_{REC}	K	receiver noise temperature
T_{REF}	K	reference noise temperature
T_{SKY}	K	sky radiometric temperature
T_{SC}	K	scattered radiometric temperature
$\overline{T}_{SL}$	K	side-lobe apparent temperature
T_{SYS}	K	system noise temperature
T_{UP}	K	upward-emitted atmospheric radiometric temperature
$T_\perp, T_\parallel$	—	Fresnel transmission coefficient for perpendicularly (horizontally), parallel (vertically) polarized wave, respectively
T_*	K	T with uppercase subscript = radiometric (or noise) temperature
t	s	time
$\tan \delta$	—	tangent of δ, $= \varepsilon''/\varepsilon'$
$\mathbf{u}$	m s^{-1}	velocity
u	m s^{-1}	speed
V	m^2	resolution volume
V, v	V	voltage
V_{ac}	V	ac (fluctuating) component of V
V_{agc}	V	AGC voltage
$\overline{V} = V_{dc}$	V	dc value of V, average value
V_d	V	detected voltage
V_e	V	envelope voltage
V_{IF}	V	IF voltage
V_n	V	noise voltage
V_{out}	V	output voltage
V_s	V	signal voltage
V_{syn}	V	synchronous detector output voltage
$W(\cdot)$	m^2	normalized roughness spectrum
$W(\omega)$	—	frequency weighting function
w_v	%	snow liquid-water content (wetness), percent by volume
w_w	%	snow liquid water content (wetness), percent by weight
$w(t)$	—	time weighting function
Z	Ω	impedance

Symbol	Units[a]	Name
Z	$m^6 m^{-3}$, $mm^6 m^{-3}$	reflectivity factor (of cloud, rain, or snow)
α	$Np\,m^{-1}$, $dB\,m^{-1}$	attenuation constant
β	$rad\,m^{-1}$	phase constant
$\beta_{1/2}$	rad, degrees	antenna half-power beamwidth
β_h	rad, degrees	horizontal (along-track) beamwidth
β_{minor}	rad, degrees	minor-lobe width
β_{null}	rad, degrees	antenna beamwidth between first nulls
Γ	—	reflectivity
Γ_c, Γ_i	—	reflectivity (coherent, incoherent)
γ	$Np\,m^{-1}$	propagation factor ($\gamma = \alpha + j\beta$)
γ	Hz	linewidth parameter
δ	rad, degrees	phase shift
δ	s	bit length in binary phase code
$\delta(\cdot)$	*	Dirac delta function
ε	$farad\,m^{-1}$	permittivity
$\varepsilon', \varepsilon''$	$farad\,m^{-1}$	real, imaginary part of ε
ε_c	—	complex dielectric constant, $\varepsilon_c = \varepsilon' - j\varepsilon''$
ε_r	—	relative complex dielectric constant, $\varepsilon_r = \varepsilon_c/\varepsilon_0 = \varepsilon_r' - j\varepsilon_r''$
$\varepsilon_r', \varepsilon_r''$	—	real, imaginary part of ε_r
ε_x	—	relative complex dielectric constant of material x
$\varepsilon_x', \varepsilon_x''$	—	real, imaginary parts of ε_x
ε_0	$farad\,m^{-1}$	permittivity of free space, $8.85 \times 10^{-12}\ farad\,m^{-1}$
η	Ω	intrinsic impedance
η_a	—	antenna aperture efficiency
η_l	—	antenna radiation efficiency (due to ohmic losses)
η_M	—	antenna main-beam efficiency
η_m	—	antenna stray factor, $\eta_m = 1 - \eta_M$
θ	rad, degrees	angle of incidence
θ, θ_a	rad, degrees	antenna elevation angle
θ_B	rad, degrees	Brewster angle for total transmission
θ_c	rad, degrees	critical angle for total reflection
$\kappa_a, \kappa_e, \kappa_s$	$Np\,m^{-1}$, $dB\,km^{-1}$	volume absorption, extinction, scattering coefficients
$\kappa_{ec}, \kappa_{er}, \kappa_{es}$	$Np\,m^{-1}$, $dB\,km^{-1}$	cloud, rain, snow extinction coefficients
λ	m, cm	wavelength
λ_0	m, cm	free-space wavelength
λ_g	m, cm	guide wavelength
μ	$henry\,m^{-1}$	magnetic permeability
μ_0	$henry\,m^{-1}$	magnetic permeability of free space, $4\pi \times 10^{-7}$ $henry\,m^{-1}$
μ_r	—	relative magnetic permeability, $\mu_r = \mu/\mu_0$
$\xi_a, \xi_b, \xi_e, \xi_s$	—	absorption, backscattering, extinction, scattering efficiency of a particle
ξ, η	m	coordinates along, perpendicular to isodops
ρ	—	correlation coefficient
ρ	$g\,m^{-3}$, $g\,cm^{-3}$	density of a material
ρ_{air}	$kg\,m^{-3}$	density of air
ρ_b, ρ_i, ρ_s	$g\,cm^{-3}$	densities of bulk soil, ice, snow
ρ_{ij}	—	normalized cross-correlation coefficient
ρ_v	$g\,m^{-3}$	water-vapor density
σ	$S\,m^{-1} = \Omega^{-} m^{-1}$	conductivity
σ	$W\,m^{-2}\,K^{-4}$	Stefan-Boltzmann constant, 5.67×10^{-8} $W\,m^{-2}\,K^{-4}$

Symbol	Units[a]	Name
σ	m^2	radar scattering cross-section
σ_b	m^2	backscattering radar cross-section of a particle
σ_v	$m^2 m^{-3} = m^{-1}$	volume backscattering coefficient (radar reflectivity)
σ_x	(of x)	standard deviation of variable x
σ^0	—	differential scattering cross-section (per unit area), also called scattering coefficient
σ_{pq}^0	—	scattering coefficient when transmission is at polarization q and reception at polarization p
τ	s	integration time
τ	s	relaxation time
τ, τ_p	s	duration of a pulse (pulse length)
τ_d	s	dwell time
τ_θ	Np	atmospheric opacity at zenith angle θ
$\tau(r_1, r_2)$	Np	optical thickness between r_1 and r_2
Υ	—	transmissivity
Υ_c, Υ_i	—	transmissivity (coherent, incoherent)
ϕ	rad, degrees	phase angle, phase shift, azimuth angle
χ	rad, degrees	grazing angle
χ	rad, degrees	real angle of transmission
χ	—	dimensionless Mie size parameter, $\chi = 2\pi r/\lambda$
χ^2	*	parameter of χ^2 distribution
$\chi^2(\tau, f_D)$	$V^4 s^2$	generalized ambiguity function
Ω	sr	solid angle
$\Omega_M, \Omega_m, \Omega_p$	sr	antenna solid angle (main-beam, minor-lobe, pattern)
ω	$rad\,s^{-1}$	angular (radian) frequency
ω_c	$rad\,s^{-1}$	carrier angular frequency
ω_D	$rad\,s^{-1}$	Doppler angular-frequency shift

[a] The asterisk * indicates that the symbol does not have unique units.

Abbreviations, Acronyms, and Names of Systems and Satellites

ac	alternating current (varying component)
A/D	analog-to-digital
AGC	automatic gain control
AMSU	advanced microwave scanner unit
AN/APQ-97	military designation of a Westinghouse side-looking airborne radar
AN/APQ-102	military designation of a Goodyear synthetic-aperture radar
AN/APS-94	military designation of a Motorola side-looking airborne radar
AN/DPD-2	military designation of a Philco-Ford unfocused synthetic-aperture radar
ATR switch	anti-TR (anti-transmit-receive) switch
B-scan	Radar display of range and angle
COHO	coherent oscillator
Cosmos 243, 384	USSR satellites
CRT	cathode-ray tube
CW	continuous wave
dc	direct current (average value)
DFVLR	Deutsche Forschungs- und Versuchsanstalt für Luft- und Raumfahrt e.V.
DME	distance-measuring equipment
DMSP	Defense Meteorological Satellite Program
EHF	extremely high frequency
EMI P391	8.6-mm SLAR produced by EMI, Ltd. (U.K.)
ENR	excess-noise ratio
ERIM	Environmental Research Institute of Michigan
ESMR	electrically scanning microwave radiometer
FET	field-effect transistor
FFT	fast Fourier transform
FM	frequency modulated
FOV	field of view
GaAs	gallium arsenide
GEMS	Goodyear Electronic Mapping System
GOES	geostationary operational environmental satellite
HELOSCAT	helicopter-borne MAS
HF	high frequency
IF	intermediate frequency
IFOV	instantaneous field of view
IMPATT	impact avalanche and transit time (diode)
ITU	International Telecommunication Union
JPL	Jet Propulsion Laboratory

Fawwaz T. Ulaby, Richard K. Moore, and Adrian K. Fung,
Microwave Remote Sensing: Active and Passive,
Vol. I: Microwave Remote Sensing Fundamentals and Radiometry   ISBN 0-201-10759-7

LAMMR	large antenna multifrequency microwave radiometer
LF	low frequency
LO	local oscillator
Mariner	U.S. satellite
MAS	microwave active spectrometer
MIC	microwave integrated circuit
Meteor	U.S.S.R. satellite
MF	medium frequency
M.I.T.	Massachusetts Institute of Technology
MSU	microwave scanner unit
MTI	moving-target indicator
NASA	U.S. National Aeronautics and Space Administration
NOSS	National Oceanic Satellite System
NEMS	Nimbus E Microwave Spectrometer
Nimbus	U.S. satellite
NRL	U.S. Naval Research Laboratory
PDF	probability density function
PIN	*P*-region–Intrinsic-region–*N*-Region semiconductor diode
PPI	plan-position indicator
PRF	pulse repetition frequency
radar	radio detection and ranging
RADSCAT	radiometer-scatterometer, flown on Skylab
RAR	real-aperture radar
RF	radio frequency
rms	root-mean-square
S-193	designation of 13.9-GHz radiometer-scatterometer flown on Skylab
S-194	designation of 1.4-GHz radiometer flown on Skylab
SAR	synthetic-aperture radar
SASS	Seasat-A Satellite Scatterometer
SAW	surface acoustic wave
SCAMS	scanning microwave spectrometer
SCANSAR	scanning synthetic-aperture radar
Seasat	U.S. satellite
SHF	superhigh frequency
Skylab	U.S. spacecraft
SLAR	side-looking airborne radar
SMMR	scanning multichannel microwave radiometer
SPDT	single-pole double-throw (switch)
SSM/I	Special Sensor M/I (microwave environmental sensor)
SSM/T	Special Sensor M/T (microwave temperature sounder)
STALO	stable local oscillator
TE	transverse electric (perpendicularly or horizontally polarized)
TEM	transverse electromagnetic
TIROS	U.S. satellites (television infrared observation satellite)
TM	transverse magnetic (parallel or vertical polarized)
TR switch	transmit-receive switch
TWT	traveling-wave tube
ULF	ultralow frequency
UHF	ultrahigh frequency
VCO	voltage-controlled oscillator
VHF	very high frequency
VLF	very low frequency

Index

Numbers set in *italics* designate pages on which complete literature citations are given.

Abramowitz, M., *435*
Absorber reflection coefficient, 416
Absorption coefficient, 212, 225, 267
  for atmospheric gases, 279–280
  for clouds, 309–314
  for oxygen, 274, 276–279
  for rain, 318–324
  for snow, 326–328
  for volume of spherical particles, 306
  for water vapor, 269–275
Absorption cross-section, 289
  of water or ice particle, 310
  Rayleigh approximation for, 295
Absorption efficiency factor, 289
  Mie solution for, 293–294
  Rayleigh approximation for, 295
Absorption spectrum of atmosphere, 280–281
Absorptivity, 187
  of dielectric slab, 246
Active microwave remote sensing, *see* Radar
Active noise sources, 401
Advanced Microwave Scanner Unit (AMSU), 15, 442
AGC (automatic-gain-control), 384, 442
AGC demodulator, 388
AGC (Hach) radiometer, 384–390
Air, *see* Atmospheric density, atmospheric temperature
Airy pattern, 130
Albedo (single scattering), 212, 239, 242, 332
Altshuler, E. E., 332, 334, 337, *343*
Amplifier, *see* RF amplifier, Mixer, and Video amplifier
AMSU (Advanced Microwave Scanner Unit), 15, 442
AN/APQ-97, 8–9, 45, 47, 442
AN/APQ-102, 9, 442
AN/APS-94, 9, 47, 442
Antenna
  aperture efficiency, 103, 133, 414
  beamwidth between first nulls, 101
  directivity, 101–102
  effective area (aperture), 103, 131–133
  far-field (far-zone or Fraunhofer) region of, 119–120
  feed, 167
  Fresnel region of, 117, 120
  gain, 104
  half-power beamwidth, 101
  main-beam efficiency, 100, 207, 413–414
  main-beam solid angle, 100
  minor-lobe solid angle, 100

  near-field region of, 117, 120
  normalized radiation pattern, 97
  pattern solid angle, 100
  polarization, 122–124, 143
  principal planes, 97
  radiation efficiency, 104, 208, 413–414
  radiation pattern (or radiation intensity), 97, 187
  reflectors, 167
  stray factor, 100, 207
  types, 94, 165
  see also Aperture, Array, Dipole, Horn, and Slot Antenna
Antenna temperature, 53, 204, 412
  and antenna radiation efficiency, 207–208, 413
  due to self-emission, 208
  main-lobe contribution, 206
  of a discrete source, 205
  relation to apparent and brightness temperatures, 202–203
  side-lobe contribution, 206
Aperture antenna
  and Fourier transform relations, 121–122
  and polarization, 122–124
  and scalar diffraction, 115–116
  and vector diffraction, 142–143
  beamwidth of, 125, 136–138, 141
  directivity of, 127, 139–141
  effective area of, 131–133
  far-field radiation condition for, 121
  radiation from, 114, 119–120, 143
  with cosine illumination, 141–142
  with Gaussian illumination, 182
  with linear-phase illumination, 134–140
  with parabolic illumination, 141
  with triangular illumination, 141
  with uniform illumination, circular, 128–131, 141
  with uniform illumination, rectangular, 124–128, 141
  with $(1-\rho^2)^n$ illumination, 141
Apparent temperature, 201, 215
  general solution for, 216
  in a scatter-free medium, 217
  main-lobe, 206, 223
  of homogeneous medium, 230
  of layered media, 245
  of non-homogeneous observation cell, 224
  relation to brightness and antenna temperatures, 202–203
Area, elemental, in spherical coordinates, 96